Introduction by

FREDERIC A. BIRMINGHAM

Random House · New York

First Printing

Published in New York by Random House, Inc., and simultaneously in Toronto, Canada, by Random House of Canada, Limited.

Library of Congress Catalog Card Number: 52–7523

Manufactured in the United States of America

Contents

List of Illustrations

FREDERIC A. BIRMINGHAM

Introduction

IF THE proper study of mankind is Man, as a great writer once observed, then *Esquire*—the Magazine For Men—is truly published with a happy propriety.

But we must confess to a suspicion that Man is better studied in company with his improper playmate, Woman. She is his lifelong pursuit, take it any way you will.

And so *The Girls from Esquire* was conceived.

We suddenly discovered that *Esquire* had in its back numbers a treasury of fiction, comment, and fun based on that interesting and unpredictable animal which Oscar Wilde warned was meant only to be loved, not understood.

It takes a brave man, and a sturdy one, to read this book, and it took dogged and determined men to assist in its compilation. They were given pencil and pad, provisions enough for many months, mostly in dehydrated form, plus flashlights, stimulants, the kind of high-register whistles that only a dog's sensitive ear can detect, the blessings of the editor—then released into that dark library where lurk the leatherbound copies of *Esquire's* back issues. Their orders were explicit. Seek out Woman in her infinite variety. Find stories of her. Find the things she wrote. See to the jokes about her, and the japes she played back. Quote the puzzled and angry and happy and wrong men who made Her a proper study. *Esquire* has captured Her in its pages: find Her.

Some of them cut their way out with machetes and came back alive. One, a matted and clotted wreck we could name only through his Social Security number, carved on an old rejection slip, whispered his findings and then staggered off to work out his days on another magazine devoted to biscuit recipes and flower arrangements. Another paused to reveal his findings, leaning heavily on a bust of Havelock Ellis. Women, he declaimed, are the greatest living proofs of evolution, because they can be divided into two groups: those who look like birds and those who look like horses. We reminded him of the Pennsylvania woman who was discovered after a twenty-year search chained to her bed in the attic. *She* looked like a Pekinese, we pointed out. "Just proves you can't trust women," said the researcher, heading out for a double Martini.

When the great search was over, we were pleased and not too surprised to discover that *Esquire's* most eloquent writers had always turned to the great subject simply by the forces of gravity and levity. It's been over eighteen years since *Esquire* itself first appeared; the well-known *Bedside* anthology repeated the ancient theme in over 650,000 copies. And so now, concentrating mostly on recent issues, we work out our noble fate.

It would be wrong to go to press without a gracious bow to the girls who read *Esquire,* and frequently write to it. They have contributed uniquely to this volume in their own way. Every magazine, of course, has its secondary and tertiary readers—people who borrow or chance upon it in odd places like clubs and dentists' waiting-rooms or airplanes and enjoy the fruits purchased by the original buyer. A general magazine, or a family magazine, doesn't pay much attention to these so-called peripheral readers, since they are normally pale and somewhat less interesting specimens of the same group which compliments the magazine by actually buying it. But *Esquire's* periphery is a flaming orb composed of a great portion of female readers who have rebelled against their sad lot of seeing pages of *Esquire* only over the shoulders of their men. They are the ones who steal *Esquire* most often, and it is by all odds the most stolen magazine in the business. Women cop it from libraries, club rooms, and their husbands' brief cases with an enduring and affectionate larceny that we heartily condone. To them, the girls of *Esquire,* we dedicate this book.

They write us letters, too. *Esquire's* mail is probably the gaudiest in the business. We hear from Maharajahs who want us to send them some ordinary gadget, diamond encrusted for the regal touch, and we hear from *Fräuleins* looking for a husband. In a month, we read intimate pages describing life in a Sumatran jungle and in a South American corral; the number of men who write from the Korean battle line would make up a sizable fighting force; college presidents, freshmen, congressmen and exasperated wives beseech our fashion advice. But the girls, as always, write the best letters. One Kansas housewife, even in that perennially dry state, managed to show us her shapely self, fighting floods in her bathing suit. Another grandmother berated us soundly for being interested in fashion at all. Seems that Grandpa "took to wearing bow ties and fancy sport jackets" and got into trouble with one of the girls down at the plant. We didn't mean it, honest.

As richly rewarding have been the letters from lady authors. Their suggestions reveal a wide reconnaissance on the famous battle of the sexes, and leave not much doubt as to which general staff they consider will be dictating the peace terms. We would not defame these gentle damsels by betraying their confidences, but there are a few published in this anthology who are thus fair prey—and fair they are—to the most unforgettable semi-colon and author-and-editor luncheon. Helen Lawrenson, for example (May we make this clear, once and for all that she and no other was the anonymous author of the celebrated "Latins Are Lousy Lovers"?), so strongly campaigned for her theme in "What Has Become of the Old-Fashioned Man?" that at length we capitulated against our modern misgivings. It was not long after that we were wearing heavy gold jewelry, establishing ourselves as a household tyrant, and referring to automobiles as rigs. It did no good at all, of course. Helen Lawrenson is chic, beautiful, and smart, and actually rides only bicycles built for two that have been designed by Raymond Loewy.

Another fragrant breeze from the "In" box was Mary Jane Shour. "Blueprint for a Divorcee" was personally researched, she announced upon our first meeting, but we knew that it was all worthwhile when we found that this was her first published manuscript. She has had other articles in *Esquire,* since, and has been featured by other magazines in a way to make us jealous. Her other titles, "Brush Up on Your Brush Off," and "The Care and Feeding of Millionaires" show a fine authority in the field.

Another "first" was Elaine Greene's "Tears in the Ladies Room." Elaine had had it, by the time she came to us. The ladies who work with their hats on have the rarest collection of knives in business, she had discovered, and it was time that the kids who cry in the ladies room were given more for their tears than Kleenex. We secretly blessed the hatted dames; Elaine Greene now writes regularly for *Esquire.*

Betty South, Martha Gellhorn, Ilka Chase, and Cynthia Harris are wise, witty, and womanly authors who challenge the best in this collection. To them, also girls from *Esquire,* we bow in admiration, for invading the enemy's camp and coming out not only alive but garlanded.

Of the men who have written about women, we have less to

say, because you know well their names and perhaps they are more expected here. We might note, though, the joyous lack of reserve which steals over a man writing for *Esquire*. Robert Ruark has an electric style that seems to take on extra voltage when he faces and paces against an *Esquire* deadline; Morris Markey we treasured, while he was with us, for his lusty appreciation of the *Esquire* girls. We shall never forget riding with him down Sixth Avenue, in New York, headed for his beloved Luchow's, when suddenly our cab was surrounded by cowgirls on their ponies, parading uptown to Madison Square Garden for the rodeo. Morris stuck his head out of the window and regarded each and every one with the knowing eye of a broncho-busting connoisseur. Then he leaned back blissfully in the cab. "Ah," sighed M. M., "the long hours in the saddle keep their little behinds so delightfully firm." He belongs in this anthology, if for no other reason.

Paul Gallico, F. Scott Fitzgerald, John Steinbeck, Stuart Cloete, Lawrence Stallings, Budd Schulberg, and many another on our Table of Contents could scarcely have been omitted, so instinctively have they turned to the *Esquire* phase, from time to time. It is, if we may make the attempt, a curious state of mind in which freedom, relaxation, excitement, stubbornness, and downright mischievousness contend for the upper case, and frequently surprise even the author, when he discovers that somehow the girls from *Esquire* got in there, in spite of him.

It might well be (although we naturally hope that it won't happen) that some loyal reader of this volume might shake his head a little and opine that it is rather single-minded. To that gentle rebuke, we can only bring to bear the delightful story of Dr. Samuel Johnson's encounter with a sprightly Highland lass. The great man was guest of honor at a country house in Scotland, and had been scarcely seated when this sixteen-year-old minx plumped herself down in his lap, put her arms around his neck, and soundly kissed him. The company was aghast—the gravest and most celebrated philosopher of his time! But the good doctor, as always, had a ready quip. "Do it again," said he to the little wench, "and let us see who will tire first."

PART ONE: *Woman: the Necessary Evil*

"Just one more, Ma'am. The public wants to share your sorrow."

BOB PATTERSON

Babe

I MET Babe for the first time—the first of many times—at a very chi-chi party at the French Club, in Shanghai. That was the time she stole the caviar.

She was sitting at a corner table, looking limpid-eyed at her companion over the rim of her champagne glass. Her hair was blonde, her smartly cut linen dress was exciting against the deep tan of her neck and arms, and she was drunk. Not obviously drunk, in the fashion of cheap tramps, but demurely, subtly drunk, in the fashion of very superior tramps.

Her companion was a young Englishman of the ruddy-cheek and toothbrush-mustache type. His eyebrows were a little higher on his forehead than most people's. This gave him a look of perpetual astonishment. His pongee suit was very correct, in the British style—which is to say that it was tight for him in all places.

I apologized as I borrowed one of the unused chairs at their table and prepared to move it elsewhere.

"Don't apologize, and don't take it!" she said.

"I beg your pardon?"

"I said, don't take it. Sit in it. Here."

The Englishman smiled politely. Babe gave me a long, what-kind-of-a-guy-are-you sort of stare. I made the usual silly remark about not wanting to intrude.

"You're not intruding, Cousin!" she said. "You're on an errand of mercy and you don't know it. I've done my part for Anglo-American relations for today and Captain Whoozis is just about to depart; aren't you. Captain? I'll be goddamed if I'm going to hear any more about yachting at Hendon. Even for champagne."

The Englishman stood up. It was still a smile—the thing on his tomato-red face—but it was a grim smile. His look of genteel loathing included Babe and me and possibly the entire population of the

United States, including Hawaii and the Virgin Islands. "I hope you enjoy the rest of my champagne," he said.

"*Chee-lah, tzoo-loh!*" said Babe, quite casually—which is what you say in a different tone of voice to bothersome ricksha coolies, but not to inoffensive Britons who buy champagne for you. But that was Babe, as I was to find out. We got quite friendly over the Englishman's wine, and I learned a few surface facts about the attractive young woman in smart white linen who looked like a Junior Leaguer, operated like Dillinger, and had a line of dialogue that would have made Sadie Thompson seem demure.

Her name was simply "Babe."

She was originally from Nevada, but she had been in Shanghai "since Christ only knows when." She drank any kind of champagne, but preferred it when it came out of a bottle that had been paid for by someone she didn't like. ("I wouldn't let a right guy buy champagne for me. It isn't worth the dough.") And she lived in the Rue des Soeurs, in the French Concession, which made her a neighbor of mine—and that was interesting and potentially convenient.

We drank the rest of the Englishman's champagne, and I—always irresponsible after the third or fourth glass—offered to buy another. "The hell with that noise," said Babe. "We'll order another bottle and put it on the Limey's chit." Which wasn't a bad idea when you come to think of it. A man shouldn't order one bottle of champagne unless he's ready to back it up with a second.

We talked about Shanghai, which she said she hated, and the rest of the people at the party, which made for lively, baroque conversation, and about the guest of honor. My little friend was surprised to hear that the blowout had been given in honor of Chaliapin. She had thought it was for the officers of the newly arrived Lancashire Fusiliers and hadn't the faintest idea who or what Chaliapin was.

She was a glib, worldly, raffishly poised little chick in many ways, and yet naive and uninformed in other respects; but she wasn't in the least dismayed when her shortcomings came to light. She wore her smart clothes easily and well and without seeming to be aware of them. Her little face was narrow and very demure—or it would have been demure had there not been so many four-letter words coming out of it. The lashes were long, and her blonde ringlets reminded you of one of the fantastic sirens that Nell Brinkley used to draw for the Hearst papers. Across the right side of her neck was the scar of a badly healed wound. It was a strange scar; not a clean cicatrice as from a knife, but an uneven, mottled mark like nothing I'd ever seen before.

Anyway, we had quite a yarn, she and I. The guest of honor came and departed without annoying us at all; and more champagne was charged against the poor Britisher's chit without difficulty. The Chinese in charge of the champagne apparently assumed that Babe was the man's wife. Drunk or sober, though, she was a wary little character, and she finally opined that we might just as well leave a little early. "Before that Limey gets a load of what he owes . . . not that I wouldn't enjoy staying and proving to him that he did it all of his own free will."

So we blew. And by an exit that wasn't exactly the most conspicuous egress from the club. On the way out, we came upon a white-gowned coolie who was energetically trundling a small keg into the street. The blonde asked him, in fluently guttural Shanghai dialect, where the hell he was going with the keg. Looking rather hurt that the matter had been brought up, he stood silent.

"He copped it," Babe said, rather admiringly. "What's in it?"

"Black caviar, I think. Enough for all the Tsars, back to and including Ivan the Terrible."

"Oh, goody! We'll pinch it from him. I know a Russian kid over on the Rue du Consulat who'll go nuts over this." And she turned to the coolie and informed him that I was an officer of the Settlement police. His lower jaw dropped as though someone had pulled out a cotter pin. He looked at me as if he expected me to pull a portable jail out of my pocket and slap it around him.

Taking advantage of the psychological moment, Babe told him to get back to the kitchen and forever give up caviar stealing. He wasn't good at it, she said. The poor man dropped the keg, bowed, mumbled something, and trotted quickly away.

"Pick it up, Cousin! You got a car? No? Well, no matter. We'll put it in a ricksha. Hey, *wom-bah-tsaw!*" she bawled, as we emerged on the street.

The Russian kid, who turned out to be a neat little deal in blonde braids, was delighted with the loot, when we delivered it to her. Glowing from the champagne, and pleased with herself because of the good deed and the inspired stroke of larceny, she bade me a friendly farewell.

"I like you," she told me, "if only because you aren't nosy. No questions. Just action. I hate guys who've got to know what gives. The woods are full of them."

I had never seen her before, but now I seemed to see her everywhere. Being taken to the races by young fellows from the British-American Tobacco Company, and Shanghai Power, and the other foreign companies. Dancing at the Little Club or window shopping outside Madame Greenhouse's store on upper Bubbling Well Road. Oı having early breakfast down in one of the popular dives in the honky-tonk Hongkew District. She always had a wave and a hoot and a grin for me, or sometimes an acrid grimace of commentary on her escort of the moment.

But I learned nothing more of her background, her identity, or her way of getting by in a town where existence was strictly a dog-eat-dog affair.

One night, I was standing at the Number One Boy's desk at the Paramount Cabaret, waiting for my date to show, when Babe came into the place with a pink-cheeked young character who reeked of Empire. She rather spoiled the chic of her entrance—*très décolletée* and *bouffante*—by goosing me roundly and demanding to know "What's doin'?"

I jerked a thumb toward her escort, who was being very man-of-the-worldish with the Number One Boy, and asked if she had changed her mind about the British. She laughed and rubbed her finger tips against each other in the well-known cash-signifying gesture. "I love them when they're loaded, Cousin!"

When the Boy had shoved them into a ringside and returned to the portal, I tried a small-sized question. "The blonde missy; is she one of the regulars, Lum?"

Lum was usually a great man with the inside information, but he wasn't going to talk about Babe. That was for sure.

"Who is she, Lum? What's her racket?"

"No got racket." Lum wasn't liking me too well at that point.

"Don't get sore. I mean . . . how does she get by?"

I didn't get an answer until he had seated several more parties. By then my date had arrived and we had won ourselves a table. The Number One Boy had recovered his good spirits and figured out an answer. As he pushed my chair in, he murmured, "She . . . how you say? . . . make a buck here, make a buck there."

He laughed, pleased with his knowledge of Americanisms.

I learned some more about Babe from—of all people—Colonel Beauden, the commander of the Marines in Shanghai, who saw me watching her at the jai-alai one night. She was betting fat hunks of money on a big Argentine player, who was certainly justifying her faith.

"That's Babe," said Beauden. "I don't know where she gets it, but I'd rather not risk any evil-minded guesses, for she's a goodhearted wench. Made up the deficit in our fund for the orphanage—the deal we sponsor for the kids these White Russian gals are always having, with some of our men on the co-operating end. Insisted on plunking in nearly a thousand clams. Gold dollars, too. Goodhearted kid."

I thought about the reluctant philanthropy, for such causes, of the elegant lads in the throne rooms of the big American and British companies and I liked the blonde with the brown eyes and the scarred neck even more.

I didn't have a chance to talk to Babe again for many months. For one thing, I moved away from the street on which she lived, and then again, I was put on the late shift of the newspaper that paid for and often got my services, and I wasn't able to get around to the night spots so often.

Then, one night late . . . or, rather, one morning very early, I ran into Babe at the Red Rose, a White Russian dive at the juncture of Jukong Alley and North Szechuan Road, just outside the International Settlement gates.

The Red Rose was gaudy, soiled, drafty, threadbare, and very, very sad. It would have made a wonderful night club for ghosts, or for people who were considering suicide. Perhaps it was the minor-key music that the balalaika band was always plinking away at, or maybe it was the fact that the Russian lady who ran the place always wore black. She was in perpetual mourning for her husband, who had been killed in Russia by the Bolshies twenty years before. He must have been a helluva man.

This career widow from Tomsk—with her brother, a shavenheaded, beetle-browed cretin, who always looked as if he had just disposed of the body—ran the Red Rose with the assistance of probably the most variable sliding scale of prices in Shanghai. The waiters charged according to the individual patron. "Vun bottle uff vine" might cost a resident Shanghai-lander two dollars, Mex. A drunken sailor would be scraped for five bucks, while a let's-go-for-broke tourist would have to reach for a tenner, or maybe more. A White Russian would have torn the place up if asked for more than a dollar-twenty.

You entered through a long passageway, breathing gingerly as the odors of decay, cheap ylang-ylang perfume, Japanese whiskey, and ancient perspiration met your nostrils, and you remained only if you had a taste for curiosa. After a while, though, you might be glad you had stayed. Pleasantly baroque things were always happening there.

Once I heard a beautiful, if somewhat pock-marked, Korean girl sing an aria from *Madame Butterfly* in a way that would have sent the Met's best diva back to Milan for a few more lessons. Another time, a Russian lady intercepted her Portuguese gigolo there while he was entertaining another lady. She removed from his person a striped silk shirt that she had given him. Removed it stripe by stripe.

The Red Rose was very chic, in its way.

I was sitting there minding my own business and listening to the balalaika band brood over *Two Guitars* when Babe wandered in. She was beautifully dressed, as always, and wore one of the strapless, cloth-of-gold evening gowns that were then new in the Orient. She sat down at my table.

"What's doin', Cousin?"

I told her what was doing and we eventually got into one of those pseudophilosophical, post-midnight conversations about the pointlessness of life, especially life in Shanghai, especially night life in Shanghai. A glittering treadmill was all that it was, we agreed.

"What I'd give," said Babe, "to be in San Francisco, just working for a living! At the telephone company, or at Magnin's, or maybe even dishing out waves and henna rinses in some hole-in-the-wall beauty shop. At the end of the day, I'd be clopping up Post, or Sutter, on my way to a comfortable little kitchenette apartment. I'd stop off at the corner grocery for a loaf of bread and a can of tuna, something for dinner, and a couple of packs of cigarettes. Stateside cigarettes instead of these goddam Mei Li Bah bastards. And a new magazine, fresh and clean, to read. And the afternoon papers. All about Tommy Manville's latest blonde, and the theatre in the Mission that got stuck up that morning, and that prissy schmo, Dick Tracy."

She was far away from the Red Rose, and Jukong Alley, and Shanghai, as she talked. I figured that we'd be in the tears-in-the-beer stage soon at that rate, and so I tried to take a powder on nostalgia. "Mama Russky's going to sing," I said. "Bet a buck she favors us with *Dark Eyes*."

The widow was on the small stage. The anthropoid-browed brother was lurking behind a pillar. He was a one-man claque, as it were. As soon as sister's number was through, he'd start to applaud and cheer, as if he'd been stricken with a fit. Then he'd hurl a coin onto the stage—a silver buck. The decoy dollar. This

"I poked a cop. What did you do?"

gesture was supposed to precipitate a like effusion on the part of guests. It seldom did.

As Mama Russky put her hoarse contralto through the lugubrious paces of *Dark Eyes,* Babe continued to torture herself with homesickness. "That apartment would be just right for one dame. A good radio and a record-player, and the drapes would be cretonne—I'm bugs about cretonne—and the bathroom would be in coral, with a small radio to listen to while I'm soaking myself after a hard day's work. That ain't much to ask, is it?"

"Not for a broad who's wearing emerald-cut diamonds and Paris originals, it isn't."

My companion wasn't interested. She was soaking herself in a Nob Hill kitchenette apartment, listening to the radio, and wondering about her evening's date.

"He'd be a nice kid who pumped gas for Texaco, or peddled tickets for the Southern Pacific, or something like that. No *pukka sahib* English gentleman, no Shanghai slicker with a lot of gab, a lot of angles, and too much after-midnight experience."

"Don't be too sold on the idea that the home boys aren't without angles, kid. Shanghai has no monopoly on sophisication."

"Yeah, but somehow it's more tiresome out here, Cousin. Sordid—isn't that the word? There's no contrast. The wise, smart-to-the-world attitude is so damn routine here. It would be refreshing as hell to run into a guy who thought that just a plain, ordinary kiss was hot stuff.

"Like that date of mine back home who'd ring the downstairs buzzer just after I'd pressed out my blouse for work in the morning, and painted my nails, and eaten my tuna sandwich. I'd press the button to let him in and jimmy myself into a new pair of patent-leather spikes, and by the time I'd wiggled into my dress, he'd be at the door. In time to zip it up and love doing it. . . .

"Then we'd step out into the fog, and into this guy's Plymouth—he'd be about Plymouth class last year's model but plenty shined up—and we'd go to the Bal, or the St. Francis, or maybe just to a bar for highballs. And the conversation wouldn't be clever, and there wouldn't be any sharp, double-meaning remarks, and nobody would try to impress anyone else with what they were back home—the way they do here—but there would be lots of laughs, and . . ."

". . . and eventually you'd get all you wanted of that and buy yourself a ticket back to Shanghai."

"No, you're dead wrong, Cousin, I'd stay there forever. With what I know now, I'd stay there forever. *Forever.*"

Now she had me feeling low, too. Despite the drinks. I blamed it on the place.

"Let's go across the alley to the Venus for some chow. This trap is sure warping my *joie de vivre.*"

It was that very dark, very still hour just before dawn, as we came out on the bleak, honky-tonk gaiety of Jukong Alley. The neon lights were still gleaming coldly, but the street was all but empty. A scattering of hard-working beggars shivered in their rags, a few never-say-die ricksha pullers stood half-asleep between the shafts of their vehicles.

"About that Frisco stuff, that homesickness, Babe . . . why don't you leave Shanghai if you hate it like that?"

She wasn't at all corny or melodramatic about it. She just told me. "I can't go back home. Ever."

Shortly afterward, Johnny Morris, the UP bureau chief, mentioned Babe. Someone at the American Club—a Babbittish, Rotary Clublike place that I frequented as infrequently as possible—had told a typical sort of yarn about the girl: "Hawaiian family, a troupe of dancers, had got stuck in town, largely because of the unscrupulous machinations of their agent, a gentleman with a resounding reputation as a creep and a sonuvabitch. Babe sent them back to Honolulu. Of course, she had had to pawn a diamond bracelet in order to do it."

"Who the hell is she, this Babe?" someone asked.

"Babe is what they used to call a Coaster here in the old days," Johnny said. "A China Coaster is the term the old China hands had for it. This port is a mecca for hundreds of young Americans and Britishers who get two or three weeks off each year from the rubber plantations and tea farms and factories and godowns and branch offices of the Far East. They come surging into Shanghai with a year's pay and a year's backlog of hunger for bright lights, gaiety, booze, and broads. Sometimes they fall into the hands of the Russian women and the whores of Blood Alley and North Kiangse Road. If they're wiser, and luckier, they meet up with one of these women like Babe . . . who take their money, see them through their vacation, and send them back to their stations happy, hung-over, unfrustrated, and broke. Coasters, the old-timers call them. Babe is a Coaster."

"You mean, she's a . . . well, she's a kind of high-class tramp?"

"Not at all. Some of them are more broad-minded than others, but most are just party girls who provide pleasant companionship, a knowledge of the town, and protection against the more obvious gyps. These kids have a code. They collect plenty, and give plenty . . . up to a point."

It was from Babe herself, though, that I learned how she had wandered to China and how she had become a Coaster. The telling of the story was a sequel to a really strange incident.

Babe and I had been sitting at a table in Sam Levy's Venus Café, waiting for some 4 a.m. ham and eggs. She was restless and uneasy. Rather abruptly, she excused herself and slipped away from the table, taking her bag but not troubling to pick up the mink draped over her chair.

The food came, but my companion failed to return. Levy came over, said hello, and sat down. "Where's Babe?" he asked.

I told him I didn't know. Maybe she'd taken a powder. Except that her mink was still there. Well, she didn't come back. Come daylight, Sam and I were standing at the entrance to his place, looking out into the gruesome greyness of a new Shanghai day and speculating unhopefully about possibilities. "She could be at the bottom of Soochow Creek," said Sam. He had lived in China for years, and had few illusions.

"It's probably something very reasonable and commonplace," I said, hopefully.

"Like getting hit over the head with something heavy," said Sam.

I didn't like thinking of that. I had got to like the brash little blonde. I didn't like the thought of her bobbing around in the dirty waters of the Soochow. But when nine o'clock came, it was pretty clear that Babe had gone for more than a breath of fresh air. I shouldered her coat, and took a ricksha to her apartment.

There was no one there. Her *amah* hadn't seen her. I left the coat and a message to call me and went home. If a friend of yours disappeared under such circumstances in Toledo or Seattle, you might notify the cops. In Shanghai, somehow you didn't. It might be invading someone's privacy. There were so many labyrinths and by-passes in the lives of even your closest friends. . . . You were hesitant about assuming any certainties about them. Who knows? Perhaps Babe had a lover somewhere near to whom she had gone on an impulse. I hit the hay.

I dropped by her apartment again at tiffintime. The *amah*, who had been with her for years, was a little worried now. Missy no come home yet. Missy have hair appointment. No keep. The *amah* had spoken to the *amahs* of several of Babe's lady friends. Missy no stop alongside them. Bimeby she go American consul. I calmed her and asked if maybe Missy didn't have *other* friend

. . . some gentleman friend, eh? The *amah* was as indignant as if her mistress were a Mother Superior. *No mastah have got!*

Casually and as if I were just looking for an item for the paper, I dropped in on the Welshman who ran things at night at the Central Police Station. Nothing. Much later I dropped in on Sam Levy. He was sure about Soochow Creek now. And then Babe walked in.

She looked a little wilted, but she was a long way from being ready for the undertaker. I got sore, in my relief. "You might at least have told me where to send the ham and eggs."

"I'm sorry, Cousin. It wasn't my fault. Take me home, will you?"

Sam was popeyed with curiosity. "You mean you ain't going to tell us where you been?"

Babe fingered her nose at him. "Go back into the woodwork, Levy. You'll have to wait and read it in my memoirs."

She didn't say a word until we arrived at her apartment. The *amah* was waiting still, bleak-eyed with worry. Her relief took the form of indignation.

"That's right; I'm a dog, Mei-Mei," said Babe. "Now go to bed and stop worrying."

I settled down in a chair and waited morosely for a drink, as if I had been much mistreated. The blonde poured one, then opened a little cabinet next to the divan that dominated the room and took out a spirit lamp, two small jars, and a long, copper, probelike needle. She lighted the spirit lamp, which was provided with a thick glass chimney. It was flattened out at the top, out of which the crest of the flame slowly licked through a small vent.

"Of course you knew I was on opium, didn't you, Cuz?" said Babe, as she opened one of the pots.

I was silent and suddenly shocked. If I had heard about it in conversation, I would perhaps have taken it more casually, but seeing her calmly manipulating the paraphernalia as she talked somehow got me down.

"I've been on it for a long time. It's father, mother, sister, brother . . . and husband and lover to me, now, Cousin." She laughed without pleasure. "I'm a hophead."

What was there to say?

"And that accounts for last night. The yen came on earlier than it usually does. I knew of a place just around the corner from Sam's place and thought that I could get off the hook with a couple of quick pills. It isn't a bad place. A kind of a hideaway in the back of the Moon Palace Hotel, and I know Leong, the guy who runs it, pretty well. I had barely got on my hip and the cook-girl was rolling the yen-pok when . . . *ai-yai* . . . the cops. The goddam Settlement police raided the Moon Palace."

She had the pipe out now—a handsome ivory deal with the flat Peking bowl. She dipped the somewhat spatulated end of the needle into the viscous brown stuff in one of the pots, drew it out, and held it over the flame that peeped from the top of the spirit lamp. The opium wanted to drip from the needle, but she twirled it rapidly between her fingers and the gum bubbled in the heat, sputtered a bit, then began to coagulate.

"Leong locked the door and warned us to be quiet. The entranceway is flush with the wall on the outside, and the place has been cased plenty before without anyone getting wise to it. It got by this time, too. But the cops hung around the hotel the rest of the day, looking for what they could find, and Leong wouldn't let any of us out. What's worse, he wouldn't let the cook-girl light up again for fear the odor would get to them. So there we sat, the whole goddam day, looking at the walls. Until just a little while ago, when Leong let us out."

The pill was ready now. Babe rolled it back and forth on the hot glass top of the lamp, molding it to size and shape. It was no longer viscous, the banana oil having been roasted away. It was like a pellet of fresh fudge, and suddenly she fitted it onto the pipe, just over the hole in the bowl. Then she turned the bowl so that it was just over the flame; and, placing the amber mouthpiece to her lips, she started to inhale. The room was suddenly full of sweet, sweet fumes—an unforgettable odor, subtly suggestive, somehow, of beautiful evil.

Babe continued to inhale, avidly, hungrily, noisily. With each rapid intake of breath, the pill burned brightly, the rim of fire at its top eventually consuming it entirely. Then she lay back. Her eyes were half-shuttered now. She smiled at me through the slits. "Forgive me, now?"

I finished my drink very quickly and went for the bottle. It was like watching a woman commit suicide and being able to do nothing at all about it. I wanted to tell her that she was a fool, that she had no right to louse herself up in this fashion . . . but I got drunk instead.

Before I did, and while Babe prepared and smoked many more pills, I heard more of her story. I got the rest of it when I asked her why the hell she didn't get away from China, why she didn't go home.

"You mean the kitchenette-apartment deal, and the job at Magnin's?"

"Yes. Or does that look good only when you're gassed?"

"It looks good all the time. Day and night. Only, like I said before, I can't go back. Ever."

She was nearly in the other dimension now, nearly in the dream world of the poppy-pus. She spoke slowly and clearly and without emphasis or emotion, though her eyes were closed and her hands were folded lovingly over the ivory pipe. I tilted the bottle into my glass as I listened to her tell why she couldn't go home.

"I killed a girl in San Francisco. Over something so silly that I've nearly forgotten what it was. Something about a man. I've forgotten *him* all the way. The silly bastard. Wouldn't know him if he stuck his head out from under this bed.

"We had a fight—she and I—and I slid a kitchen knife into her just below the navel, blood enough to float the Ark, and some left over for the *Queen Mary,* and maybe the Vallejo ferryboat, too. She started to go fast. I was nearly bugs. I tried to bring her to, but she was plenty out. When I felt her pulse and got no answer, I was scared silly. I threw a coat on over my slip . . . that was all I had on . . . and charged out of the house. I didn't want to die in a roomful of gas. And I didn't want to crum out the rest of my life in jail. I wanted away.

"I knew a guy. The guy that every dame knows, that she doesn't love, but that she saves away in her mind to help her on a rainy day. And, Cuz, this was strictly a rainy day. He was the purser, or assistant purser or something like that, on a Dollar boat. Luckily, the boat was in and he was in his cabin. I sure got to know that cabin well—every inch of it. I stayed in it all the way to Shanghai.

"At first, he figured to get me off at Honolulu. But the customs people were too cagey, and the boat was only in port for one day. So my purser pal got me a dress and some toilet articles and we sailed. And one night, a couple of weeks later, after the boat dropped anchor in the Whangpoo, he sneaked me over the side into a bumboat . . . and I've been here ever since.

"Except for a trip I made, Christ, what a trip!"

Subconsciously, she fingered the scar on her neck.

"A few years back, my nightmare caught up with me. One morning, I get a call from the consulate. They'd like me to step in and see them. Well, I figure it could be nothing . . . and it could be the man with the handcuffs. Somehow, I feel it ain't just nothing. The panic is on again. I talked to Mei-Mei here, my *amah.* She's a good woman. She fixes me up with her brother, who has a freight sampan in the Yangtze River trade—a little job you wouldn't ride in for laughs.

"I packed a bag and dusted out of Shanghai like a duck who's just heard about the opening of duck season. With Mei-Mei's brother, and a crew of coolies, and not even Heaven to protect me. Cousin . . . *that was a trip!* We went upriver to parts that would make Shangri-La look suburban. We were away nearly six months. I slept on a mat and cooked rice for the coolies and even pulled on towrope with them when the damn mud scow had to be hauled through the no-wind parts of the river. That's where I got this scar on my neck—the damnedest rope burn you ever saw.

"I came back in the spring a different woman. I spoke good Chinese. I was through worrying about microbes forever. I wasn't even too worried about handcuffs any more. And I had learned about opium. The world was never the same for me again."

The atmosphere of the little room was strictly minor-key now. The bottle was nearly empty and the fumes of the poppy-mud had reached me, too. The normal world of yesterday was as gone as yesterday's clouds. I was living in Babe's sad, unnatural little aura of defeat, frustration, and to-hell-with-it. She went on, with a pathetic little giggle.

"Funny thing. The summons from the consulate turned out to be only some silly thing about registration. I laughed myself into a hemorrhage."

Her voice had dwindled to a fuzzy monotone. "So that's why I can't go home. Ever."

I waited until her breathing developed into a gentle snore, and then I fumbled my way out. The cold morning air went through my nose and throat like a whiff of ammonia.

I left Shanghai shortly afterward and returned to San Francisco. I was reminded next of Babe when I received a letter from her shortly before the Japanese invasion of China. It was postmarked Nanking.

"Dear Cuz: This is to let you know that I am as fine as I hope that this finds you. Things out here are same as always, only more so now that the Nips are playing soldiers again. But it means dough for Babe (all these guys selling army supplies, and so on) so why should I kick. Why don't you come back out? There's a lot of things going on which would make work for your typewriter. (Is it still as lazy as it was? Ha Ha! Joke.) Besides, I miss you.

You were always a good Joe and you were never nosy. Despite which, you learned ALL. There must be a moral to that somewhere. Drop me a line. I have a big house here and it's gotten to be a sort of a rondayvoo for a lot of the civilians doing business with the government. Best regards.

"Babe (Mrs. Babe Sadlir)"

It was the first time, oddly enough, that I ever heard her second name, or realized that she had been married.

Shortly afterward, I checked with the San Francisco police. Discreetly.

Yes, they had a record of the name. She had been named by a complainant as the person who had assaulted her some years ago. The victim hadn't been badly hurt, though, and the follow-up indicated that she had wanted to drop the matter. No prosecution. Babe Sadlir wasn't wanted in San Francisco.

Before I could get the information into a letter to Babe, the Japanese took Nanking. Later on, I learned that a foreign woman, named Sadlir, was among those who had overdelayed their departure from the city. She was missing. It was thought that she was dead. No word of her, no proof of how she died. . . . in the words of the authorities, "No disposition whatsoever."

And now, I thought, no kitchenette apartment, no cretonne drapes, no knock at the door by that nine o'clock date. . . .

JOHN STEINBECK

A Snake of One's Own

IT WAS almost dark when young Dr. Phillips swung his sack to his shoulder and left the tide pool. He climbed up over the rocks and squashed along the street in his rubber boots. The street lights were on by the time he arrived at his little commercial laboratory on the cannery street of Monterey. It was a tight little building, standing partly on piers over by the water and partly on the land. On both sides the big corrugated iron sardine canneries crowded in on it.

Dr. Phillips climbed the wooden steps and opened the door. The white rats in their cages scampered up and down the wire, and the captive cats in their pens mewed for milk. Dr. Phillips turned on the glaring light over the dissection table and dumped his clammy sack on the floor. He walked to the glass cages by the window where the rattlesnakes lived, leaned over and looked in.

The snakes were bunched and resting in the corners of the cage, but every head was clear; the dusty eyes seemed to look at nothing, but as the young man leaned over the cage the forked tongues, black on the ends and pink behind, twittered out and waved slowly up and down. Then the snakes recognized the man and pulled in their tongues.

Dr. Phillips threw off his leather coat and built a fire in the tin stove; he set a kettle of water on the stove and dropped a can of beans into the water. Then he stood staring down at the sack on the floor. He was a slight young man with the mild, preoccupied eyes of one who looks through a microscope a great deal. He wore a short blond beard.

The draft ran breathily up the chimney and a glow of warmth came from the stove. The little waves washed quietly about the piles under the building. Arranged on shelves about the room were tier above tier of museum jars containing the mounted marine specimens the laboratory dealt in.

Dr. Phillips opened a side door and went into his bedroom, a book-lined cell containing an army cot, a reading light and an uncomfortable wooden chair. He pulled off his rubber boots and put on a pair of sheepskin slippers. When he went back to the other room the water in the kettle was already beginning to hum.

He lifted his sack to the table under the white light and emptied out two dozen common starfish. These he laid out side by side on the table. His preoccupied eyes turned to the busy rats in the wire cages. Taking grain from a paper sack he poured it into the feeding troughs. Instantly the rats scrambled down from the wire and fell upon the food. A bottle of milk stood on a glass shelf between a small mounted octopus and a jellyfish. Dr. Phillips lifted down the milk and walked to the cat cage, but before he filled the containers he reached in the cage and gently picked out a big rangy alley tabby. He stroked her for a moment and then dropped her in a small black painted box, closed the lid and bolted it and then turned on a petcock which admitted gas into the killing chamber. While the short soft struggle went on in the black box he filled the saucers with milk. One of the cats arched against his hand and he smiled and petted her neck.

The box was quiet now. He turned off the gas for the airtight box would be full of gas.

On the stove the pan of water was bubbling furiously about the can of beans. Dr. Phillips lifted out the can with a big pair of forceps, opened the beans and emptied them into a glass dish. While he ate he watched the starfish on the table. From between the rays little drops of milky fluid were exuding. He bolted his beans and when they were gone he put the dish in the sink and stepped to the equipment cupboard. From this he took a microscope and a pile of little glass dishes. He filled the dishes one by one with sea water from a tap and arranged them in a line beside the starfish. He took out his watch and laid it on the table under the pouring white lights. The waves washed with little sighs against the piles under the floor. He took an eyedropper from a drawer and bent over the starfish.

At that moment there were quick soft steps on the wooden stairs and a strong knocking at the door. A slight grimace of annoyance crossed the young man's face as he went to open. A tall lean woman stood in the doorway. She was dressed in a severe dark suit—her straight black hair, growing low on a flat forehead, was mussed as though the wind had been blowing it. Her black eyes glittered in the strong light.

She spoke in a soft throaty voice, "May I come in? I want to talk to you."

"I'm very busy just now," he said half-heartedly. "I have to do things at times." But he stood away from the door. The tall woman slipped in.

"I'll be quiet until you can talk to me."

He closed the door and brought the uncomfortable chair from the bedroom. "You see," he apologized, "the process is started and I must get to it." So many people wandered in and asked questions. He had little routines of explanations for the commoner processes. He could say them without thinking. "Sit here. In a few minutes I'll be able to listen to you."

The tall woman leaned over the table. With the eyedropper the young man gathered fluid from between the rays of the starfish and squirted it into a bowl of water, and then he drew some milky fluid and squirted it in the same bowl and stirred the water gently with the eyedropper. He began his little patter of explanation.

"When starfish are sexually mature they release sperm and ova when they are exposed at low tide. By choosing mature specimens and taking them out of the water, I give them a condition of low tide. Now I've mixed the sperm and eggs. Now I put some of the mixture in each one of these ten watch glasses. In ten minutes I will kill those in the first glass with menthol, twenty minutes later I will kill the second group and then a new group every twenty minutes. Then I will have arrested the process in stages, and I will mount the series on microscope slides for biologic study." He paused. "Would you like to look at this first group under the microscope?"

"No, thank you." He turned quickly to her. People always wanted to look through the glass. She was not looking at the table at all, but at him. Her black eyes were on him but they did not seem to see him. He realized why—the irises were as dark as the pupils, there was no color line between the two. Dr. Phillips was piqued at her answer. Although answering questions bored him, a lack of interest in what he was doing irritated him. A desire to arouse her grew in him.

"While I'm waiting the first ten minutes I have something to do. Some people don't like to see it. Maybe you'd better step into that room until I finish."

"No," she said in her soft flat tone. "Do what you wish. I will wait until you can talk to me." Her hands rested side by side on her lap. She was completely at rest. Her eyes were bright but the rest of her was almost in a state of suspended animation. He thought, "Low metabolic rate, almost as low as a frog's, from the looks." The desire to shock her out of her inanition possessed him again.

He brought a little wooden cradle to the table, laid out scalpels and scissors and rigged a big hollow needle to a pressure tube. Then from the killing chamber he brought the limp dead cat and laid it in the cradle and tied its legs to hooks in the sides. He glanced sidewise at the woman. She had not moved. She was still at rest.

The cat grinned up into the light, its pink tongue stuck out between its needle teeth. Dr. Phillips deftly snipped open the skin at the throat; with a scalpel he slit through and found an artery.

With flawless technique he put the needle in the vessel and tied it in with gut. "Embalming fluid," he explained. "Later I'll inject yellow mass into the venous system and red mass into the arterial system—for blood stream dissection—biology classes."

He looked around at her again. Her dark eyes seemed veiled with dust. She looked without expression at the cat's open throat. Not a drop of blood had escaped. The incision was clean. Dr. Phillips looked at his watch. "Time for the first group." He shook a few crystals of menthol into the first watch glass.

The woman was making him nervous. The rats climbed about on the wire of their cage again and squeaked softly. The waves under the building beat with little shocks on the piles.

The young man shivered. He put a few lumps of coal in the stove and sat down. "Now," he said. "I haven't anything to do for twenty minutes." He noticed how short her chin was between lower lip and point. She seemed to awaken slowly, to come up out of some deep pool of consciousness. Her head raised and her dark dusty eyes moved about the room and then came back to him.

"I was waiting," she said. Her hands remained side by side on her lap. "You have snakes?"

"Why, yes," he said rather loudly. "I have about two dozen rattlesnakes. I milk out the venom and send it to the anti-venom laboratories."

She continued to look at him but her eyes did not center on him, rather they covered him and seemed to see in a big circle all around him. "Have you a male snake, a male rattlesnake?"

"Well it just happens I know I have. I came in one morning and found a big snake in—in coition with a smaller one. That's very rare in captivity. You see, I do know I have a male snake."

"Where is he?"

"Why right in the glass cage by the window there."

Her head swung slowly around but her two quiet hands did not move. She turned back toward him. "May I see?"

He got up and walked to the case by the window. On the sand bottom the knot of rattlesnakes lay entwined, but their heads were clear. The tongues came out and flickered a moment and then waved up and down feeling the air for vibrations. Dr. Phillips nervously turned his head. The woman was standing beside him. He had not heard her get up from the chair. He had heard only the splash of water among the piles and the scampering of the rats on the wire screen.

She said softly, "Which is the male you spoke of?"

He pointed to a thick, dusty grey snake lying by itself in one corner of the cage. "That one. He's nearly five feet long. He comes from Texas. Our Pacific coast snakes are usually smaller. He's been taking all the rats, too. When I want the others to eat I have to take him out."

The woman stared down at the blunt dry head. The forked tongue slipped out and hung quivering for a long moment. "And you're sure he's a male."

"Rattlesnakes are funny," he said glibly. "Nearly every generalization proves wrong. I don't like to say anything definite about rattlesnakes, but—yes—I can assure you he's a male."

Her eyes did not move from the flat head. "Will you sell him to me?"

"Sell him?" he cried. "Sell him to you?"

"You do sell specimens, don't you?"

"Oh—yes. Of course I do. Of course I do."

"How much? Five dollars? Ten?"

"Oh! Not more than five. But do you know anything about rattlesnakes? You might be bitten."

She looked at him for a moment. "I don't intend to take him. I want to leave him here, but—I want him to be mine. I want to come here and look at him and feed him and to know he's mine." She opened a little purse and took out a five dollar bill. "Here! Now he is mine."

Dr. Phillips began to be afraid. "You could come to look at him without owning him."

"I want him to be mine."

"Oh, Lord!" he cried. "I've forgotten the time." He ran to the table.

"Three minutes over. It won't matter much." He shook menthol crystals into the second watch glass. And then he was drawn back to the cage where the woman still stared at the snake.

She asked, "What does he eat?"

"I feed them white rats, rats from the cage over there."

"Will you put him in the other cage? I want to feed him."

"But he doesn't need food. He's had a rat already this week. Sometimes they don't eat for three or four months. I had one that didn't eat for over a year."

In her low monotone she asked, "Will you sell me a rat?"

He shrugged his shoulders. "I see. You want to watch how rattlesnakes eat. All right. I'll show you. The rat will cost twenty-five cents. It's better than a bull fight if you look at it one way, and it's simply a snake eating his dinner if you look at it another." His tone had become acid. He hated people who made sport of natural processes. He was not a sportsman but a biologist. He could kill a thousand animals for knowledge, but not an insect for pleasure. He'd been over this in his mind before.

She turned her head slowly toward him and the beginning of a smile formed on her thin lips. "I want to feed my snake," she said. "I'll put him in the other cage." She had opened the top of the cage and dipped her hand in before he knew what she was doing. He leaped forward and pulled her back. The lid banged shut.

"Haven't you any sense?" he asked fiercely. "Maybe he wouldn't kill you, but he'd make you damned sick in spite of what I could do for you."

"You put him in the other cage then," she said quietly.

Dr. Phillips was shaken. He found that he was avoiding the dark eyes that didn't seem to look at anything.

He felt that it was profoundly wrong to put a rat into the cage, deeply sinful; and he didn't know why. Often he had put rats in the cage when someone or other had wanted to see it, but this desire tonight sickened him. He tried to explain himself out of it.

"It's a good thing to see," he said. "It shows you how a snake can work. It makes you have a respect for a rattlesnake. Then, too, lots of people have dreams about the terror of snakes making the kill. I think because it is a subjective rat. The person is the rat. Once you see it the whole matter is objective. The rat is only a rat and the terror is removed."

He took a long stick equipped with a leather noose from the wall. Opening the trap he dropped the noose over the big snake's head and tightened the thong. A piercing dry rattle filled the room.

The thick body writhed and slashed about the handle of the stick as he lifted the snake out and dropped it in the feeding cage. It stood ready to strike for a time, but the buzzing gradually ceased. The snake crawled into a corner, made a big figure eight with its body and lay still.

"You see," the young man explained, "these snakes are quite tame. I've had them a long time. I suppose I could handle them if I wanted to, but everyone who does handle rattlesnakes gets bitten sooner or later. I just don't want to take the chance." He glanced at the woman. He hated to put in the rat. She had moved over in front of the new cage; her black eyes were on the stony head of the snake again.

She said, "Put in a rat."

Reluctantly he went to the rat cage. For some reason he was sorry for the rat, and such a feeling had never come to him before. His eyes went over the mass of swarming white bodies climbing up the screen toward him. "Which one?" he thought. "Which one shall it be?" Suddenly he turned angrily to the woman. "Wouldn't you rather I put in a cat? Then you'd see a real fight. The cat might even win, but if it lost it might kill the snake. I'll sell you a cat if you like."

She didn't look at him. "Put in a rat," she said. "I want him to eat."

He opened the rat cage and thrust his hand in. His fingers found a tail and he lifted a plump, red-eyed rat out of the cage. It struggled up to try to bite his fingers and failing hung spread out and motionless from its tail. He walked quickly across the room, opened the feeding cage and dropped the rat in on the sand floor. "Now, watch it," he cried.

The woman did not answer him. Her eyes were on the snake where it lay still. Its tongue, flicking in and out rapidly, tasted the air of the cage.

The rat landed on its feet, turned around and sniffed at its pink naked tail and then unconcernedly trotted across the sand, smelling as it went. The room was silent. Dr. Phillips did not know whether the water sighed among the piles or whether the woman sighed. Out of the corner of his eye he saw her body crouch and stiffen.

The snake moved out smoothly, slowly. The tongue flicked in and out. The motion was so gradual, so smooth that it didn't seem to be motion at all. In the other end of the cage the rat perked up in a sitting position and began to lick down the fine white hair on its chest. The snake moved on, keeping always a deep S curve in its neck.

The silence beat on the young man. He felt the blood drifting up in his body. He said loudly, "See! He keeps the striking curve ready. Rattlesnakes are cautious, almost cowardly animals. The mechanism is so delicate. The snake's dinner is to be got by an operation as deft as a surgeon's job. He takes no chances with his instruments."

The snake had flowed to the middle of the cage by now. The rat looked up, saw the snake and then unconcernedly went back to licking his chest.

"It's the most beautiful thing in the world," the young man said. His veins were throbbing. "It's the most terrible thing in the world."

The snake was close now. Its head lifted a few inches from the sand. The head weaved slowly back and forth, aiming, getting distance, aiming. Dr. Phillips glanced again at the woman. He turned sick. She was weaving too, not much, just a suggestion.

The rat looked up and saw the snake. He dropped to four feet and backed up, and then—the stroke.

It was impossible to see, simply a flash. The rat jarred as though under an invisible blow. The snake backed hurriedly into the corner from which he had come, and settled down, his tongue working constantly.

"Perfect!" Dr. Phillips cried. "Right between the shoulder blades. The fangs must almost have reached the heart."

The rat stood still, breathing like a little white bellows. Suddenly he leaped in the air and landed on his side. His legs kicked spasmodically for a second and he was dead.

The woman relaxed, relaxed sleepily.

"Well," the young man demanded, "it was an emotional bath, wasn't it?"

She turned her misty eyes to him. "Will he eat it now?" she asked.

"Of course he'll eat it. He didn't kill it for a thrill. He killed it because he was hungry."

The corners of the woman's mouth turned up a trifle again. She looked back at the snake. "I want to see him eat it."

Now the snake came out of his corner again. There was no striking curve in his neck, but he approached the rat gingerly, ready to jump back in case it attacked him. He nudged the body gently with his blunt nose, and drew away.

Satisfied that it was dead, he touched the body all over with his chin, from head to tail. He seemed to measure it and to kiss it. Finally he opened his mouth and unhinged his jaws at the corners.

Dr. Phillips put his will against his head to keep it from turning toward the woman. He thought, "If she's opening her mouth, I'll be sick. I'll be afraid." He succeeded in keeping his eyes away.

The snake fitted his jaws over the rat's head and then, with a slow peristaltic pulsing, began to engulf the rat. The jaws gripped and the whole throat crawled up, and the jaws gripped again.

Dr. Phillips turned away and went to his work table. "You've made me miss one of the series," he said bitterly. "The set won't be complete." He put one of the watch glasses under a low power microscope and looked at it, and then angrily he poured the contents of all the dishes into the sink.

The waves had fallen so that only a wet whisper came up through the floor. The young man lifted a trapdoor at his feet and dropped the starfish down into the black water. He paused at the cat, crucified in the cradle and grinning comically into the light. Its body was puffed with embalming fluid. He shut off the pressure, withdrew the needle and tied the vein.

"Would you like some coffee?" he asked.

"No, thank you. I shall be going pretty soon."

He walked to her where she stood in front of the snake cage. The rat was swallowed, all except an inch of pink tail that stuck out of the snake's mouth like a sardonic tongue. The throat heaved again and the tail disappeared. The jaws snapped back into their sockets, and the big snake crawled heavily to the corner, made a big eight and dropped his head on the sand.

"He's asleep now," the woman said. "I'm going now. But I'll come back and feed my snake every little while. I'll pay for the rats. I want him to have plenty. And sometime—I'll take him away with me." Her eyes came out of their dusty dream for a moment. "Remember, he's mine. Don't take his poison. I want him to have it. Good night." She walked swiftly to the door and went out. He heard her footsteps on the stairs, but he could not hear her walk away on the pavement.

Dr. Phillips turned a chair around and sat down in front of the snake cage. He tried to comb out his thought as he looked at the torpid snake. "I've read so much about psychological sex symbols," he thought. "It doesn't seem to explain. Maybe I'm too much alone. Maybe I should kill the snake. If I knew—no, I can't pray to anything."

For weeks he expected her to return. "I will go out and leave her alone here when she comes," he decided. "I won't see the damned thing again."

She never came again. For months he looked for her when he walked about in the town. Several times he ran after some tall woman thinking it might be she. But he never saw her again—ever.

EDWARD D. RADIN

Ladies in Stripes

THERE's an old nursery rhyme about the little girl who when she was good, was very, very good, but when she was bad—oh, brother. As far as police are concerned the rhyme applies as well to the little girl's mother, grandmother and great-aunt. Cops agree with remarkable unanimity that women criminals provide them with their worst headaches.

They are not referring to the casual offenders who bump off their husbands or sweethearts, then cross their legs and sob at coached intervals before a jury. What law officials dread is matching wits with women who take up crime as a profession. For all-around slyness and downright cussedness, coupled with a genius for planning, scheming and organizing, criminals of the so-called weaker sex take all the medals with oak leaf clusters added, poison oak. It doesn't matter which field of crime is considered—murder, swindling or thievery—women have run up unenviable records in all categories.

No con man can match the artistry of Cassie Lydia Chadwick, few killers have been as callous as Lyda Myer, and police fervently hope there'll never be another "fence" like "Ma" Mandelbaum.

Although Ma operated shortly before the turn of the century, cops down at Centre Street police headquarters in New York City still rap wood whenever her name is mentioned.

Fredericka Goldberg Mandelbaum looked like something the three witches in Macbeth might have distilled during a bad night. Barely five feet tall, she weighed well over 200 pounds and waddled like a pachyderm. Her nose was long and droopy, her chin sharp and pointed, her eyebrows bushy as a pair of hedgerows. Her coarse black hair was rolled up into a bun on the top of which she perched a tiny bonnet, dripping with ostrich feathers.

German-born, she appeared one day at the dry-goods store of

Wolfe Mandelbaum in the heart of New York's lower East Side, and badgered him into giving her a job. From there on she moved in. Before Wolfe was able to utter a feeble protest Fredericka hooked him into marriage, took firm control of his business and became the most notorious receiver of stolen goods America has known.

She didn't wait for thieves to steal and then hope that they would bring the loot to her. She recruited the top pickpockets, burglars, safecrackers and bank robbers and welded them into an international cartel of crime. Her agents ferreted out crooked merchants so that she could dispose of any kind of merchandise. Ma teamed men together, financed those who needed money between jobs, and was the final arbiter in disputes. She placed loft burglaries on an organized basis, bought horses and wagons to transport the stolen cloth and arranged convenient drops to hide the goods.

The shabby store became the crossroads of the crime world, where the criminal élite gathered to bring their loot, and get their orders from Ma. With its customary sardonic humor, the underworld had named her "Ma" in recognition of her harsh, evil temper and her heart of stone. When one of her thieves crossed her, Ma put police on his trail and had him caught red-handed.

She lived in an apartment above the store, the entrance to which was barred by a heavy steel door concealed behind red curtains. It was luxuriously furnished, but there was a conspicuous absence of any identifying marks on the furnishings. Behind the fireplace was a cleverly constructed dumbwaiter to whisk incriminating evidence upstairs and out of sight.

Ma became so preoccupied with the many phases of her criminal career that she grew careless and a bolt of stolen cloth was found in her store. Although the notorious legal team of Howe and Hummel portrayed her as an innocent victim and a jury acquitted her, she was soon caught again. When it became evident during trial that the cops really had the goods on her this time, she jumped bail and fled to Canada, then a refuge for American criminals. She lived there in obscurity for several years and vanished.

Ma Mandelbaum left one legacy to crime, her protegée—pretty, curvaceous Sophie Elkins, known as Lady Lyons. She was sweet sixteen, a captivating beauty and the best pickpocket in New York City when she came under the aegis of Ma Mandelbaum. Ma predicted a brilliant future for her. She helped it along by arranging a romance between Sophie and Ned Lyons, safecracker extraordinary.

The bride and groom left for a grand tour which was rudely interrupted when Lyons was sent away to prison for his part in a bank robbery and Sophie was picked up for helping herself to department store finery. To her associates it was incredible that Sophie could have bungled such a simple matter as shoplifting. It soon was evident that Sophie wanted to be caught. She joined her husband in prison, first arranged for his escape, and then, talking herself into the job of minding the matron's children, obtained a wax impression of a key to a seldom used door, and ambled out to freedom.

Sophie took an active part in all types of bank robberies, from blowing open a vault with "soup," to bemusing cashiers with guileless questions while confederates slipped out with all visible cash. When the Pinkertons finally plastered enough of her pictures in banks to hamper her work, Sophie turned banker herself, opening an establishment for women only, offering widows investments guaranteed to return a safe and sane fifteen to twenty per cent. Posing as a wealthy woman who was doing all this out of charity, she fleeced thousands, and the bubble burst only after she had fled with all the cash.

Although she continued to be known as Sophie Lyons, she discarded her husband after he became careless and piled up several arrests. Sophie was one of the few all-around women in crime. While she still had her beauty and figure she went in for blackmail; she wasn't above lifting a fat wallet or an expensive watch and she made frequent trips abroad during which time hotel guests reported staggering losses in jewelry. During one visit to Paris her suite adjoined that of Mrs. Pierre Lorillard, wife of the tobacco magnate. A week later Mrs. Lorillard discovered her gems gone and was comforted by her kind and understanding neighbor.

During the height of her career Sophie moved to Detroit because it was so convenient to slip over the border to Canada. For those who are firm believers in the theory that crime doesn't pay, the story of Sophie is a bit hard to take. She did serve several minor prison terms and toward her end seemed to have a change of heart when she donated money for a home for wayward girls, but died in luxury after devoting her later years to managing her large properties.

While Sophie was cruel in fleecing widows with her fake bank, she was nowhere as heartless as Lyda Trueblood Dooley McHaffie

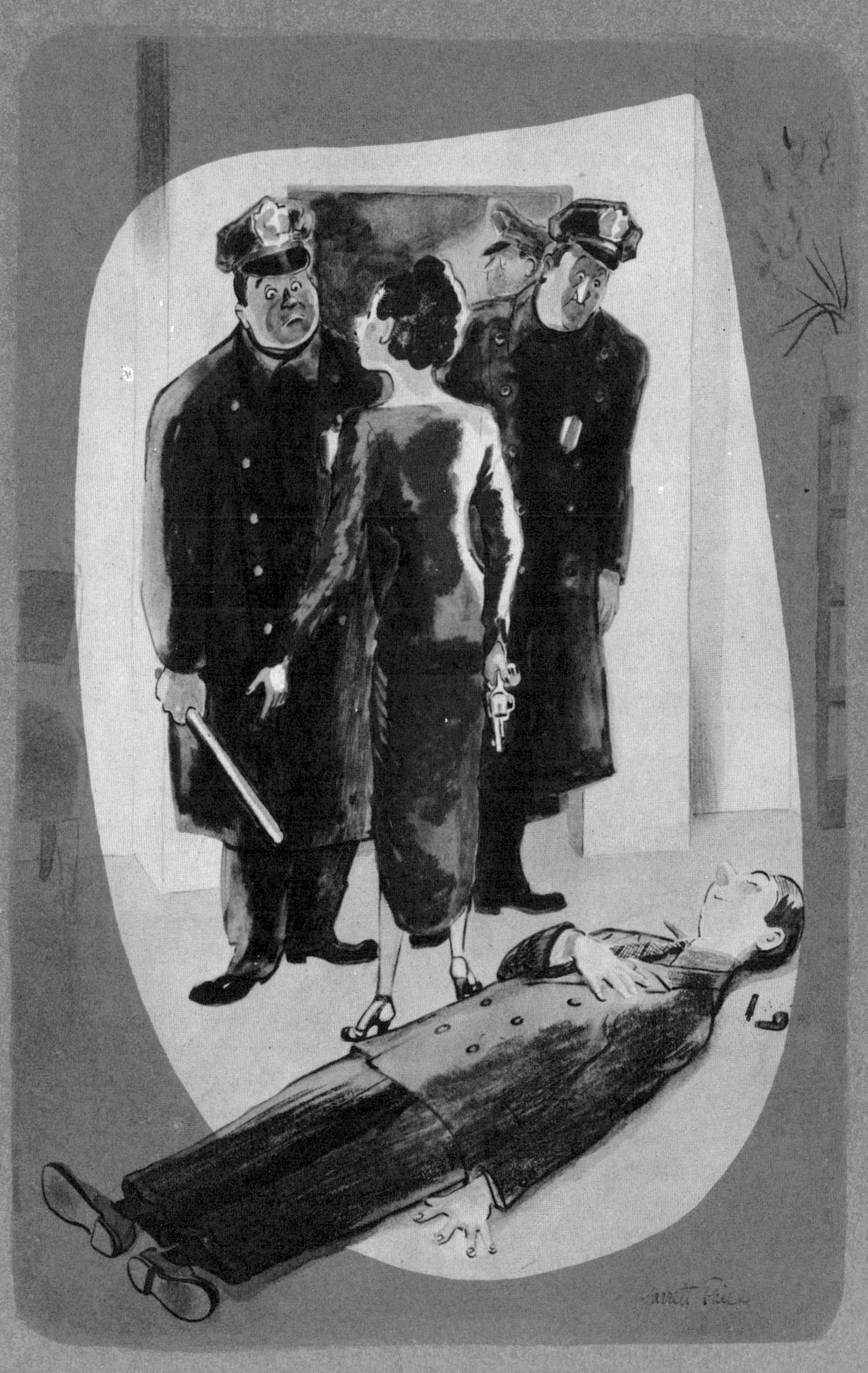

"He forced me to it....Kept on buying more and more life insurance."

Myer Southard, who appears in court records as Lyda Myer. Lyda entered the hall of infamy not because she was a mass murderer, but because of the way she laughed.

Some thought it was hysteria when her roar of mirth split the air while the body of Ed Myer, her husband of one month, was lowered into its grave, but there were others who wondered out loud. One of these skeptics was Deputy Sheriff Virgil Ormsby, who set out to investigate. Almost everybody in Twin Falls, Idaho, knew twenty-seven-year-old Lyda, who liked handsome men, uniforms, and a good laugh.

There was nothing about the opening phases of the investigation to indicate that anything was wrong. Lyda and Ed Myer had kept their marriage a secret at first, spending only their wedding night together, and then Ed had returned to the ranch where he was foreman, and waited for Lyda to finish up some business matters. Three weeks later she spent her second night with her new husband. He was sick the next day, and died in the hospital.

Lyda had been a widow when she wed Myer. She had been married before to Bill McHaffie, owner of a prosperous café in Twin Falls. McHaffie had sold out the café, bought a ranch in Montana and gone there with Lyda. He'd died a year later during the flu epidemic and she'd returned to Twin Falls.

Ormsby heard rumors that McHaffie wasn't her first husband. At Keytesville, Missouri, Lyda's birthplace, he found that at the age of nineteen she had married her childhood sweetheart, Bob Dooley. Bob and Lyda had gone to the Far West to open a ranch. Bob's brother, Ed, had gone along to help them. They'd been away about a year when Ed was brought back in a box for burial. It was hard to tell whether Lyda was sobbing or chuckling during the funeral services. A month later Lyda was back with another box. Her husband, Bob, had died suddenly, too. This time Dooley's father was certain she laughed. Lyda left with the proceeds of the Dooley brothers' insurance policies.

With three sudden deaths scored up for Lyda, Ormsby hurried to Montana. The doctor wasn't too sure that McHaffie had died of flu, but it was during the epidemic and it seemed reasonable. He admitted that the symptoms might have been poison. Ormsby then picked up word that after McHaffie had died Lyda had been seen with Harlan C. Dewis, a truck salesman, and so he checked the death records. Lyda had married Dewis and he had died suddenly, and hilariously.

With such facts Ormsby had no difficulty getting the bodies

exhumed, and each one was found loaded with arsenic. Lyda had built up a handsome fortune on insurance plus the properties of her various husbands.

The undercover investigation lasted over six months and by that time Lyda was gone from Twin Falls. Ormsby began a hurried search for her. In San Francisco he discovered she had married again. Her new husband was a sailor named Southard. The sailor was traced to Honolulu where Hawaiian police picked up Lyda and reported Southard still alive. Lyda was convicted of the murder of Ed Myer and sentenced to ten years to life imprisonment at the Idaho State Penitentiary. In 1931 she escaped, but was picked up the next year in Topeka, Kansas.

Con men are considered the top group, the intellectual giants of the criminal world. Con artists such as Yellow Kid Weil and Fred (Deacon) Buckminister, have boasted about taking suckers over in deals ranging from $25,000 to $100,000. They are penny-ante characters compared to Cassie Lydia Chadwick.

For most confidence work the choice victim is a successful businessman, puffed up with his own importance, who is like a fish out of water when he gets out of his own field. He is sucked into the deal through what the Yellow Kid called "a touch of larceny in his heart," plus an elaborate build-up that requires several good men and a few lesser fry.

But Cassie had her own methods. First of all she operated alone and, for her suckers, selected levelheaded successful bankers equally at home in any kind of a business deal. Her entire equipment consisted of an eyebrow-lifting story and an envelope of worthless paper. Her take was somewhere between three and thirteen million dollars. She caused at least one bank failure and was responsible for runs on dozens of financial institutions.

Cassie was born plain Lizzie Bigley, one of many children of a poor Canadian farmer. While still in her teens she breezed into Ontario, handed shopkeepers her visiting card which read, "Miss Bigley, heiress to $15,000," and ran up large charge accounts. She tried forging a note, after disillusioned merchants recalled their goods, and was arrested. When witnesses testified that she appeared in a barbershop, had her hair cut short, and asked for a false mustache, the jury acquitted her on grounds of insanity. She was crazy like a fox.

Now ready for richer game, she crossed the border into Cleveland. For the next decade various wealthy men and women in Cleveland and Toledo who had strayed from the straight and narrow marital path received subtle communications from a fortune-telling Miss Bigley. However, if her palm was crossed with currency, she lost all memory. In Toledo she lapsed into her old habit of forgery and was sent away for ten years but after a stay of only three she was released, changed Lizzie into Cassie, and was ready for her life's work.

Dr. LeRoy S. Chadwick, twenty years her senior and a member of the very upper crust in Cleveland, admired Cassie when she massaged his foot when it ached. He wound up by offering her marriage.

Cassie whipped through the doctor's fortune in short order, and with her credit well-established, put her master plan in operation.

One Sunday she waited after the sermon to discuss a personal matter with the pastor of a wealthy church attended by John D. Rockefeller, Sr. She hinted that there was something deep dark and hush-hush in her past and asked him to introduce her to a reputable banker who would keep her secret. The pastor gave her a letter to a Boston banker.

After pledging him to silence, Cassie told the banker she was the illegitimate daughter of Andrew Carnegie, the steel king, then still alive. When the banker asked for some proof, she was ready with her coup. Witnesses accompanied her to New York where she drove up to Carnegie's town house. They saw her ring the bell, disappear from view and appear a half hour later with a large envelope in her hands. She sped back to Boston and produced a promissory note for a half-million supposedly signed by Carnegie. The banker was properly impressed. Cassie made the banker promise that he never would let Carnegie know that she was borrowing money, since "father won't like it."

Cassie made several loans and repaid them promptly, even throwing in a bonus, but each time she borrowed the bite became larger and larger. With part of the money she purchased some good sound securities and one day invited Ira Reynolds, Cleveland banker, to her home. She also confided her deep dark secret to him while she was busy placing securities in a folder. The good securities were where banker Reynolds could see them without any trouble. She stuffed the folder full and told Reynolds that it contained stocks and bonds worth fourteen million. After sealing it with wax, she asked if he could keep it in the bank vault. She added that he could open the package and inspect the securities. After glancing at the good ones still on the desk he gallantly brushed aside the suggestion and issued a receipt showing that Cassie L. Chadwick had placed in the bank vault for safekeeping a folder containing securities valued at fourteen million.

Armed with the receipt, Cassie told her story and borrowed from bankers left and right. She paid off her loan to one with sums from another, with the amounts borrowed pyramiding up. She went along for years until the original Boston banker got cold feet about the size of the loan and brought suit against Reynolds to forbid him to dispose of the "fourteen million" in the folder. Far too late Reynolds caught onto Cassie's game. Other bankers presented their claims. C. T. Beckwith, head of the Citizens National Bank of Oberlin, Ohio, which went bankrupt, had advanced her $240,000 in bank funds and $102,000 personally. He died a few weeks after the exposé.

The dam burst when a group of bankers went to Carnegie and the steel king said the note bearing his signature was a forgery and added most emphatically that he did not have any illegitimate daughters. The folder was opened and found to be stuffed with worthless paper. Cassie was arrested, convicted of grand larceny and sentenced to the Ohio State Penitentiary for ten years. In October, 1907, she died in prison.

Needless to say, con men are still shooting at her record.

The Silence of Mr. Prendegast

"Avril Mason used to be the most beautiful woman I have ever seen," Prendegast said.

I was staying with the Masons. Someone had given me a letter of introduction to them, and they had asked me to visit them, so I was interested in what Prendegast said. He lived on the next farm and I'd dropped in to see him, the way one does in Africa. I needed exercise and had gone for a ride; and then, seeing his homestead, I'd thought I'd drop in. I was curious about him because Avril had said, "He's a queer character. We don't see much of him, and when we do see him he doesn't say a word."

Well, he seemed disposed to talk now. Perhaps because I was a stranger, perhaps because I was a writer and people seem to talk to writers. Writers are out of their world, unreal to them, like griffins and unicorns.

When I'd introduced myself, Prendegast had said, "The writer?" and I had said, "Yes."

"I read a lot," he said, "and I've enjoyed your books."

I was flattered and pleased, and took to him at once—this being human nature. But I was particularly interested in what he said about Avril. It confirmed what I had thought myself when I met her. She'd been beautiful. Twenty years ago or so, she must have been lovely. She still had the bone in her face, the structure was there; she still had great dark brown eyes; she still had a good figure and good legs. Her hair was grey now, of course, but she had masses of it, and it was strong and vital, with a natural wave. She blued it heavily and used a lot of make-up, but the beauty was all there underneath. She was like a picture postcard that someone has written over. Time had written over her picture, blurring it a bit, smudging it, fading it; but the picture was there, and Prendegast's remark brought it out again.

Avril Mason was beautiful (he went on). She had the kind

of beauty that brings a man's heart into his mouth, and she was, as far as I was concerned, the very last kind of neighbor I could have wanted. In fact, if I had been asked what sort of people I should like least, I should have said a beautiful young woman with an invalid husband. At least I should have said that if I had been smart enough to think of it.

I'll never forget meeting her. I was sitting on the stoep figuring out some stock returns when she walked in. I was in a filthy mess, sweaty and covered in dust, having just come from the cattle kraals. Nothing more unlikely than a woman like Avril Mason walking up the steps of a South African farm stoep could be imagined. I looked up from my figures and there she was. Tall, dark, slim, beautifully turned out in a white suit with white gloves and a white felt hat.

"You're Mr. Prendegast?" she said.

I said yes, and then, "Where's your car? I didn't hear it."

"I left her at the back," she said.

I said nothing. I just stared, I think. She really left me speechless. It was a minute before I asked her to come in and sit down, and called the boy to make tea.

By this time I'd taken her in. The details of her dress, her lovely hands and slim legs and ankles. Her hair was long and she wore it in a knot at the back of her neck like she does now, only of course it was brown then—a lovely, rich, dark brown. Sepia color with almost a touch of red in it. Her eyes were brown, velvety soft. They were the color of dark sherry, very large and set wide apart, and they gave her a young, innocent look. Her eyes have changed a lot. I guessed her to be about twenty-five, and as it turned out I was one year out. She was twenty-six. It was years since I'd seen anyone like her.

She said, "We've been looking at farms and have more or less decided to buy Avalon."

It was quite undeveloped then. Just bare veld.

"I hope you do," I said.

"We'll buy it," she said. "I've just decided."

And I felt that her meeting me had clinched the deal in some way. As a matter of fact, that's an understatement. I knew it, but did not want to know it. I knew from the way she had looked at me, and from the quick way she was breathing.

Then the *we* dawned on me. "'We,'" I said. "You said we. Is there someone with you?"

"Yes," she said, "my husband. He's an invalid—at least he's not at all well. And Phyllis. They're in the car."

"I'll go and get them," I said, getting up.

She went on, "My husband is Frederick Mason—Freddy Mason."

"The polo player," I said.

"Yes," she said. "He was badly wounded and has to live a quiet life in the country. That's the reason why we're buying a farm." Then she said, "This is good horse country, isn't it?"

I said, "Yes. We're high here. No horsesickness to speak of, and except for Mooi River and parts of the Karoo and Free State it's the best place I know."

"Then that settles it."

I said, "I'll fetch them," and went out.

The car was a big green Cadillac. In the front seat there was a native driver, and at the back were her husband and Phyllis.

"Come in," I said, "and have some tea."

Mason said, "Thanks," and got out of the car carefully. He was a man of about forty and looked very ill. Phyllis followed him. "This is Miss French—Phyllis French," Mason said.

We shook hands. "My name's Prendegast," I said.

Miss French was a small woman of about thirty—a rather fragile-looking washed-out blonde. She had tired blue eyes and she seemed very quiet. I remember thinking then that she looked rather like a governess.

They followed me in and we all sat down.

"My wife has told you, I suppose, we're thinking of buying the place next door," Mason said.

I said, "Avalon."

"Yes," he said, "but it really depends on my wife." He smiled at her. "She's got to make the decision."

"We'll buy it," she said.

"You've made up your mind, then," he said.

She looked at me under her lashes. "Mr. Prendegast has decided me."

I found later that this was typical of her. The double bluff in which the absolute truth was used to disguise the truth.

"What did he tell you?" her husband asked.

"He says it's good horse country; and then, having a civilized neighbor . . ."

I said, "Not so civilized."

She said, "Civilized enough."

Mason said, "I've got to lead a quiet, open-air life. She told you, I suppose."

I said yes, and then asked Miss French how she would like it.

"I don't really know," she said, "but I like a quiet life. Books," she said, "and music . . ."

"Phyllis is a highbrow," Mrs. Mason said, and laughed.

"And you?" I asked.

"Me?" She laughed again. "I can be happy anywhere."

Not much more was said, as far as I remember. The conversation became general and centered more or less on farming, cattle and horse breeding, shooting, the question of labor, and similar topics. They stayed only an hour and then left for Nylstroom, where they were spending the night at the hotel. They were going back to Johannesburg the next day to close the deal. When they said good-bye, Mrs. Mason said, "We're staying at the Carlton, if you want to get hold of us, or are coming into town." I said I only went to Joburg once a year, to see the dentist. "I hate the place," I said. And that was the last I saw of them for some time.

They were, however, in my mind quite a lot, because I couldn't get them out of it. Her looks, the sick husband, the sad-looking secretary or whatever she was. Why would people like that want to come into the wilds? What would they do with themselves? Avalon is a big place. Five thousand morgen—a morgen here, as you no doubt know, is a little over two acres. It was, as I said, quite undeveloped then but had good grazing and plenty of water. But it was hard to visualize them there. They belonged in England, America, or the South of France. It all puzzled me; and then I accepted it the way one does. One can't go on puzzling forever, and people should know their own business best.

What did puzzle me, though, was her interest in me. I'm not a ladies' man. Never was. But the look she'd given me meant something or I thought it did; and then I put that out of my head too. I was very busy losing a lot of stock with a pride of lions that had come in from the reserve, and one of my best bulls was sick. A bull meant a lot to me then. A bull's half the herd, especially when you're grading up on native cows. Funny, now that I can afford it I seldom lose anything. But then it was different—lions, wild dogs, leopards, jackals, every damn thing. Of course the place was wilder then. (He spoke almost regretfully. He was silent for a few minutes and then went back to Avril.) I was in such a mess when she saw me. That's what finally made me decide I'd been imagining things.

I smiled. Poor Prendegast didn't know women. He was a fine-looking man even now, and must have been magnificent then. Strong, bronzed, smelling of sweat and cattle. I saw him, in my mind, on his stoep with his returns in front of him. I saw his dusty face furrowed with sweat around the eyes and nose. I saw his strong hands holding the pencil. And I saw Avril as she was then. Sleek, svelte, finished to the last degree, excited by a man like this—the silent, lonely rancher of the novelists. A man. A new type. With her husband ill and no good to her, the picture was very clear. To come into the bush was the one thing she could never have done without a pastime; and for a woman like her there was only one kind of amusement—men. But he hadn't seen it then, and I rather doubted if he saw it now. Rough and strong, an outdoor man, virile but at the same time what we call a gentleman. He read a lot and he'd been about before he settled here. He knew how to behave, which knife and fork to use at dinner and things like that, so that the paradox of his existence had intrigued her. Why should he live like this alone, unmarried, miles from anywhere?

And then, like all women, even the best of them, she wanted power. Here was something she could get into her power by the use of her beauty. A strong man she could either use or shatter. But I didn't say anything to him. I wanted him to go on. I was sure he would, because no one talks as much as a silent man once the silence has been broken.

"Go on," I said, "tell me the rest."

"The rest?" he said. "All right, I'll tell you. Maybe you'll put it in a book sometime. . . ."

The rest, as you can imagine (Prendegast went on), is where I made a bloody fool of myself. And a cuckold of Mason. I'm not excusing myself, except that as a farmer I know very well that morality doesn't jibe with biology, and a girl of twenty-six, especially one like Avril, can't live without a man in her life. For two years I was that man. Mason got worse. It's only lately he's taken a turn for the better.

It began with the rides. I used to take her for rides. I knew this country like the palm of my hand. She was just friendly at first, giving me the rope I needed to hang myself. I was in love with her. I was mad about her. I could think of nothing but her. And then one day I showed her the Bushman cave in the Berg. It's only about three miles from the house and about eight from here. You can get the horses up to within a couple of hundred yards of it and leave them tied in a thick patch of bush. Then you've got to climb for about fifteen minutes before you come to it. There's a nice Bushman painting in the cave—a giraffe in ocher yellow with black markings. The cave's as big as a small room and has a little spring on one side that's a mass of maidenhair fern. It's what you'd call a romantic spot, with a view over the low country, and the drip of water, and the moss and the ferns. I'll show it to you one day if you like.

Anyway, that's where it happened. I'd hardly got her there before she was in my arms . . . I must confess that she did not match my ardor. I did not know then, as I do now, that such was her instinctively subtle way of increasing my longing for her. It was not long before she was openly as mad about me as I was about her. I'd never known a woman like her before. She was all woman. Sometimes I thought of the Bushmen who had made love there for hundreds, perhaps for thousands of years, till they were shot off like animals when the Boers first settled in the country. As I held her, I often thought of it. And of men and women, and the strange things that happen between them. I felt nothing about Mason. In this sense he was dead. He wasn't a man. You couldn't take something from him that he hadn't got.

We made a bed of maidenhair fern. We took my two dogs with us, and they'd have given us notice if anyone came near. Looking back on it, it's unbelievable, but then it was the only reality. We'd meet on horseback and ride there day after day. She's a wonderful horsewoman, you know. Learnt to ride as a child on a sheep station in Australia. That only came out later when she had to manage the ranch. She'd been brought up to it, and then had got out of it owing to her looks. There'd been a good many men in her life before Mason, I gathered. But he'd found her irresistible and had married her. It would be impossible to call her immoral. Morals didn't mean anything to her. She was a woman. A beautiful animal who had made herself into a sophisticated woman of the world.

Well, that's the way it was till Max came onto the scene. Maximilian Ferdinand von Freidheim. He bought Elandsfontein—that's the farm on the other side of me—for its shooting. We used to laugh about him. He always wore riding breeches, boots, and a slouch hat. It was his idea of what a man should wear in Africa. He was a baron, all right—I got a friend to look him up in the *Almanach de Gotha*—and in some way related to the Hapsburgs. He built himself a big house near the Masons' boundary. Elandsfontein is L-shaped and runs right around my place. I bought it afterwards, but that's a long way ahead. As I said, we used to laugh about him, and all the time she was having an affair with him. I have no doubt that when she was with him she used to laugh about me—the simple farmer who was stupid enough to fall in love with a woman like her. I think she told him she was just amusing herself with me, to keep suspicion from falling on him. That was her story to me about Max.

"Darling," she used to say, "it wouldn't do if I rode only with you. And besides he plays the piano so well."

Phyllis used to take him messages from Avril, and Phyllis loved his music. He had a Bechstein grand and played magnificently.

I interrupted Prendegast at that point. "I was wondering about Phyllis," I said. "She must have known what was going on."

"Some of it," Prendegast said. "She knew about me, but thought Max was a blind, which was why she let him make love to her."

"You mean he made love to Phyllis, too?"

"Yes," Prendegast said. "She often went over to his place on her pony—she had a little cream Basuto mare with black points (what you call a buckskin in America, I think)—and looked very well on her. Though I must say I'd no idea she could really ride until . . ."

"Until what?" I said.

"I'm coming to that," he said. "I've left out some bits. Anyway, you've got the hang of the story now. A beautiful woman with a sick husband and two lovers that she played off one against the other, making fools of them both. It was a triangle," he said, "with Avril, me, and Maximilian. Mason was on the sidelines; and Max had a little secret triangle of his own with Avril and Phyllis."

"Yes," I said.

"Well, I must go back a bit. You can see that money was no object with the Masons."

I said yes, again, because it was obvious that money had been poured into Avalon. The house was lovely and beautifully furnished; there was a park where they kept their brood mares, a wonderful garden, and a swimming pool two hundred feet long.

They went into it in a big way from the beginning (Prendegast said). Within a year they had ten thoroughbred mares and a grey stallion by the Syrian Prince who was by the Tetrach. Avril used to ride him a lot, but not to meet me—you couldn't tie him, and he was hard to mount. But I should have realized that Phyllis knew about horses when, one day, while we were all together having tea at Avalon, Phyllis said, "I'm sure Pasha could jump a house. Just look at his quarters."

Avril said, "He won't jump."

And Phyllis said, "He'll jump wire."

"Only to get at a mare," Avril said.

"It's just that *you* can't make him," Phyllis said.

"No one can make him jump," Avril said. "He doesn't like it."

That little conversation slipped out of my mind till much later. But to get back to Maximilian. He was very rich, too. I was the poor man there. I was ranching for my living while they were checkbook farmers, amusing themselves breeding a few horses to run in local races and running a herd of mediocre whitefaces.

Well, there it was; and, when you come to think of it, a pretty nasty mess, too. And, like all such messes, it was filled with latent tragedy, though none of us suspected it at the time. I was even very happy in my love for Avril, and things had begun to pick up for me. A couple of good calf crops with a big percentage of heifers, and Max's hunting had cleaned out a lot of vermin. I was sitting here where we are now, just as I was when I first saw Avril, when it happened. I was reading *An American Tragedy*—which was a bit of a coincidence—when I heard a horse galloping like hell. It was coming from the direction of Avalon, straight as a crow flies. I jumped to my feet. There were no gates that way. To get to Avalon you have to come round the way you did today. And then, to my astonishment, I saw Phyllis coming hell for leather on Pasha. She was leaning over his neck and her hair was streaming out all mixed up with his mane.

My God, I thought, the fence—five barbed wires, with fourteen-pound iron standards eight yards apart, with four droppers between them. It didn't occur to me then that she must have jumped six fences before she came to this one. I ran out just in time to see her give the stallion his head and call to him. He changed legs, gathered his quarters under him, and soared like a bird into the air. He jumped big. When he landed with his forelegs, his hind were two foot above the top wire. She never checked him, but came right on, through the rosebushes in the garden, and only pulled up when his nose was practically on the stoep.

I went to his head. He was blowing hard; great gusts of air came from his flaring nostrils. He was nearly black with sweat, but he knew me well and rubbed the thick curds, where the reins had chafed him, against my chest.

"My God, Phyl," I said, "what's up?"

She threw her leg over the horse's neck and almost fell at my feet.

I caught her by the arm. "What is it?" I said. "And what will Avril say?" Avril let no one ride that horse.

"Damn Avril," she said. "She's killed him. She shot him. She pushed the pistol right into his chest and shot him."

"Shot who?"

"Max," she said. "Avril has killed Max."

I called a boy to take the horse and put him in one of my boxes, and then I led Phyllis into the house and got her a drink of brandy. I lit a cigarette and gave it to her.

"Now tell me everything," I said.

She gave a sort of choking sob, and then, pulling herself together, said, "She shot him when she found he was my lover."

"What?" I said.

"Yes," she said. "He was my lover. We were going to be married."

"My God," I said. "But why?"

"You fool," Phyllis said. "Can't you see it?"

"Why?" I said again.

"Jealousy," she screamed. "He was *her* lover, too."

I poured myself a drink. I needed one. So she had tricked me, the way I'd tricked Mason. The way she'd tricked lots of men. Phyllis was crying softly, now.

I said, the way one does at such times, just for something to say, "I never knew you could ride like that. Why, you ride better than Avril." It was odd, using her name like that, as if nothing had happened.

"Like Avril?" Phyllis said. "Why, I taught Avril to ride."

"What happened then?" I asked. "Was she accused of murder?"

"No," Prendegast said. "There was an inquest, of course, and she said she killed him in self-defense when he tried to assault her. She'd torn her clothes to prove it. She'd torn them herself after Phyllis left, and the fact that she'd shot him at such close range clinched the matter. Actually, Phyllis said, she walked right up to him and shot him. His silk shirt was all scorched with the powder blast. Anyway, he was a bad 'un, Max was, and no loss to society. I advised Phyllis to say nothing because nothing would have been gained by it, and a lot of dirty linen would have come to light.

"You see, Avril had something on Phyllis. They'd been brought up together, but Phyl had been in a lunatic asylum for a while, and Avril was always threatening to let it out if she ever left her, or didn't do what she told her. That was why Phyl had never married before. This time she thought she was safe, because she'd told Max. But now the boot was on the other foot and she had something on Avril; and once she got over the shock, she blossomed out. Very pretty she was, now that she'd lost that worried look. Max hadn't meant much to her, she realized afterwards, except as a way out, an escape, and it sort of eased her mind, my knowing and not being upset. But that's why we never had any children."

"No children?"

"Yes," he said. "We wouldn't take the chance."

"You married Phyllis, then?" I said.

"Yes," he said, "I married her, and for fifteen years we were very happy. Then she died. Come," he said, and got up. "I'll show you her grave."

We went through the garden till we came to the paddock fence; and there, cutting into it, was a little enclosure with an iron gate. It was planted with giant aloes. "I didn't put roses," he said, "because they'll die if they're not taken care of. But aloes go on. Nothing eats them, nothing can hurt them. And she loved them."

"Is this the place?" I pointed to the fence.

"Yes," he said, "this is where she jumped Pasha. He died only ten years ago. Avril gave him to us as a wedding present, provided she could use him at stud when she needed him."

"What nerve," I said.

"She's got guts," he said. "All guts and no heart. Phyl had both," he said. "Plenty of both, and the light has gone out since she died." He coughed, and then he said, "Afterwards, I made a clean breast of it to Mason. About me and Avril, I mean. And he asked me if I thought he was a complete fool.

" 'You knew?' I said.

" 'I knew that she couldn't live without love,' Mason said. 'And I knew she'd picked on you when she decided to buy the farm.'

" 'You knew then?' I said.

" 'Yes,' he said. 'If it had been a city, there would have been lots of men. I didn't like that. But I was out of the running and I didn't want to lose her. Just to see her gave me pleasure—just to watch her walk, watch her move. Like a race horse.' "

At dinner that evening, Avril asked me what I'd been doing. "Have a nice ride?" she said.

I said, "Yes, I rode over to Prendegast's."

"The silent rancher," she said.

"I'm going to see him again tomorrow," I said. "He's said he'd take me to look at a Bushman drawing of a giraffe in a cave."

"I'll come with you," she said. "I'd like to see it again. I haven't seen it for years."

What nerve the woman had, I thought. She looked lovely in a white evening dress with red and green sequins on the hips. She wore a diamond star in her blue hair, and a double rope of pearls. It was difficult to associate this well-preserved and distinguished woman with the story Prendegast had told me, but I believed every word of it. It was all there under the white-sequined dress, the girdle, the pearls and diamonds, the hair-bluing and eye shadow. Eve was there, and Artemis the huntress, and the harlot and the slut that exist latently in so many women. What matters is how much of it there is. It's a matter of proportion, and Avril had too much of it. Just as she had too much beauty and too much nerve. She was dangerous as an unsheathed sword.

I never saw the cave, because a wire came calling me back to town, but I often wish I'd stayed on to see Avril and William Prendegast, both in their fifties, looking at the scene of their romance. I've often thought of Prendegast's words: ". . . a woman like a race horse," and of Mason—a man who could look truth in the face, which is more than most men can do.

The truth. What is truth? How much was love? How much was cynicism on Mason's part? What had held Avril to him? I'd heard Prendegast's story. How different would Avril's have been, or Mason's? And it had happened twenty-five years ago. What I had seen was the residue of Life, the sediment of an old emotion, of old pain that now was just a story.

MARTHA GELLHORN

About Shorty

I DO NOT remember her name. She had a pug-dog face and she was twenty-five years old. A pug-dog face is not necessarily unattractive. She was sunburned and had small square teeth; when she smiled, her gums showed. She smiled, she laughed, she giggled. And her gums showed and her snub nose wrinkled and her round blue eyes, with the light eyelashes, looked confidingly upon the world. Her hair was very blonde and cut short; the job seemed to have been done with a nail scissors. The hair was not thick—ragged, but fluffy. She was of what they call medium height and she had a good body. Men would notice this; but women, deceived by the unpainted face, would not consider it.

What can her name have been? Trudi perhaps, only it wasn't Trudi. It was a German nickname, ending in "i," the kind of nickname that made you think of "Shorty." I have to call her something. She now becomes Shorty.

They brought her to my hotel room, in Madrid, one late afternoon in the winter of 1937. I was feeling sorry for myself as I had flu and had been abandoned while everyone went out to look at the war. The men were far too merry for my taste; they had found Shorty somewhere and were enjoying themselves. She giggled at their jokes and she listened in awe to their knowledgeable war prophecies; they had observed her shape with satisfaction. There was little amusement in Madrid that winter and less food, and all we ever had for entertainment was each other and anyone else we could dig up. Women were scarce too, foreign women who understood English especially. I thought I was prettier than Shorty, but not as successful. I would not have been able to giggle so enthusiastically at such mediocre jokes. The men were showing off. I disliked Shorty, for a lot of instant virtuous reasons, because I was jealous.

After a while, they all went away, looking for a room that had liquor in it and a more welcoming host. Later that night, Jim Russell came back and told me about Shorty. She was, it seemed, a good girl. She was a German, as "Aryan" as can be, married to another German who was a Jew. Her husband was a doctor in one of the International Brigades. We all knew him. We thought he was the finest man in Spain. We could not have said why, except that he was not dramatic; he was funny; he never talked about the Cause; he did not spare himself, slaving with less than the minimum of equipment to help the wounded, who were numerous enough. His name was Otto—I remember that. Shorty had been working near Valencia in a home for the newly created orphans of Madrid. Shorty and Otto were an admirable couple, unlike the rest of us, who had passports and salaries and were attending this war in the rare modern capacity of press tourists. In Spain, in those days, you felt like a profiteer and a monster if you had cigarettes, let alone a passport and any other place to go when you got sick of this.

Someone gave or bought Shorty a dress. She had been more alluring really, in a sort of Elizabeth Bergner way, when she arrived in blue dungarees and the ragged boy's haircut. Her hair grew and she curled it; she used lipstick and presently mascara. She turned very womanly. She should have stayed in Valencia where she knew what she was about. Otto was nearly always at the front. And Shorty liked to have a good time; she was obliging, grateful, humble, and not weighed down with intelligence.

When we first heard or saw or guessed that Shorty had become the mistress of a Russian journalist, my gentlemen war-correspondent friends were surprisingly angry. It appeared they had all been honorable and undemanding because of Otto, because they loved Otto, and now this lousy little tart was cheating on him and he would certainly find out and it would break his heart. The men did not blame the Russian, of course; he was only doing what anyone would do, if you didn't happen to know Otto.

I was exceedingly noble about this. I told Jim Russell and Owen James, one night in my room, that they were grotesque; probably Otto had a girl too, and why not? War was long and life was not guaranteed here to stay; poor Shorty had had a tough time and if she wanted a little pleasure, she had a right to it. They howled me down. Now that Shorty had displeased them, I was again the apple of their eyes, by default, due to the lack of competition. I could afford to be noble. Besides, in a general way, I found this free use of the Scarlet Letter tiresome and dishonest. Gradually

I became Shorty's champion, and her friend. That is to say, I was as much her friend as I could be. Our pasts and presents and futures were too different; my follies were not hers; I have always thought there is a secret basis of pity in the friendship of most women, and that is a crumbling rock to build on. Shorty pitied me, I think, because I was so pompously determined to do my job like a real newspaperman (an idiot job of watching other people do theirs). I pitied her because apparently she could not learn by experience and she was unable to form and enunciate the word "No." So we were friends.

The Russian pulled out, with predictable speed. I imagine Shorty adored a man into the ground. Shorty looked bewildered for a while, like a puppy who has licked your hand and been slapped for its pains. She stayed in her room, waiting in the classical manner for the telephone that does not ring. Then her native jollity reappeared and she was back at Chicote's bar and in the hotel lobbies and the cluttered dirty bedrooms we called home; and a Frenchman, convalescing from a leg wound, replaced the Russian. The Frenchman returned to his brigade, and a Canadian, who was working for the Quakers, took over.

By now, Shorty was classed as one of what Jim Russell named the whores de combat. These few ladies were distinguished from the large professional body because they did not receive money for their services. As I grew to know Shorty, I realized that she loved all these passing men and continued to love Otto. This operation was possible, due to a cloudy, romantic German turn of mind which was very boring to listen to, and very pathetic.

We were out of Madrid a good deal, driving to the various fronts in whatever transport we could buy or borrow or talk away from its rightful owner. The men had become casual about Shorty, saying, simply, hello kid, whenever they saw her, and acting as if she weren't there. She was doing no work for the war, so she had nothing to say that would interest them; and the taboo, established for Otto's sake, prevailed. Shorty lived in another hotel but she visited us, occasionally, to beg. There were few enough gifts to give—extra cigarettes, an envelope full of sugar, a partially used cake of soap. The men gave Shorty what she asked for, if they had it, with affable contempt. And when any of us happened to stop at Otto's brigade headquarters and he wanted news of Shorty, the men were vague. She's doing okay, they'd say, seems in okay health, looks okay. It was amazing, in such a small war, where everyone appeared to know everyone else, that Otto hadn't heard.

The spring that year was more beautiful than it had ever been anywhere before, probably because of the long ugly winter that preceded it. We loved Spain, we the voluntarily uprooted, and we took a personal pride in the spring and in the grace it laid upon this land that we felt to be ours. We had watched many brave people pull Spain through the winter, and though we had done nothing but accomplish an act of presence, still we owned the country too, in a small but devoted way. The spring healed us. Quarrels had grown up during the winter, based on propinquity, dirt, lack of food and heat, the harassing daily German artillery fire, the fact that no one, notably our editors, was interested in what we wrote and apparently no one believed us. Now, in this new sun and this new greenness, we became friends again; and, due to the weather, we decided we were going to win the war.

The spring did something for Shorty too. She had become haggard and pale under the orange rouge she used, and her blue eyes, no longer full of gayety, looked stupid and hurt and alarmed and wary. Suddenly she put on her dungarees and left for the front, near Teruel as I remember, to be a nurse. In that war anyone could do anything, what with the widespread lack of specialized training and the labor shortage. The men were friendly to her just before she left. She seemed to be the original Shorty again—her face washed, her hair ragged and uncurled, going forth like a good girl to do her part. It was there, wherever she was, that Shorty met the Spanish colonel whom we called Juanito.

We knew Juanito too and had decided he was very likely the second finest man in Spain. I had always found Otto handsome, but this was a question of taste. Otto had a lean, swarthy, brilliant face, with a bony nose and lively eyes; he was not very tall, stooped and shabby, and he had beautiful hands. I liked his mouth particularly, and his voice. Perhaps he wasn't handsome. But there could be no argument about Juanito: he was a beauty. And he was much more—he was a man who had never heard of defeat, any kind of defeat. Otto was brave in a way that does not show and also never ends; Juanito was brave in the superb, heart-lifting way that ends you up dead.

Shorty fell in love with Juanito, and since she did not understand Spanish very well she must have interpreted Juanito's conversation eagerly, to suit herself. I am certain Juanito would not make a woman believe that he loved her with a true undying passion and wished to have her as his wife, if he had no such idea. I do not think Juanito loved anything truly and undyingly except Spain,

"We had a fight and he took back everything he'd given me."

and I think he was far too busy with the war to want a woman except for whatever brief delight she could offer. Shorty wrote two letters, from the shelled farmhouse where she was working. One was to me and the other was to Otto. I know about Otto's because she told me. She said that at last she had found the one love of her life, there was no turning back, she had explained to Otto and though she would always love him too in a different way, she could no longer be his wife, *etcetera* and *etcetera.* I showed my letter to the men, since we all saw Otto from time to time and we had to know how to treat him. Jim Russell opined that it would have been a good thing if the shell that landed down the hall from Shorty, last winter, had landed in her room. Shorty, they agreed, was on Franco's side, distracting Juanito from his work and destroying Otto.

Destroy Otto she did, as far as anyone can tell about anyone else simply by looking. His brigade was making an attack in the north, and Owen James and Jim Russell and I had to go up there to write about it, and we could not avoid Otto. Otto must have been thirty-three or -four, that spring, but he wasn't a young man any more. The brilliance had left his face and his skin was stone-colored and heavy; his eyes seemed to hurt him and the fine things that had always been in them, wisdom and compassion and hope, were gone. He did not speak of Shorty nor of anything else. He ordered us out of the terrible two rooms where he was working, with the wounded spread on the floor like a stinking human quilt; he said he had too much to do to bother with journalists; why didn't we pick up guns and be useful? Even writers ought to be able to see the attack was going badly.

Ten days later, when we were back in Madrid, Otto was killed. Someone reported he had been working in the trenches; it was a direct mortar hit. We checked; he was dead. Jim Russell and Owen James got drunk that night, in a somber untalking way, and suddenly Jim Russell said that if he ever ran into Shorty he would break her neck; even, if he had time, he would look her up for this purpose. Not that Shorty had anything to do with the mortar shell; no one was dumb enough to think that; people got killed or they didn't, that was how it was; but you didn't have to kill them twice—not if they were Otto.

I do not know how Juanito disembarrassed himself of Shorty. It isn't anything I want to imagine. But he did it, and the Canadian who worked for the Quakers came to Madrid in the early summer and said he'd seen Shorty in Barcelona. What is she doing, I said.

What does she always do, he said. We did not see Shorty again. She was crossed off as a war casualty, and forgotten.

We got out of Spain all right, at the end. We had passports and money. But that defeat was ours; we carried it with us in our hearts, in our brains, where it mattered. I daresay we all became more competent press tourists because of it, since we never again cared so much. You can love only one war; afterwards, I suppose you do your duty, use up your life in your own way, think as elevated thoughts as you can manage. Our little group split up, taking all those airplanes that go to all those places. We had, it seemed, picked a fine trade and could be busily employed from then on.

I was in Paris in the summer of 1939, returning from China. The idea was to hang around and be handy for the oncoming European war. Some French colleague, who was hard up for copy, interviewed me; I said a few inspiring things about the gallant Chinese—who, in fact, seemed to me as unlucky, badly led, and doomed as anyone then extant—and the colleague, in that droll Frenchy way, wrote not only my dreary remarks, but a description of my clothes and my allegedly flower-filled room at the Plaza Athénée. The next morning Shorty telephoned me. An hour later she arrived.

I had unthinkingly decided Shortly was dead. This is a bad habit you acquire from attending wars; so many people actually are dead that if anyone disappears for a while you jump to conclusions. Shorty was wonderfully, unrecognizably, adorably alive.

The pug-dog face shone, not with its usual or former mindless merriment, but with something so seldom seen that I could not at once place it. It turned out to be peace. They say women acquire a Madonna-like expression when they are pregnant, and I doubt the truth of this; there can be no universal biological rule. But Shorty had it. Shorty looked smoothed out, certain, serene, and happy in a way that made you think sentimentally of rivers, clouds, and wide fields quiet under the sun. She bulged in the unbecoming, accepted manner, and she announced in a voice of joy that she threw up all the time. Her baby was coming in two months. It would be a girl. Why? Because it must not be killed in a war. I did not argue this. She had forgotten the sexually impartial effectiveness of aerial and artillery bombardment. She was married. I did not point out that this was still a stylish habit for women in her condition. Her husband was named Louis Lefèvre, and he ran the luggage section of a Paris department store. She did not tell me where or how she had met him, nor how she had left Spain. Her husband, she said proudly, had no political ideas at all and, due to a weak heart, wasn't even in the army. Good, said I. They lived in the suburbs in their own house; it was entirely paid for. She was going to get real papers, just like anyone else, real citizenship papers; she was going to have a passport. Splendid I said.

Then I inquired if there was anything she needed and Shorty was very grand about her husband's salary, their furniture, their house again, and her husband's father who was retired and lived in another house, which he also owned himself, near the Loire.

Did I think there was going to be a war, Shorty asked, suddenly anxious. She was easy to lie to; anyone happy has a way of staying happy as long as possible. She gave me her address. I must look her up the next time I was in Paris; she wanted me to meet her husband. She would have the baby ready to show me. It is all I ever wanted, Shorty said, just one baby—if I could only get one, that was all I wanted. But we never had time, you know, since 1933, and no place to live and no papers and war. I'm glad you've got it, I said. I would like to name her after you, Shorty said, because you are my friend. I am sorry I cannot. But I have always known what I was going to call my baby and I have waited a long time so I have to do it. What is it, I said. Myrtle, she said, pronouncing it as a French word, with a German accent. *Oh well,* I thought, *the child can probably invent some nickname for herself later, to get over that horrid handicap.*

I was busy writing a lot of nonsense about would-there-be-war-wouldn't-there-be-war—and then it came, as it had to by then. I was sent to Poland and after that to Finland, and though I meant to write Shorty saying I hoped the baby was fine and that she and her husband were fine (as if anyone in Europe could be) I did not. But I got a rest at Christmas and came back to Paris with the notion that I had to see it once more before it was broken into rubble. Paris was as beautiful as you could hope, if you were looking at it for what you believed to be the last time. It was soft with snow, and quiet, and I walked around having a final heartsick love affair with the city. I decided that, these days, people would be well advised to love nothing; and this reminded me of Shorty and her baby and it was Christmas and a present was in order. I telephoned her. Her voice sounded the way she had looked in the summer, it was fantastic for any voice, here and now, to sing and exult in this way. But I would not go to her house; I said I had too much work. I imagined her house must be a glorious place, from her voice, and I did not want to take my despair into it.

She came to see me, and the peace had not left her face. I could hardly believe how she looked. She seemed to have arranged in her mind that the war was not coming here, it would be fought neatly in the north along the Maginot Line where it belonged. No harm could strike this city; no evil could befall. She had Myrtle, and such happiness, given only by God, would obviously be protected by Him. She spoke of Myrtle as if she were already twice as beautiful as Helen of Troy; she spoke of the pink-and-white room she had fixed for Myrtle. I did not ask if she needed anything. The only thing she needed was a world forever at peace. Presently I went back to Finland, which was cold and certain to be defeated.

I could not get Shorty on the telephone the next time I was in Paris and I wasn't there long. I left, together with a good proportion of the citizenry. Shorty and Myrtle and the husband with the weak heart must already have gone to the retired father, to the house near the Loire that was still, and one passionately hoped would remain, safe. After that there was only the war, all the years of it, and Shorty in Occupied France where I could not have reached her had I thought about her, which I didn't.

The international conference was well attended by many of the former Spanish War correspondents. I do not know about the others, but I felt that I had lived longer than was decent, and judging by the appearance of my friends, who had also been wandering around the wars, we all looked that way. One afternoon, limp with boredom and prickly with contempt, I was taking my ease in the Luxembourg Palace press bar when Owen James came in. I had seen him once in Italy, during the Cassino winter, but our real bond was Spain. We fell upon each other with suitable rejoicing. We settled the affairs of the world. We told each other how this international conference ought to be and wasn't. And then, for no reason at all, he mentioned Shorty.

Do you remember Jean Roche, he said (Jean Roche was a French correspondent in Madrid, who wore the largest horn-rimmed spectacles I have ever seen on anyone). Sure, I said. Well, he kind of kept up with Shorty in Paris after the war. (The war, for us old boys, was always Spain.) He met her husband. I had dinner with Jean last week. He told me about Shorty. It seems she and her baby and her husband moved down somewhere in the country with her father-in-law. Then the krauts took over. It was okay for a while; you know, nothing gets organzied too fast. But the krauts started settling in and checking up on everybody and seeing everything was on the level. Shorty didn't have any papers;

there wasn't enough time for the red tape between her being married and the war declared. And she was a German anti-Fascist—which, as you know—is what the krauts would not take—and had been in Spain, which was really bad, and her first husband was a Jew—and that's the kiss of death. So it seems Shorty sat around there thinking about all this. Jean Roche got the story from her husband. And then one day she walked out the front door and disappeared.

But why, I said, why? Well, Owen James said, she left a note, so her husband told Jean Roche. She said she didn't want to bring danger to her baby. He was to look after the baby, that was all; and she didn't want to cause trouble for the kid.

I said nothing, and we had two more brandies. But now, I said, but now that it's over, hasn't anything happened? No, Owen James said, she's gone; I guess you have to assume she's dead. How dreadful, I said (and the word sounded insulting to me—tiny, feeble, a caricature). How perfectly awful. I remembered Shorty in her happiness. Owen James wouldn't have known what she had; Owen James wouldn't know about the peace on her face. Then somebody bounced into the bar and said that the whole Jugoslav Delegation was boycotting the session, and everyone rushed for the press galleries. I did too. I have not thought about Shorty since.

This week, I am in New York, that mammoth stone ant heap, buying unseasonal summer clothes. The sky sparkles in these parts, and those who can go about wrapped in furs. I am buying silks and cottons, as I am leaving for South America on a long insignificant assignment about something or other. It seems that the calendar is confused for South America, and they have summer while other folks have winter. I do not know why, in the middle of inspecting without interest a pale green flowered print for wear during the cocktail hour, I should have remembered Shorty. I do not know why at all. I only know that she is here. It occurs to me that, if you live long enough, there are more people you would like to forget than people you would like to remember. I would like, for instance, to forget Shorty as I have forgotten her name.

MORRIS MARKEY

Lady of the Evening

THE TALE is of man's folly: the particular kind of folly that youths, being very wise, deplore in their fathers and then, having grown to slippers and a pipe, weep for in their sons. Quite incidentally, perhaps, it is also the tale of a girl called beautiful by many, many people, who was murdered in her bed one fine night.

The night was a Wednesday. It was the 14th of March, 1923. The scene was New York.

In Carnegie Hall, which is at 57th Street and Seventh Avenue, the Schola Cantorum sang choral music that night while the wealth and the elegance of the town sat enthralled with their rendition of Brahms and of French and Italian madrigals. Two hundred yards down 57th Street, the committee ladies of the Reverend John Roach Straton's Baptist Church completed plans for the protracted revival meeting of a child preacher named Uldine Utley.

Immediately across the street from this vast and holy edifice there was a short row of buildings, originally designed with careful taste for the families of the notably prosperous, and now converted into apartments for the fastidious. In the top-floor apartment of the most seemly of these houses, the beautiful young woman was pursuing her career.

It was a career peculiar, in a certain sense, to that decade of the Twenties. Indeed, with all respect to the Schola Cantorum and Brahms, the song written in celebration of this career was the most popular music in all the town. At the Music Box Revue a lovely creature leaned back upon her chaise longue, the very perfection of an odalisque, and purred while her stage lover sang *Lady of the Evening.*

There were, in those brief days, many ladies of the evening. Their scented nests were tucked into half the apartment buildings of mid-Manhattan.

Of course, there was nothing essentially new about this. There have been mistresses, there have been courtesans, since "burning Sappho loved and sung" amid the Isles of Greece. But here was a little while in our times when men of wealth and, as they say, position, mistook a total naiveté for sophistication. Some of them simply threw discretion to the winds. And so the return which they earned upon their pursuit of the fleshpots, and their total ignorance of womankind, was summed up in a single word: disaster.

Our particular lady of the evening, deploying her charms in behalf of her lover that night of March, called herself Dot King. But the detectives of the Broadway Squad knew her name was Anna Keenan. Please understand that this girl was not a prostitute in the ordinary sense. She simply enjoyed nice things. She liked to be well kept by a man, and she was not only passively willing but honestly eager to bestow upon her protector all the delights and the happiness she could manage.

At eighteen, she had hired out as a nursemaid. Her stunning looks persuaded Jack Lannigan, once headwaiter at Reisenweber's Restaurant (the splendid fame of which is now almost forgotten) to take her under his wing. But only a little while went by before it was plain that her sights were set far beyond the opulence and position of even a headwaiter. So by the time she was twenty she left Lannigan to bestow her startling favors upon a Wall Street broker. His fortune disappeared in the 1919 crash and Dot King felt no obligation to continue her deep affection for him.

In New York, thereafter, she found several providers. Some of them were simple scoundrels. One or two were gentlemen of substance, misunderstood at home and touched to the quick by dreamful eyes, a perfect body, and every aspect of devotion save devotion itself. Not one of the men who kept her in this time, so far as an outrageously inept police investigation could determine, was an outright criminal. She lived in apartments her lovers provided for her, dressed in gowns from Paris, and wore tasteful diamonds. She was not a gaudy creature, but an impeccably dainty one.

It was almost exactly noon of Thursday, March 15, when her colored maid, Ella Bradford, entered the elevator in the building at 144 West 57th Street and went up to the apartment. She had her own key, since Miss King often slept quite late. She spent a moment or two in the living room, started coffee in the kitchen, and then peeked into the bedroom.

She knew at once that Dot King was dead.

There was an almost overwhelming reek of chloroform in the bedroom. And on the bed in a pink silk nightgown was a corpse.

They had no radio squad cars in those days, but even so the police came rather quickly when Ella Bradford set up the alarm with her screams. Detectives from the Precinct Station and uniformed men in the neighborhood swarmed into the apartment.

They found a handful of chloroform-soaked cotton on the floor, and one of them later reported that it had been at least ten feet from the bed. A bottle which had held cholorform had been tossed in a corner. The closets had been rifled. And before the day was out it was decided, from examination of bills and receipts, from inquiry among the shops, that gowns and furs worth $10,000 were gone. The jewelry boxes had been emptied, but there was no way to determine the value of the diamonds and sapphires that had been stolen. As it later developed, $1000 in cash was missing, also.

The Broadway Squad knew that Dot King's frequent companion in the speakeasies was a fellow named Albert Guimares, who lived at the Embassy Hotel and told people that he was an importer. So detectives went to the Embassy, and searched Guimares' room, and arrested him for violation of the Sullivan Law when they found an empty revolver in a dresser drawer.

Down at headquarters in Centre Street, Guimares talked without restraint. Dot King had been in love with him, though he could not possibly afford the money to keep her. Somebody else, with real money, was keeping her. She had given Guimares a $1200 watch, and a $750 fur coat. She had let him pick out a pair of jeweled cuff links priced at $400, and had paid for them in cash. He knew that the money for these gifts came from another man, but he did not know the man's name. That was his story.

He admitted that Dot King had spent Monday and Tuesday nights with him in a Broadway hotel. When they had lunch together on Wednesday, she told him her rich man was coming to her apartment that evening. She must go to the beauty shop. And then she must go home and rest so that she might be proper company for the gentleman who paid her rent and bought her clothes.

Guimares helped her into a taxicab and never saw her again. His alibi was flawless. Many people had seen him during the rest of the afternoon, which was not a critical time anyway in the chronology of the murder. And he had dined at the Beaux Arts Restaurant, near Bryant Square, with two men. One of them was Albert

Hanan, grandson of the shoe manufacturer and a citizen of unassailable probity. Hanan told police that Guimares was with him until a late hour. The time linked with the arrival of Guimares at the Embassy, and employees there said that he had gone immediately to his room and had not left the building until the arrival of the police. After twelve days, the police released Guimares from charges.

Now upon the scene enters Mrs. Anna Keenan, the dead girl's mother. She was under no illusions about the way of life her daughter had pursued. "But she never went around with gangsters or bootleggers," Mrs. Keenan said. "She didn't have to. She was the kind of girl who attracted fine men. Men like Mr. Marshall, who has been so nice to her."

"Who is Mr. Marshall?"

"I don't suppose that's his real name. You know how important these men are, and generally they're married and have to be careful. He's from out of town somewhere. I know that. And I know that money doesn't mean a thing to him."

The Homicide Bureau men went looking for Mr. Marshall.

John Thomas, night elevator man in the apartment building where Dot King had lived and died, had seen a good deal of Mr. Marshall.

"He was here that Wednesday night when she got killed," he said. "Sure he was. His secretary, Mr. Wilson, got here about seven o'clock, and then about twenty minutes later Mr. Marshall showed up. Mr. Wilson always came in ahead of time. I guess he was seeing that the coast was clear. As soon as Mr. Marshall came, Mr. Wilson left. He always did that.

"There was a lot of people Miss King knew and they knew all about Mr. Marshall, but he didn't know much about them. They always called him 'Champagne Jack.' I figured the guy was a sucker, but it wasn't any of my business. It was all a long way over my head."

"What time did you take Mr. Marshall down in the elevator?"

"I can't remember taking him down at all. But, like I say, I didn't pay much attention. I might have taken him down without even knowing who was in the car. And he might have walked down the steps. It was only three flights."

The hunt was on, now, in full cry, for Champagne Jack. And it was perhaps their concentration upon this that led police to neglect the plodding routine that solves most murder cases.

It happened that I worked on this affair for a New York news-

"Really, Miss Pringle....Statistics show a big percentage of women die old maids!"

paper, and one day I handed the Acting Chief of the Homicide Bureau, Detective Division (Captain Arthur Carey), a list of questions:

Was the window to the fire escape opened or closed?

Were the lights in the apartment on or off when Ella Bradford arrived?

Were fingerprints taken from the chloroform bottle?

Had any effort been made to trace the chloroform purchase?

Was the bed clothing rumpled to indicate a struggle?

Had the clothing she wore *that night* been stolen along with the rest? If not, how was it disposed in the bedroom?

Was there a comprehensive interrogation of John Thomas, to find out, as best he could tell, who rode his elevator that night?

Was there any evidence to show how the murderer gained entrance?

There were several more questions, but the Homicide Bureau gave no satisfactory answer to any in the list. Their reticence was not a matter of what we call, in these days, "security." They simply did not know. The groundwork that might have been provided for the answers had been destroyed by the mob of policemen and detectives who had crowded the place, searching every nook and cranny with neither design nor efficiency. Windows had been pushed up and down. Lights had been punched on and off. Furniture and other objects had been moved about before the photographers and other experts could get there.

Nothing very convincing was offered even upon the approximate time of death. The best that we could learn was a rather halting opinion that Dot King had been alive when the dawn came up, that she had been murdered only a few hours before Ella Bradford arrived.

While most of thir energies were being devoted to the search for Mr. Marshall, the police brought in for questioning half-a-hundred characters of the speak easy world whom Dot King had known. But the questions were perfunctory. Alibis were exchanged back and forth in a plausible sort of way. Plausible enough for Centre Street, anyway. Nobody was held.

Public announcement of the finding of Mr. Marshall did not fall to the lot of either the police or the District Attorney. By what shrewd devices I never learned, the game was bayed to covert by reporters for the New York *Journal*. All the rest of us trying to report the case were humiliated one afternoon to read the great black headlines of our competitor.

Mr. Marshall was worthy game indeed. His true name was John Kearsley Mitchell. His family was Philadelphia Main Line—proud blood to say the least. He was the son-in-law of Colonel E. T. Stotesbury, a partner in the house of J. P. Morgan.

Mr. Wilson, the "secretary," was John H. Jackson, a New York lawyer.

Ferdinand Pecora, who is now a Judge of the New York Supreme Court, was Acting District Attorney then. He did the only thing possible under the circumstances. Looking upon our frustration and our contempt for professional investigators whose failure had allowed our competitor to outdo us, he summoned John Mitchell to his office and invited us to interview him.

When we walked in and took chairs, we looked at a man in his early fifties who sat close beside Pecora's desk. He was a handsome man, with a frame which must have been powerful in his football days. His hair was greying, and this perhaps gave accent to the scarlet flush upon his face.

Pecora said at once that there were no charges of any sort against Mitchell. He was not being held. There was no possible chance that he could be guilty of the murder of Dot King.

These firmly categorical statements were not really necessary. For not even the most callow student of human nature, looking into John Mitchell's open, well-bred face, and listening to the story he told in a voice extraordinarily calm and contained under the circumstances, could think of him as a killer.

He was not reluctant in answering our questions, but neither was he glib. He knew that we knew he had been considerable of a fool. But his breeding made it impossible for him to try the invariably fatal gambit of trying to be a pal among a roomful of reporters.

One evening, about two years before, he had been dining with the lawyer, Jackson, at the Brevoort. This beautiful girl came into the room. She seemed to be looking for someone, and a little upset because this someone was not there. These were Prohibition days, of course, and there was no bar where she might sit and wait. Mitchell told Jackson to invite her to their table, and Dot King joined them. She was waiting for a girl friend, she said. The girl friend never showed up.

That was the beginning—that night in the midst of the "Love Nest" era, when many a man of substance rose to the bait, not only the bait of a desirable female, but to the very spirit of the times.

As a matter of fact, Mitchell did not see her at frequent intervals during those two years. There was no such thing as Café Society, he was not a playboy, and he lived in Philadelphia. His business, his obligations to his family and to the real Society in which he moved made it difficult for him to get to the pretty little place in 57th Street as often as he might have wished. But he paid the bills. He bought gifts. It cost him a thousand dollars every time he did see her, and he gave her that sum on the Wednesday night that she died, when he bade her farewell and walked down the stairs to find a taxicab. This was the money stolen by the murderer.

Occasionally, when he could think of no possible excuse for going to New York, he sent word to her to meet him in Atlantic City, and motored from Philadelphia to meet her there. Indeed, he had spent the previous week end with her in one of the Boardwalk hotels, leaving her late Sunday night—whereupon she had hurried back to Broadway and Guimares.

There is no doubt that the infatuation of this rich and middle-aged aristocrat with the beautiful Irish nursemaid, who had been mistress to half-a-dozen sharp Broadway operators, was a very real thing. In all men, from kings to bootblacks, there is the leveling touch of lust. Perhaps it is more frequent in kings because they have the money for it.

Mitchell wrote many letters to his mistress on 57th Street. Ella Bradford told the investigators that she had seen them arrive. She said that when there was no possibility of Mitchell coming for the night, and when therefore Dot King's shady pals were in, conversation sometimes got dull. Whereupon Miss King would bring out the letters and show the boys and girls what it was like to have a high-class lover.

When everybody had enjoyed a good, if slightly envious laugh, they generally went out in a body to some speak easy. And, generally, Miss King did not get home before 3 o'clock in the morning, when Ella Bradford was relieved by arrangement of all her duties, and so could go home.

The letters were missing from the apartment—all but one. It was a confession of total love, written by an amateur in such matters. An example of Mitchell's enchantment lies in one phrase from the rather embarrassing paragraphs: " . . . I would like to kiss your little pink toes . . . "

Ella Bradford, as is the way with servants, had heard a great deal more of the talk among Dot King's dubious crowd than anybody realized.

"I'll tell you this. Sometimes I heard them talking about blackmail on Champagne Jack. I heard one of them say, 'We get our hands on these letters Dot's been reading us, and brother, we got that sucker cold. It's a pushover.' "

There is no way to discover beyond doubt whether blackmail was at the heart of the murder. There is no way to be sure that Mitchell, confronted with this appalling club in the hands of a man who had his letters, did not let his identity be "discovered" —either by confession to official authorities who tipped the story to the New York *Journal* in return for favors received, or to the Hearst press itself.

But there is room for sober speculation:

Suppose that the little crowd of men and women who clustered about Dot King because she had a source of money—the men living by their wits and the women comforting them and making a glamorous front for them—suppose they decided one night, when Dot wasn't around, to get Champagne Jack's letters, and bleed the rich guy for the rest of his life?

Suppose, again, they said to Dot King, "Give us the letters and you're good for ten grand a year from now on, without having to sleep with that old bore."

And suppose that some remnant of decency rose up in the Irish blood of a Broadway wanton and she said, "Get out of here! The guy has been good to me. I'm not going for any blackmail racket."

So, then, the boys and girls decided to do the job on their own. They figured out a scheme that was simplicity itself. Watch and wait for a time when Jack would come calling from Philadelphia. Any time he called, Dot would be half-crocked when he left, with champagne and with love. Wait for him to leave. Then dip up the stairway. Knock Dotty a little colder with a touch of chloroform. Find the letters, and take everything in the apartment to make it look like the job of an ordinary cat burglar. Dip down the stairs again. The night elevator man would be the only problem because he was the only servant on duty in the building. They knew him. As we have seen, he couldn't recollect whether he had given Mitchell a ride back down.

Whether this might be a solution of the case of Dot King's murder is pure conjecture. But one item of specific evidence remains. It is negative evidence, though such things are not to be scorned.

Not one single thing stolen that night from Dot King's apartment ever showed up—neither in the homes of the women who knew her, nor in the pawnshops. Her furs and gowns, and probably her jewelry, were familiar articles to half the speakeasy doormen, half the headwaiters, in the speakeasies of the town. The speakeasies were dependent for their existence upon the good will of the police.

No item stolen on the night she died was ever seen again.

PART TWO: *All for Love*

"Are you sure you *take* this *to be your lawful wedded husband?"*

JAMES JONES

Two Legs for the Two of Us

"No," SAID the big man in the dark blue suit, and his voice was hoarse with drunkenness. "I cant stay. I've got some friends out in the car."

"Well, why didn't you bring them in with you, George?" the woman said in mock disgust. "Don't let them sit out in the cold."

George grinned fuzzily. "To hell with them. I just stopped by for a minute. You wouldn't like them anyway."

"Why, of course I'd like them, if they're your friends. Go on and call them."

"No. You wouldn't like them. Let the bastards sit. I just wanted to talk to you, Sandy." George looked vaguely around the gayness of the kitchen with its red and white checkered motif. "Jesus, I love this place. We done a good job on it, Sandy, you know it? I used to think about it a lot. I still do."

But the woman was already at the kitchen door and she did not hear. "Hey out there!" she called. "Come on in and have a drink."

There was a murmur of words from the car she could not understand and she opened the screen door and went outside to the car in the steaming cold winter night. A man and woman were in the front seat, the man behind the wheel. Another woman was in the back seat by herself. She was smoothing her skirt.

Sandy put her head up to the car window. "George is drunk," she said. "Why don't you go on home and leave him here and let me take care of him?"

"No," the man said.

"He's been here before."

"No," the man said sharply. "He's with us."

Sandy put her hand on the door handle. "He shouldn't be drinking," she said. "In his condition."

The man laughed. "Liquor never bothers me," he said.

"Poor George. I feel so sorry for him I could cry."

"No, you couldn't," the man said contemptuously. "I know you. Besides, it aint your sympathy he wants." He thumped the thigh of his left leg with his fist. It made a sound like a gloved fist striking a heavy bag. "I pawned one myself," he said.

Sandy moved as if he had struck her. She stepped back, putting her hand to her mouth, then turned back toward the house.

George was standing in the door. "Tom's a old buddy of mine," he grinned. "He was in the hospital with for ten months out in Utah." He opened the screen.

Sandy stepped inside with slumped shoulders. "Why didn't you tell me? I said something terrible. Please tell him to come in, George, he won't come now unless you tell him."

"No. Let them sit. We got a couple of pigs from Greencastle with us." He grinned down at her belligerently through the dark circles and loose lips of an extended bat.

"Ask them all in, for a drink. I'm no Carrie Nation, George. Tell them to come in. Please, George. Tell them."

"All right. By god I will. I wasn't going to, but I will. I just wanted to see you, Sandy."

"Why don't you stay here tonight, George?" Sandy said. "Let them go on and I'll put you to bed."

George searched her face incredulously. "You really want me to stay?"

"Yes. You need to sober up, George."

"Oh." George laughed suddenly. "Liquor never bothers me. No sir by god. I aint runnin out on Tom. Tom's my buddy." He stepped back to the door. "Hey, you bastards!" he bellered. "You comin in here an have a drink? or I got to come out and drag you in?" Sandy stood behind him, watching him, the big bulk of shoulder, the hair growing softly on the back of his neck.

There was a laugh from the car and the door slammed. The tall curly-haired Tom came in, swinging his left side in a peculiar rhythm. After him came the two women, one tall and blonde, the other short and dark. They both smiled shyly as they entered. They both were young.

"Oh," said the short one. "This is pretty."

"Its awful pretty," the blonde one said, looking around.

"You goddam right its pretty," George said belligerently. "And its built for utility. Look at them cupboards."

George introduced the girls by their first names, like a barker in a sideshow naming the attractions. "An this heres Tom Hornney," he said, "and when I say Hornney, I mean Hornney." George laughed and Tom grinned and the two girls tittered nervously.

"I want you all to meet Miss Sandy Thomas," George said, as if daring them.

"Sure," Tom said. "I know all about you. I use to read your letters out in Utah."

George looked at Sandy sheepishly. "A man gets so he cant believe it himself. He gets so he's got to show it to somebody. Thats the way it is in the army."

Sandy smiled at him stiffly, her eyes seeming not to see. "How do you want your drinks? Soda or Coke?"

"They want Coke with theirs," Tom pointed to the girls. "They dont know how to drink."

"This is really a beautiful place," the blonde one said.

"Oh my yes," the short one said. "I wish I ever had a place like this here."

Sandy looked up from the drinks and smiled, warmly. "Thank you."

"I really love your place," the blonde one said. "Where did you get those funny spotted glasses? I seen some like them in Woolworth's once."

George, laughing over something with Tom, turned to the blonde one. "Shut up, for god sake. You talk too much. You're supposed to be seen."

"Or felt," Tom said.

"I was only being polite," the blonde one said.

"Well dont," George said. "You dont know how."

"Well," said the blonde one. "I like that."

"Those are antiques, dear," Sandy said to her. "I bought them off an old woman down in the country. Woolworth has reproductions of them now."

"You mean them are *genuine* antiques?" the short one said.

Sandy nodded, handing around the drinks.

"For god sake, shut up," George said. "Them's genuine antiques and they cost ten bucks apiece, so shut up. Talk about something interesting."

The short one made a little face at George. She turned to Sandy and whispered delicately.

"Surely," Sandy said. "I'll show you."

"See what I mean?" Tom laughed. "I said they couldnt hold their liquor."

Sandy led the girls out of the kitchen. From the next room

their voices came back, exclaiming delicately over the furnishings.

"How long were you in the army?" Sandy asked when they came back.

"Five years," Tom said, grinning and shaking his curly head. "My first wife left me three months after I got drafted."

"Oh?" Sandy said.

"Yeah. I guess she couldnt take the idea of not getting any for so long. It looked like a long war."

"War is hard on the women too," Sandy said.

"Sure," Tom said. "I dont see how they stand it. I'm glad I was a man in this war."

"Take it easy," George growled.

Tom grinned at him and turned back to Sandy. "I been married four times in five years. My last wife left me day before yesterday. She told me she was leaving and I said, Okay, baby. Thats fine. Only remember there wont be nobody here when you come back. If I wanted, I could call her up right now and tell her and she'd start back tonight."

"Why dont you?" Sandy said. "I've got a phone."

Tom laughed. "What the hell. I'm doin all right. Come here, baby," he said to the blonde one, and patted his right leg. She came over, smiling, on his left side and started to sit on his lap.

"No," Tom said. "Go around to the other side. You cant sit on that one."

The blonde one obeyed and walked around his chair. She sat down smiling on his right thigh and Tom put his arm clear around her waist. "I'm doin all right, baby, aint I? Who wants to get married?"

George was watching him, and now he laughed. "I been married myself," he said, not looking at Sandy.

"Sure," Tom grinned. "Dont tell me. I was out in Utah when you got the rings back, remember? Ha!" he turned his liquor-bright eyes on Sandy. "It was just like Robert Taylor in the movies. He took them out in the snow and threw them away with a curse. Went right out the ward door and into the snowing night.

"One ring, engagement, platinum, two carat diamond," Tom said, as if giving the nomenclature of a new weapon. "One ring, wedding, platinum, diamond circlet.—I told him he should of hocked them."

"No," Sandy said. "He should have kept them, then he could have used them over and over, every other night."

"I'll say," Tom said. "I'll never forget the first time me and

George went on pass in Salt Lake City. He sure could of used them then."

"Aint you drinkin, Sandy?" George said.

"You know I don't drink."

"You used to. Some."

"That was only on special occasions," Sandy said, looking at him. "That was a long time ago. I've quit that now," she said.

George looked away, at Tom, who had his hand up under the blonde one's armpit, snuggled in. "Now this heres a very fine thing," Tom said, nodding at her. "She's not persnickity like the broads in Salt Lake."

"I didnt really like it then," Sandy said.

"I know," George said.

"George picked him up a gal in a bar in Salt Lake that first night," Tom said. "She looked a lot like you, honey," he said to the blonde one. The blonde one tittered and put her hand beneath his ear.

"This gal," Tom continued, "she thought George was wonderful; he was wearing his ribbons. She asked him all about the limp and how he got wounded. She thought he was nuts till she found out what it was made him limp." Tom paused to laugh.

"Then she got dressed and took off; we seen her later with a marine." He looked at George and they both laughed. George went around the table and sat down beside the short one.

"You ought to have a drink with us, Sandy," George said. "You're the host."

"I dont feel much like being formal," Sandy said.

Tom laughed. "Me neither."

"Do you want something to eat?" Sandy asked him. "I might eat something."

"Sure," Tom said. "I'll eat anything. I'm an old eater from way back. You got any cheese and crackers?"

Sandy went to one of the cupboards. "You fix another drink, George."

"Thats it," Tom said. "Eat and drink. There's only one think can turn my stommick," he said to the blonde one. "You know whats the only think can turn my stommick?"

"Yes," said the blonde one apprehensively, glancing at Sandy. "I know."

"I'll tell you the only thing can turn my stommick."

"Now, honey," the blonde one said.

George turned around from the bottles on the countertop, pausing dramatically like an orator.

"Same thing that can turn my stommick."

He and Tom laughed uproariously, and he passed the drinks and sat down. The blonde one and short one tittered and glanced nervously at Sandy.

Tom thumped George's right leg with his fist and the sound it made was solid, heavy, the sound his own had made out in the car.

"You goddam old cripple, you."

"Thats all right," George said. "You cant run so goddam fast yourself."

"The hell I cant." Tom reached for his drink and misjudged it, spilling some on the tablecloth and on the blonde girl's skirt.

"Now see what you did?" she said. "Damn it."

Tom laughed. "Take it easy, baby. If you never get nothing worse than whiskey spilled on your skirt, you'll be all right. Whiskey'll wash out."

George watched dully as the spot spread on the red and white checked tablecloth, then he lurched to his feet toward the sink where the dishrag always was.

Sandy pushed him back into his chair. "Its all right, George. I'll change it tomorrow."

George breathed heavily. "Watch yourself, you," he said to Tom. "Goddam you, be careful."

"What the hell. I dint do it on purpose."

"Thats all right, just watch yourself."

"Okay, Sergeant," Tom said. "Okay, halfchick."

George laughed suddenly, munching a slab of cheese between two crackers, spraying crumbs. "Dont call me none of your family names.

"We really use to have some times," he said to Sandy. "You know what this crazy bastard use to do? After we got our leather, we use to stand out in the corridor and watch the guys with a leg off going down the hall on crutches. Tom would look at them and say to me, Pore feller. He's lost a leg. And I'd say, Why thats turrible, aint it?"

Sandy was looking at him, watching him, her sandwich untouched in her hand. Under her gaze George's eyebrows suddenly went up, bent in the middle.

"We use to go to town," he said, grinning at her. "We really had some times. You ought to seen their faces when we'd go up to the room from the bar. You ought to see them when we'd take our pants off." He laughed viciously. "One broad even fainted on me. They didnt like it." His gaze wavered, then fell to his drink. "I guess you cant blame them though."

"Why?" Sandy said. "Why did you do it, George?"

"Hell," he said, looking up. "*Why?* Dont you know *why?*"

Sandy shook her head slowly, her eyes unmoving on his face. "No," she said. "I dont know why. I guess I never will know why," she said.

Tom was pinching the blonde one's bottom. "That tickles mine," he said. "You know what tickles mine?"

"No," she said, "what?"

Tom whispered in her ear and she giggled and slapped him lightly.

"No," George said, "I guess you wont. You aint never been in the army, have you?"

"No," Sandy said. "I havent."

"You ought to try it," George said. "Fix us one more drink and we'll be goin."

"All right, George. But I wish you'd stay."

George spread his hands and looked down at himself. "Who?" he said. "Me?"

"Yes," Sandy said. "You really do need to sober up."

"Oh," George said. "Sober up. Liquor never bothers me. Listen, Sandy. I wanted to talk to you, Sandy."

Under the red and white checked tablecloth George put his hand on Sandy's bare knee below her skirt. His hand cupped it awkwardly, but softly, very softly.

"I'll get your drink," Sandy said, pushing back her chair. George watched her get up and go to the countertop where the bottles were.

"Come here, you," George said to the short dark one. He jerked her toward him so roughly her head snapped back. He kissed her heavily, his left hand behind her head holding her neck rigid, his right hand on her upper arm, stroking heavily, pinching slightly.

Sandy set the drink in front of him. "Here's your drink you wanted, George," she said, still holding the tabled glass. "George, here's your drink."

"Okay," George said. "Drink up, you all, and lets get out of this."

The short one was rubbing her neck with her hand, her face

twisted breathlessly. She smiled apologetically at Sandy. "You got a wonderful home here, Miss Thomas," she said.

George lurched to his feet. "All right. All right. Outside." He shooed them out the door, Tom grinning, his hand hidden under the blonde one's arm. Then he stood in the doorway looking back.

"Well, so long. And thanks for the liquor."

"All right, George. Why dont you stop drinking, George?"

"Why?" George said. "You ask me why."

"I hate to see you ruin yourself."

George laughed. "Well now thanks. That sure is nice of you, Sandy girl. But liquor never bothers me." He looked around the gayness of the kitchen. "Listen. I'm sorry about the tablecloth. Sorry. I shouldnt of done it, I guess. I shouldnt of come here with them."

"No, George. You shouldnt."

"You know what I love about you, Sandy girl? You're always so goddam stinking right."

"I just do what I have to," Sandy said.

"Sandy," George said. "You dont know what it was like, Sandy."

"No," she said. "I guess I dont."

"You goddam right you dont. And you never will. You'll never be . . ."

"I cant help the way I'm made."

"Yes? Well I cant neither. The only thing for us to do is turn it over to the United Nations. Its their job, let them figure it out."

Tom Hornney came back to the door. "Come on, for Christ sake. Are you comin or aint you?"

"Yes goddam it I'm comin. I'm comin and I'm goin." George limped swingingly over to the countertop and grabbed a bottle.

Tom stepped inside the door. "Listen, lady," he said. "What the hells a leg? The thing a man wants you dames will never give him. We're just on a little vacation now. I got a trucking business in Terre Haute. Had it before the war. There's good money in long-distance hauling, and me and George is goin to get our share. We got six trucks and three more spotted, and I know this racket, see? I know how to get the contracks, all the ways. An I got the pull. And me and George is full-time partners. What the hells a leg?"

George set down the bottle and came back, his right leg hitting the floor heavy and without resilience. "Tom and me is buddies, and right or wrong what we do we do together."

"I think thats fine, George," she said.

"Yeah? Well then, its all all right then, aint it?"

"Listen, lady," Tom said. "Someday he'll build another house'll make this place look sick, see? To hell with the respectability if you got the money. So what the hells a leg?"

"Shut up," George said, "Lets go. Shut up. Shut up, or I'll mash you down."

"Yeah?" Tom grinned. "I'll take your leg off and beat you to death with it, Mack."

George threw back his head, laughing. "Fall in, you bum. Lets go."

"George," Sandy said. She went to the countertop and came back with a nearly full bottle. "Take it with you."

"Not me. I got mine in the car. And I got the money to buy more. Whiskey never bothers me. Fall in, Tom, goddam you."

Tom slapped him on the back. "Right," he said. And he started to sing.

They went out of the house into the steaming chill February night. They went arm in arm and limping. And they were singing.

Si-n-n-g glorious, glorious,
One keg of beer for the four of us,
Glory be to God there's no more of us,
'Cause . . ."

Their voices faded and died as the motor started. Tom honked the horn once, derisively.

Sandy Thomas stood in the door, watching the headlights move away, feeling the need inside, holding the bottle in her hand, moisture overflowing her eyes unnoticed, looking backward into a past the world had not seen fit to let alone. Tomorrow she would change the tablecloth, the red and white checkered tablecloth.

IRWIN SHAW

The Convert

"FANNIE says she's sure he's been a little crazy since he got out of the hospital," said Sara. "Are you listening to me, Justin?"

"Yes," said Trotter, sighing a small, inward sigh, looking up from the *Times* neatly folded beside his plate on the breakfast table.

"After all," Sara said, her teeth crunching loudly on the bacon, "it's your friend, not mine; you've known him since your freshman year at Yale, and I should think you'd be worried about him."

"I am worried about him," Trotter said. "Terribly worried."

"You don't sound it."

There was no answer to this, so Trotter silently poured himself some more coffee.

"A man his age," Sara said, "in his delicate health. With two half-grown children, barely recovering from that kidney operation . . . Please, don't look at your watch. Your office can wait another ten minutes."

"Sorry," Trotter mumbled.

"After seventeen years of marriage," Sara said, "suddenly to get up one morning and calmly announce, 'I'm leaving.' That's not normal, you know, not even for these days." She stared harshly at Trotter as though she half-believed he thought it was normal. "No explanations, no excuses, just good-bye and I'll be at the New Weston." She leaned forward keenly. "Did he tell you anything?"

"I haven't seen him for a month," Trotter said. "Leave me out of this."

"Fannie thought maybe he spoke to you. She's going frantic. She cried in our living room from two until five-thirty yesterday afternoon. Naturally," Sara said, in a tone of bitter resignation, "I'm the one who finally bears the brunt."

There was no answer to this, either, so Trotter poured himself some more coffee.

"I told her," Sara said, "that you'd go talk to Rudolf."

"Oh, Lord," Trotter cried, involuntarily. "What did you do that for? I can't go poking my nose into other people's marriages. I have enough trouble keeping my own . . ."

"Justin," Sara said, warningly. "Be careful."

"I didn't mean that, of course," Justin said hurriedly. "Manner of speaking. What I mean is, marriage is something between two people, and nobody thanks anyone for interfering . . ."

"You've known them for twenty-five years. You went to Yale with him."

"I went to Yale with two thousand other people," Trotter said loudly. "Still, I don't go around irresponsibly telling them they ought to go back to their wives."

"Don't twist my words," Sara said. "You know what I mean. He's been your best friend, and you always said you liked Fannie."

"Even so," Trotter said, forlornly knowing he was not going to come out the winner in this argument, "there are certain things you don't get involved in, and marriage and divorce are two of them. If only you could get women to understand that for once . . ."

"I'm not interested," Sara said, "in another of your ridiculous lectures on the subject of women. It seems to me that a grown man should have a certain sense of responsibility to the people around him, the people he's loved and been friendly with for so many years. Good God, you're always worrying about what's happening to the Greeks and the Albanians and the coal miners, the least you should be willing to do, when two of your closest friends are having a crisis, is to see if there's any way you can help. I'm not asking you to *do* anything, all I'm asking, for poor Fannie's sake is . . ."

"All right," Trotter said, "all right. I'll call him today."

He called Rudolf's office after the first flurry of the morning appointments was over. Rudolf's voice over the phone sounded tired and pathetically grateful as he said he'd be delighted to have lunch. Neither he nor Trotter said anything about their wives. That could wait till later, Trotter thought, when it could be led up to gracefully and diplomatically.

After hanging up, Trotter got out the *Times*. He leaned back comfortably, rustling the pages with pleasant lack of restraint, but the door opened and Pat came in with a sheaf of papers to be signed.

"Not working today?" Pat asked in that voice of hers that always made you think she was secretly making fun of you, even if she was only asking you the time. Pat had been working with him for twelve years, and had gone through three husbands in that time, and was now a handsome grey-haired woman of forty, in brilliant clothes, who made every man in the office slightly nervous and slightly exhilarated whenever she passed near him.

Trotter sighed. He folded the *Times* neatly and put it aside. Then he started to sign the contracts Pat had brought in.

"Heard something this morning," Pat said off-handedly. "Something about you."

"Good?" Trotter asked, signing away.

"Pretty good."

"What?"

"Afraid I can't tell."

"Damn it," Trotter said loudly. "Women. If you wanted to keep it to yourself, why didn't you just keep your mouth shut? If you just came in here to . . ."

"Do you know that new girl?" Pat asked blandly. "Clark's secretary?"

Trotter stopped working on the papers before him and screwed up his eyes, trying to remember. He had a general, hazy memory of dark hair and a slight tendency to plumpness somewhere in the outer office. "What about her?" he asked.

"Name's Gloria," Pat said. "Gloria Chapin. Not bad-looking in the blowzy way most men like." Pat lit a cigarette with slow care.

"Well?"

"She likes you," she said, and watched his face.

Trotter shook his head a little wearily. "Pat," he said, "will you stop annoying me."

"Her own words were even a little more specific," Pat went on, grinning, blowing smoke, ignoring him. "She likes you, she told Miss Evans, in a direct, physical way."

Absurdly, Trotter felt himself beginning to blush. Ridiculous, he thought, at the age of forty-three. "You ought to fire her," he said stiffly.

"Secretaries are too hard to get these days. Got to put up with a lot of things. Even boss chasers."

"It's disgraceful," Trotter said, looking angrily at Pat, who was obviously vastly amused. "If you want to know what I think about it, I think it's sordid. Young girls these days," he went on, thinking of his own fifteen-year-old daughter with new surmise, "are not as well-bred as they ought to be. I frankly don't think we ought to encourage that type of person in our office and I do think that you ought to examine her work very carefully and see if she's really worth keeping around here, considering everything . . ."

"My," Pat said, grinning, "aren't we stuffy some days."

She waved and went out, leaving a faint trouble of perfume on the air. Trotter stared after her. Sometimes, he thought resentfully, that woman imposes on her position.

But he couldn't refrain from looking at Miss Chapin on his way out to lunch. He hurried through the office and glanced sidelong at the desk in front of Clark's door. Miss Chapin was still there, bending over the typewriter. She had on a tight black crepe dress and her hair was very dark and shiny around her shoulders. She was quite full-breasted, too, in the eager, bursting way that is the despair of women over thirty, and the highlights glinted alarmingly on the dull plump crepe. She looked up suddenly as Trotter passed and a slow, disturbing smile, crammed with implication, crossed her smooth round face as she bent, her head tilted, over her typewriter.

Trotter never stopped moving. But he glared at her as he swept by and he was morosely pleased as he reached for the door that the girl dropped her eyes and hastily, and he was sure guiltily, applied herself to her work.

Rudolf did not look well. His eyes were worried, his complexion quite grey, and he merely played with his lunch. His clothes, which were always very proper and handsome in a neat, dull way, made his haggard, worn face more noticeable and disturbing than otherwise, and Trotter felt a pang of anxious regret as he glanced across his London broil at his battered friend.

"You look fine," he said, with false cheeriness. "I guess you're over the operation completely by now, Rudy."

"I'm over the operation all right," Rudolf said, pushing away his plate, "but I look awful. Don't kid me."

"I'm sorry," Trotter said humbly. "I didn't want to alarm you."

"That's all right," Rudolf said dully. "It's nothing physical. It's all in the mind."

At least, Trotter thought, he realizes it. That's the first step to recovery. But he did not press Rudolf to talk. All in due time, he thought, it will all come out. He ordered a cigar and leaned back, smiling in what he hoped was a simple, confiding, reliable manner at his friend.

"I suppose," Rudolf said flatly, "Fannie has been around telling you what a horrible man I am."

"Well," Trotter said, "to tell the truth, she hasn't said a word to me. But she has said one or two things to Sara."

"She's right," Rudolf said darkly. "I am a horrible man." He shook his head, like a man who has fallen and is wondering if he will be able to stand up. "I just can't help it," Rudolf said. "Finally, there was nothing else I could do."

"Look," said Trotter. "If it's too painful, don't talk about it."

"I don't care," Rudolf said haggardly. "I can talk about it. I've kept it bottled up for so long it may do me good to get it out."

"I suppose," Trotter said delicately, "it's a woman."

"Well," Rudolf said, obviously trying to phrase it precisely, "yes and no. That is, not exactly."

Trotter looked obliquely at his friend.

"It all started in the hospital," Rudolf said, speaking not across the table to Trotter, but to his own inward confessor. "I was in a weakened condition and for three days after the operation I thought I was going to die."

"Yes," Trotter said, his voice reflecting a hospital gravity. "We all did."

"I lay in that bed looking up at the ceiling, telling myself, now it is going to happen. I felt . . ." Rudolf paused, "annoyed." He shook his head pensively. "I didn't know what I was annoyed about, but I was annoyed. As I lay there thinking this is the end, I felt that I'd made a complete mess of my life."

"Now, Rudy," Trotter protested, half in his own defense, because his and Rudolf's lives had been startlingly similar, "I wouldn't go so far as to say that. You've been pretty successful, by most standards. You've got a good job, a fine family, two fine children . . ."

"A mess," Rudolf said crisply. "Then on the third day, when I was at my worst point, when I could hear the worms chewing on my coffin, the nurse came in and gave me an alcohol rub." He stopped and looked over Trotter's head, lost and reflectful, thinking of the low ebb of his days.

"Yes?" Trotter said helpfully, puzzled.

"First," Rudolf said softly, "she bathed my forehead. Then my face. She poured the alcohol into her hands and rubbed it on my skin. Sitting here right now I can smell that alcohol. Alcohol has the most perfect smell in the world. I couldn't see her face because it was pretty dark and my eyes weren't functioning very well. But I felt her hands on me, curing me, and, well . . . maybe you'll think I'm vain, but it's what I felt . . . curing me and . . . *appreciating* me."

Trotter put his chin on the back of his hand and looked gravely down at the tablecloth.

"Then," Rudolf said finally, "I knew what had been annoying me as I lay dying. Women."

The waiter padded over to the table and Trotter carefully signed the check. The waiter went away.

"Women," Rudolf said. "I realized then that what I had been thinking about all those three days, which I thought were going to be my last three days on earth, was women. The women I'd had, and more often than that, the women I hadn't had."

Trotter took a small sip of water. Deranged, he thought, cracked as a Civil-War chamber pot.

"I know," Rudolf went on softly, "it sounds immoral. Even frivolous. A dying man, who should be composing his soul and making his peace with his conscience. Remember that waitress, the fat one, in the Hotel Garde in New Haven, in 1925?"

"Yes," said Trotter, thoughtfully.

"I remembered her," said Rudolf. "And old man Noonan's daughter. The Greek professor."

"Yes," said Trotter.

"Then I remembered the girl who worked in Lord and Taylor's in 1926, and that big, loud girl who was always coming home from France."

"Yes," said Trotter, faintly.

"Then I remembered a lot of girls you never saw. Lying there, in that stiff bed, in the hospital, with everybody coming in to watch me die, the different colors of their hair, the soft ones that were like silk cushions and the athletic ones with legs like steel springs and the artistic ones downtown who made a big production of it, and the Chilean girl I used to meet in a speakeasy on 45th Street."

Maybe, Trotter thought weakly, maybe he is not really cracked.

"Since 1931," Rudolf said, "since the birth of the girl, I have been faithful to my wife. I don't like to say this about Fannie. She is a fine woman in many ways. But the truth is, making love to my wife in the last ten years has been like marching through a drained marsh."

Trotter nodded thoughtfully, then realized what he was doing and kept his head rigid on his neck.

"My life," Rudolf said, sounding, Trotter thought, like a character in a Russian play, "was painted grey. When a man thinks he is dying he has a tendency to look back clearly on what he has done. I remembered I used to walk along the street and look at the girls and I'd go home to dinner and I'd sit there as though somebody had put me in a vault and was slowly pumping the air out. I didn't know why I felt like that, then, but those days in the hospital I knew. What my subconscious mind was telling me, then, was look at the way that coat wraps around that woman, look at the way those hips move, look at those faces, look at that hair, look at those legs. Aren't they wonderful? They're not for you. Never for you. I didn't realize it then, but I was frustrated for ten years. Don't laugh."

"I'm not laughing," Trotter said, and the fact was he had rarely felt less like laughing.

"My subconscious mind just felt there was no use in remaining alive," Rudolf said. "Now I feel guilty about Fannie and the children, although I must confess, in thinking about them, too, in the hospital, I realized they were as boring a brace of children as I'd ever come across . . ."

"Rudy!" Trotter said, shocked.

"I know it sounds awful," Rudolf said sadly. "But I just hope for your sake, that before you die you don't have any time to reflect on what your life has been like. Clarity," he said, "awful, honest clarity. I came out of that hospital a haunted man."

"You did seem somewhat . . . somewhat . . . remote."

The two men sat in silence for a long time. Then Trotter said, softly, and as delicately as possible, "How has it been . . . uh . . . since you left home?"

"Awful," Rudolf said. "For a week, it was quite . . . uh . . . satisfactory. But then the nurse's husband came home from Chicago, and they were reconciled. She wouldn't let me see her again."

There was another silence, and both men stared morbidly at the tablecloth, thinking of the insecurity of human happiness.

"No others?" Trotter asked.

"I don't know any others. I've never been so lonely in my life."

"You know," Trotter said gently, sorrowing for his friend in his hour of great trouble, "it's likely to grow worse. As you get older, you know . . ."

"I know," Rudolf said starkly. "I know."

"Don't you think," Trotter asked, "that perhaps it would be a good idea to give it up, go back?"

"I've thought of it a thousand times." said Rudolf, "and each time I'm on the verge of going to the phone and calling my home I just can't do it." He stared down at his clenched hands, his face

"Fifty thousand dollars and the championship isn't all you lost, baby."

ravaged by his sorrowful obsession. "I don't know what I'm going to do, Justin," he said, his voice low and hoarse, "I just don't know. Ah," he stood up, "it doesn't help to talk about it. I have to get back to the office now, anyway."

Trotter stood up, too. "How are things," he asked, glad to change the subject, "down at your office?"

"Awful," Rudolf said flatly. "Couldn't be worse."

They went out in silence. Rudolf shook his hand in a hot, pathetic, long grip when they parted, and Trotter watched his friend walk slowly away like a sick old man with bad legs. The pursuit of joy, Trotter thought, is one of the most tragic things in life.

"Well," Sara said, over dinner that night, "did you talk to him?"

"Yes, dear," Trotter said.

"How is he?" Sara sniffed harshly.

"Not good," said Trotter. "Not good at all."

"Serves him right," said Sara. "Why did he do it?"

Trotter hesitated a moment. "He . . . uh . . . didn't say."

"Are you lying to me, Justin Trotter?" Sara demanded, holding a forkful of mashed potatoes menacingly in the air.

"No," Trotter lied. "Really, Sara. I couldn't ask. It obviously was very private."

"You and your damned idea of privacy. What can I tell Fannie? She's been calling all afternoon."

"Tell her," Trotter said, "tell her to stop worrying. He'll be back in two weeks."

But Rudolf wasn't back in two weeks. He wasn't back in two months. Fannie came to the house and was lying on the couch one evening, dabbing at her eyes with witch-hazel pads, when Trotter came home, and Sara reported grimly later on that night that Fannie hadn't heard from Rudolf for a month, outside of the usual check, and was in utter despair.

"All right," Trotter said wearily, "I'll call him tomorrow and see what's happening, if I can."

The next morning, from his office, Trotter called his friend.

"Sorry," Rudolf's secretary said with brisk professional regret, "Mr. Markham's not in at the moment. He hasn't come in yet. I expect him in in about an hour."

"Please have him call me," Trotter said, hanging up, and looking gravely at the clock. It was ten-thirty already and if Rudolf wasn't getting in for another hour, it showed an alarming tendency on his friend's part to let things slip, Trotter thought. He would try to talk to him firmly and sensibly about that when they met. Rudolf had been rather shaky down at his office in the last year or so, Trotter knew, and this wouldn't help. Poor man, Trotter thought, going from bad to worse.

It was nearly one o'clock before Rudolf called. "I'm terribly sorry I was out," Rudolf said, and Trotter was delighted to discover that his voice was not as desperate as Trotter had feared. "I'd love to have lunch with you, but I'm afraid it's impossible this week, Justin, old man. I've got a pretty heavy schedule this week. How about next Monday? Fine. Fine. Oh, yes," he said, in answer to Trotter's hurried question, "I'm all right. Quite all right."

Trotter put on his hat and coat. Now he would have to eat lunch alone. He had not made any other arrangements for lunch because he had thought that he and Rudolf would have it together. In the corridor, waiting for the elevator, there was a familiar figure. He looked more closely and saw that it was Miss Chapin. She had on a leopard-skin coat and no hat, and her dark hair cascaded, in a way that Pat would call blowzy, over the pale lemon and black of the coat collar. Miss Chapin smiled plumply at him.

"How do you do, Mr. Trotter?" she said, her dark eyes crinkling in imitation, Trotter was sure, of some movie actress. "Going to lunch?"

"Yes," said Trotter, ringing vigorously for the elevator.

"Isn't it awful," Miss Chapin said, her voice soft and sad, "to have to eat lunch alone?"

"I like it," Trotter said loudly. "I like to eat lunch alone. It gives me a chance to think."

How brazen, he thought angrily, how full of sly invitation. He turned his back deliberately on the girl and faced the elevator door. I really should talk to Pat about this girl this afternoon, he thought. She must be a disastrous influence in the outer office.

Next Monday morning Rudolf called Trotter and postponed the lunch until Friday. Then on Friday Rudolf called again. "I'm terribly sorry," he said, "but I'm afraid I can't make it today either. I'm just being rushed off my feet."

"Any day you say," said Trotter firmly.

"Tuesday," Rudolf said. "Absolutely."

"Good," said Trotter. "Let's really make it this time, Rudy."

"Absolutely," said Rudolf and hung up.

Things must really be getting rough for him, Trotter thought, his hand still on the phone, if he feels he has to avoid old friends.

That night Trotter went to the theatre with his wife. Sara was developing a cold and kept sniffling and sneezing and complaining that her head was feeling stuffed. In the lobby at intermission, when he was digging out an extra handkerchief for Sara, he saw Rudolf. Rudolf was in a dinner jacket and laughing, and he was in the middle of a party of handsomely dressed people who were dominating the crowded smoky lobby with an air of slightly drunken exhilaration. Rudolf had a girl on his arm and when Trotter looked at the girl he took a long, deep breath.

She was a tall blonde creature with bare shoulders rising from a heartbreaking green dress. She had deep blue eyes and a full dizzying body and as she hung on Rudolf's arm, looking intently into his eyes, she looked like the full declension of the verb to yield.

"My God," Sara said, through her wet handkerchief, "will you look at that!"

Trotter, who was already looking, looked some more.

"If she's twenty," Sara said, "I'll give the Vice Society a hundred dollars. So . . ." she said, accusingly, as though Trotter were obscurely responsible, "that's what that old fool's been doing! Disgraceful!"

Rudolf caught sight of them then, and waved. Trotter smiled wanly at Rudolf, and half waved back, but Sara grabbed his arm and whispered harshly, "Come on. Inside."

On Tuesday morning Rudolf called. "Do you mind eating at Bruno's?" he asked when he got on the wire. "I got a little rushed and I arranged to meet someone there, if it's all the same to you."

"Of course," Trotter said, although Bruno's was considerably fancier and more expensive than any of the places he usually patronized. "Anything you say."

"One o'clock," Rudolf said. "And it's on me."

Before Trotter could protest Rudolf had hung up. In his own way, Trotter thought, he's making up for the sense of guilt he feels toward us all. Poor Rudolf, Trotter thought, I suppose I'd better give it to him straight. Tell him, for his own good, he can't go through with it. He'd better go back to his wife, his children, his old life. Trotter sat at his desk, carefully rehearsing the soft, intelligent, worldly phrases with which later on that day he would try to salvage what was left of his friend's happiness.

Rudolf was sitting at a corner table with a woman. He stood up when he saw Trotter coming over to the table, and smiled widely at him. They shook hands and Rudolf introduced Trotter to the woman, whose name was Carlotta something, and who had a sultry, dark look about her and who was, Trotter thought dazedly, one of the most attractive women he'd seen in years.

"All right, now darling," Rudolf said, "now go off and buy yourself lunch. This is business now and little girls can't listen."

"Will you try to make it, Rudy," the woman said, standing up, shining and glisteningly elegant in a pale grey suit, "tomorrow night?"

"I may drop in for a moment," Rudolf said, holding her hand lightly, "after the theatre. Run along."

She smiled at him in a way that no woman had smiled at Trotter since 1929, and walked, swaying beautifully, out of the room.

Trotter blinked. Then he turned to Rudolf. "Listen," he said, "I didn't want to interfere. We can always eat lunch, you know, any time."

"Nonsense," Rudolf laughed. "She'll keep." He waved to the waiter and three waiters arrived. "What'll you have to drink?" he asked Trotter.

"Well . . ." Trotter said, looking down at the old fashioned glass in front of Rudolf, "I don't . . ."

"An old fashioned for Mr. Trotter, please," said Rudolf. "And another one for me."

"Are you drinking?" Trotter asked. "I thought the doctor . . ."

Rudolf grinned. "I don't believe in doctors," he said. Trotter peered anxiously at his friend while Rudolf ordered lunch for them both. It was true that Rudolf looked very well. He was cutting his hair shorter these days, in a kind of college-boy style that sat very well on his well-shaped head, and went handsomely with the stiff, grey-streaked hair. And his color was very good, as though he had been out in the sun for a long time. Rudolf's clothes, too, were different, light, soft tweeds and a soft blue shirt and rather bright red bow tie. If you didn't know him and his years and his troubles, you would swear, Trotter thought, that he was a bouncing young man of thirty-five.

"I'm awfully sorry," Trotter said, "that I haven't got in touch with you all these months, Rudy. But I've been terribly busy and I had seven weeks in Cleveland on a job and . . ."

"Perfectly all right, Justin, old man," Rudolf said. "Fact is, I've been pretty busy myself, what with one thing and another. I was away, too. For two weeks. Skiing."

"Skiing?" Trotter asked faintly.

"That's where I got my sunburn," Rudolf said. "The Laurentians.

I hadn't skied for ten years but an awful lot of it came back. You ought to try it, Justin," Rudolf said seriously. "You look a little peaked."

"Do I?" Trotter said.

He sipped at his drink and studied Rudolf's face. He wondered if Rudolf had lost his job by now. If he hadn't, how had he found time for two weeks of skiing in Canada? Still, if Rudolf wasn't going to talk about it, he wouldn't either.

"How did you like the show the other night?" Rudolf asked. "I say you in the lobby."

"Oh, yes," Trotter said. "Very nice." Then he remembered. "That girl you were with," he said. "Lord she was pretty. Very blonde. Big. In a green dress. She looked as though she was on loan to you from M-G-M."

"Honestly, Justin," Rudolf said, wrinkling his brow and looking at the ceiling, "I just can't seem to remember which . . ."

"Pale blonde hair," Trotter said patiently and with new respect for the rich social life of a man who could forget a girl like that, "combed to the back and to one side, and blue eyes and . . ."

"Oh, yes," Rudolf laughed apologetically. "Of course I remember. Janice. She *is* quite nice, isn't she?"

"Yes," said Trotter evenly.

"We went skiing together. She's a lovely skier."

Trotter thought of Rudolf and the tall blonde girl slipping silently down the gleaming snowy holiday hillsides and later on sitting dreamily in a snug lodge before the fire, with hot rum in mugs on the table, and . . .

"She has a father complex," Rudolf said. He was eating busily now, a large steak, very rare, with mushrooms. "You'd be suprised, Justin, how many modern young women have father complexes. They can't stand younger men. They're always looking for someone who reminds them of their father and I . . ."

The waiter came over, plugged in a phone and put the instrument on the table. "For you, Mr. Markham," he said.

"Excuse me, Justin," Rudolf said as he took the phone. Then, "Hello. Oh, hello, Alice. Now, Alice, darling, I told you, I just can't get away till Tuesday. You go on ahead with the others and I'll hop a plane Tuesday morning and I'll be in Havana and have dinner with you that night. I promise. I really do promise."

Trotter heard a dim, soft murmur rising and falling huskily in the earpiece of the phone. Havana, he thought erratically, planes, Alice, Janice, Carlotta . . . From the rich texture of the voice in the phone, swelling and falling over the indistinguishable words, he somehow was certain that it was one of those small, curved women you sometimes saw at the opera, who looked as though they had been turned out by Austrian confectioners. He looked away from Rudolf, who was still talking breezily and elliptically into the phone. A party of three handsome women were being seated at a table on the other side of the room. All three waved and smiled softly across the rich room and for a moment Trotter squinted puzzledly and almost waved back. Then he turned and saw that Rudolf was smiling at them, and waving to them debonairly with his free hand.

Trotter kept his eyes on his plate and ate methodically.

Finally Rudolf hung up. "I must apologize," he said. "But I suppose Alice wanted to be sure to get me, so she called me here."

"How are things at the office these days?" Trotter asked as delicately as possible.

"Oh, fine," said Rudolf, waving at a tall beauty in a mink coat who was smiling widely at him from the bar. "They finally seem to have caught on to how valuable I am. I thought you knew. They made me a partner last month."

"Oh," said Trotter flatly. "Congratulations."

"I hate to rush you, old man," Rudolf said, looking at his watch, "but I promised to go to a run-through of Margaret Sloan's new play this afternoon. I got trapped into it over the week end. It begins at two-thirty, though, and it's over on 49th Street . . ."

"That's all right," Trotter said thinking of Margaret Sloan, whose picture he saw on the cover of a dozen movie magazines. "I have to be getting back to my office."

"Is there anything in particular," Rudolf asked seriously, "that you wanted to talk about?"

Trotter hesitated for a fraction of a second, remembering his carefully rehearsed speech of the morning. "No," he said, "I just wanted to see you. See how you were."

"Fine," said Rudolf, heartily. "This has been fine. Let's make a regular thing of it."

"Sure," said Trotter. "Glad to."

Rudolf signed for the check and they went out, amid bows and smiles from the help and salutations by various ladies situated at tables around the room.

Outside, in the daylight, Rudolf's tan looked more impressive than ever, and the red tie shone brilliantly.

"Can I drop you?" Rudolf asked.

"No, thanks," said Trotter. "I'd better walk off the old fashioned. Well . . . I . . . uh . . . I'm pleased you're feeling better."

"Oh, yes," said Rudolf. "Yes, indeed."

"By the way," Trotter asked, because curiosity finally overcame him. "Do you ever see that woman, the alcohol-rub one?"

Rudolf grinned. "Once in awhile," he said "He husband went back to Chicago." He waved and sprang lightly into a cab, buoyant, immoral, youthful. The cab clanged away and Trotter walked slowly toward his office.

He opened the door of the office abstractedly, and the noise of typewriters made him blink and look up. At the desk nearest the door Miss Chapin was sitting, typing swiftly. She stopped for a moment and looked up. Then, a little fearfully, she dropped her head and went on with her work.

Trotter stood at the door. Miss Chapin's hair fell in a dark, thick swirl over her shoulders and her dull crepe dress caught the light of the afternoon sun in a dozen places. Still wears black silk stockings, Trotter thought, as he started toward his own office past her desk.

The clatter of her typewriter sounded in his ears as he approached her, and the sound of the crepe rustling against her body as she moved made a thin, piercing music in his brain.

He stoped before her desk. "Good afternoon, Miss Chapin."

The typing stopped. The smooth, fair young face looked up, the dark hair falling back. Then the eyes crinkled in a sly, victorious smile. "Why, Mr. Trotter," Miss Chapin said. "You almost frightened me."

They stared at each other dumbly for a moment, then slowly, with a high, delicious, premonitory thunder beating within the walls of his chest, Trotter moved on toward his own office.

JOSEPH WECHSBERG

New York Is Full of Girls

There was a heavy turnover among the musicians on the *Ile de France,* which was the flagship of the Compagnie Généràle Transatlantique when I worked aboard as violinist in the early Thirties. Some members of the orchestra got drunk and pestered middle-aged American ladies in the corridors. Others stayed sober and were found in the staterooms of young ones. We had at least one new man on every outbound voyage among the nine of us who played in the first-class and the four who made up the tourist-class orchestra.

For a ship's musician the *Ile de France* was a plum assignment. The pay was the same as on the other French Line boats—one thousand francs per month, about the equivalent of forty dollars—but the *quête,* the customary collection at the end of every trip, which was evenly divided among all musicians, often surpassed our combined salaries. No wonder that in order to get the coveted job people fell back on graft and shady politics.

I remember a rather bad second violinist who stayed on for months because he happened to be a nephew of the chief engineer and played chess with his uncle. One trumpeter went sour on his high notes, but had to be nursed along. His wife was a distant relative of a board member of the French Line. And Alain, the *batterie* player, later admitted that he got his job by bribing a *sous-directeur* in the steamship company's personnel department.

Alain was hired as a clarinetist and tenor saxo. By the time we found out that he played neither the clarinet nor the tenor saxo, the *Ile de France* was halfway through the Channel. Alain played the *batterie,* drums, cymbals, tambours, bells, castanets, all percussion instruments. He was a slim, disjointed fellow with friendly eyes and a shy, good-natured smile, the sort of man you would trust with your wallet, fountain pen or fiancée.

He had a weakness for all kinds of apéritifs, also kirsch, beer, brandy, gin, rum, Benedictine, wine, Scotch, champagne. He couldn't hold any of them. After three drinks he became talkative and started to tell us about his wife and his *amie*. He had a wife in New York and *une amie* in Paris. Things became complicated because his wife wanted to visit Paris, and his *amie* had a cousin in New York and wanted to go there. Alain had a hard time persuading the two ladies to stay where they were.

"I explained to my wife that Paris is no place for a lady," he said. "I told her that the men there either drink or play music, so she gave up the idea of making the trip."

We gathered that Alain's wife severely disapproved of both alcohol and music. She didn't like Alain's playing the *batterie* aboard ship and wanted him to stay in New York and get a more dignified job with her father, who was in the fur business. "I finally appeased her by explaining that we musicians aboard are not allowed to buy alcohol," he said.

I asked him whether he was in love with his wife. He looked at me in astonishment and said, "What a question, *mon petit* Joseph! One can see you are not a Frenchman. Of course I am in love with her. Is there anything more exciting for two people in love than to depart and meet again?"

Alain always kept a couple of bottles in the drawer under his bed. He bought his liquor aboard by the half-dozen bottles because we had a fifty per cent reduction on the wholesale price. He kept lying on his back, reached down with his left hand, opened the drawer, seized the bottle, took a long swallow and put the bottle back. "My wife works for a group which wants to bring back prohibition. She's the treasurer. Makes me feel deeply ashamed," he said, and extended his hand for another drink.

On the day before the *Ile de France* docked in New York, Alain would stop drinking and start to wash his mouth with milk. Someone had once told him that one can smell alcohol on a man's breath for twelve hours. "I make it twenty-four hours," Alain said to me. "So would you, if you knew my wife."

I understood what he meant when the ship docked in New York and his wife came to pick him up. She was slim and slender and had very pretty legs. In fact, she would have been quite attractive if she hadn't tried so desperately to look cold and smart. She had a husky alto-saxo voice and spoke in brief, staccato sentences.

"Amelia never uttered a sentence that contains over ten words," Alain said. His wife didn't think this was funny. Nothing seemed funny to her. She probably thought that smiling was bad for a woman's complexion because she never did smile. She inspected his stateroom with the icy pitilessness of an eager second lieutenant who is out to restrict his men for the week end, but Alain had washed away every trace of alcohol.

Things were slightly different when the *Ile de France* left New York, eastbound. Usually, we would sail at midnight. As soon as the tugboats began to tow the ship away from the pier and Alain had waved the last good-bye to his wife down there, he went to his room and strengthened himself with four or five drinks. From then on he was never quite sober again. Like many musicians I've known, he performed best when he was pleasantly intoxicated.

We docked in Cherbourg where a vivacious redhead would come aboard. She knew everybody aboard ship and everybody knew her. She wore high heels and had electrifying hips. She always looked like she was in a bathing suit, no matter how many clothes she had on. Vivienne tenderly kissed Alain and kissed the rest of us, though not quite so tenderly, and said to Alain, "Couldn't you wait to get drunk until I came?" She poured herself a drink. She would turn on the portable gramophone in Alain's stateroom, and a moment later she would be in the arms of Emile, our pianist, who was an excellent dancer. "*Chéri,* I'm going with you to New York," she said to Alain once. "My cousin invited me again. She said I can get a good job in New York. They like French *chanteuses* there. Paris, *j'en ai mare.*"

"Don't be silly," Alain said. "You've got a good job in Paris. What would you be doing in New York all day long? The days are very long in New York. People get up much earlier than in Paris. It gets boring."

Vivienne shrugged and continued to dance again with Emile. Alain watched her, a tender expression in his eyes. "She's a good kid," he said to me. "She sings in a *boîte* near the Bastille. She's quite *une artiste* but I keep telling her to forget about New York and to stay here. There are no *boîtes de nuit* in New York. Just bars and night clubs. That's a hell of a difference. Besides, what would I do with her in New York?"

I said, "Does she know that you have your wife in New York?"

Alain shook his head in astonishment. "*C'est une drôle de question,*" he said. "One can see that you are not a Frenchman, *mon petit* Joseph. Why should anybody know of anything that doesn't make him happier?"

We left Cherbourg a few days later for another trip to New York. It was August and the *Ile de France* was crowded, with people sleeping in bathtubs and on billiard tables. Once again Alain was easily the favorite member of the orchestra. He was as popular on the promenade deck as a gossip columnist in the Stork Club. He would walk around shaking hands and in no time he had half a dozen invitations for free drinks. Two hours after saying good-bye to Vivienne, who had come to Cherbourg to see him off, he was installed in the first-class bar.

His host was an elderly gentleman with a pinkish, clean-shaven face, white hair parted on one side, and a double chin. It was a warm day and the gentleman was sitting there in his shirt sleeves and braces. He held his thumbs under his braces and let them snap back against his chest. He radiated optimism and the sacred principles of free enterprise. As I passed by, Alain introduced me to Mr. Harbrough.

"Mr. Harbrough is president in charge of the mushroom division of a large food concern," Alain said.

"Vice-president," Mr. Harbrough interrupted modestly, and hiccuped.

Alain shrugged disdainfully. "Americans don't appreciate the good things in life. Putting fresh, delicious, tasty mushrooms into dead, cold tin cans. *Dieu d'un dieu!*"

"They taste like fresh ones—only better," Mr. Harbrough said. "That's our slogan." He ordered more drinks.

"Americans got no fantasy," Alain said. "No imagination. Mushrooms in cans! Imagine, *mon petit* Joseph, what they would say if they knew I had a wife in New York and *une amie* in Paris."

Mr. Harbrough stared at Alain for a long moment and emitted a trombone laugh that shook the glasses on the table. "I'll let you in on a little secret," he said, in a voice as secretive as a foghorn. "I'm a married man myself. We live in San Francisco. But I got plenty of business in the East." He let his braces snap back and said solemnly, "New York is full of girls." He smacked his lips as though tasting mushrooms, and repeated, "Yes, sir, New York is full of girls."

Alain looked pleased. "Maybe San Francisco isn't really in America," he said. "Maybe the earthquake taught them that life is short and must be fully lived. Tell me, how do you manage with all your women?"

"Organization," Mr. Harbrough said. "It's all a matter of organization. I've been telling my wife more lies about New York than a politician could think of. She now believes that the place stinks. Never goes East with me."

Before we left, Mr. Harbrough invited all members of the orchestra for a drink after the evening concert. "We'll drink to the lovely girls of New York."

I went down with Alain. The musicians' quarters were on B deck, complete with a small dining room and pantry, and a rehearsal room which was used for anything but rehearsals. We got dressed and went to the dining room where we played our one-hour evening concert, and afterward dance music. We were right in the middle of *Singing in the Rain,* which has a very important *batterie* part, when the sound of the drums suddenly stopped. We all turned around and looked at Alain. He sat there, pale and motionless, staring into space. His hands were swinging the drum sticks, but they didn't touch the tambours. I was afraid that he would scream out at any moment.

He seemed to be staring toward the rear of the dining room. I looked there myself. My heart sank. This could be no hallucination. There, way behind, was Vivienne, sitting at a table all by herself. She had just taken off her fur cape. I didn't know whether she had anything on underneath. From our platform one saw only her bare shoulders and arms. She looked like a million dollars or twenty-five million francs, whichever you prefer.

She got up and came toward our platform. She wore a royal-blue evening dress that started way below her shoulders. As she walked through the dining room, one could almost hear the necks of the men jerk toward her. Then the women looked sharply at their men and the men had to lower their eyes to their plates.

Vivienne stopped in front of the orchestra and said, "Well, here I am!" She clapped her hands to the chorus of *Singing in the Rain,* and started to dance on her toes. The *chef d'orchestre* got panicky and told me to take Vivienne and Alain to the bar.

On the way there, Vivienne chatted happily. Alain seemed stunned. "Was it too late for you to get off in Cherbourg?" he said. "Didn't they ring the bell? We must get you back on the first ship from Plymouth."

"But I'm *not* going back, *chéri,*" she said. "I'm going to New York, with you! I told you that my cousin invited me again. So I made up my mind. And I thought I'd surprise you."

"But you *can't* go to New York," Alain said, with desperate urgency. "You have no ticket—besides, what would you do there?"

"I have a tourist-class ticket," Vivienne said. She sounded angry. "I gave the *maître d'hôtel* a tip and he'll let me eat in the first-class dining room. And I know exactly what I'm going to do in

New York. First, we're going to paint the town red. Then I'll go and visit my cousin."

Alain seemed too weak to answer. I looked at him from the side and for the first time I understood the novelists' saying that a man has suddenly grown old. Alain's hands were trembling. He gulped down his drink with reckless abandon.

After a while Mr. Harbrough came in from the dining room. He wore his dinner jacket and patent-leather shoes and looked almost distinguished now. When he saw us, he shook hands with himself over his head and bellowed, "Tried the *Champignons Sauté* for dinner. Far below our standard quality. I told the chief steward, they should try *my* canned mushrooms!"

I introduced Mr. Harbrough. He sat down and ordered champagne. I went back to the orchestra and told the boys not to count on Alain for the evening. One of the fellows took over the drums, but things went badly. Emile, the pianist, messed up his solo breaks and our first saxo, usually a very reliable man, fell down on his passages. Everyone was worried about Alain.

"We could send his wife a wire that he isn't aboard," Emile said. The chef contributed his bit of advice, suggesting that Vivienne be confined to the ship's hospital.

"But she is in excellent health," I said.

"I am on very excellent terms with the doctor," the chef answered. The 'cello-player coldly suggested that we hang a heavy stone around Vivienne's beautiful neck and throw her overboard. The 'cello-player had had his disappointments with women.

I didn't have the courage to go back to the bar after the concert. Alain came to his room late after midnight, and woke up everybody. He was in bad shape the following day and the day after. Once Vivienne came down to our quarters, but they had a fight and he threw her out.

After that Alain continued drinking in solitary confinement, while Vivienne played shuffleboard with Mr. Harbrough. She also played deck tennis with him, and bet with him on the races, and ate at his table, and drank with him in the bar and danced with him on the prom deck. Alain rejoined the orchestra and took up his drums, but he was in a permanent stupor and didn't seem to care about anything. Sometimes Vivienne danced close to the orchestra. When she whirled past the *batterie,* she'd put her cheek on Mr. Harbrough's silk lapel to make Alain jealous, but he looked the other way.

Once he said to me, "She could have stayed in Paris and we would have been happy. Very happy." He looked after Vivienne. "Very, very happy . . . Let's go to the bar, *mon petit* Joseph. I need a drink."

Captain's dinner was on the last evening before we docked in New York. After the dance Mr. Harbrough invited the entire orchestra to his de luxe suite. Of course Vivienne was there. She kissed each of us. She kissed Alain, much longer. He wanted to say something, but then he shrugged and raised his hand and let it flop down in front of his face. He went over to the table and poured himself a water glass full of champagne and gulped it down. As a rule, he never took any drinks after Captain's dinner and was well set on his milk-mouthwash cure but this time he didn't seem to care.

The party went on all night. There was a piano in the drawing room and Vivienne sang her entire repertoire. Alain sat in a deep chair, watching her with half-closed eyes. Mr. Harbrough yelled for more champagne and Alain said, "Shut up, you barbarian mushroom. Can't you listen when *Mademoiselle* sings?"

It was dawn when I came back to my cabin and fell into my bed. I was dead tired. I must have slept through all the noises accompanying the *Ile's* arrival in New York—whistles and foghorns, electric cranes grinding, luggage being shoved on deck. The chain of the anchor woke me up. It rolled over deck, just above my head, and came to a sudden halt when the anchor reached ground. I jumped up and looked through the porthole. There was Pier 48 and crowds of people.

I dressed in a hurry and ran up on deck. The first passengers were leaving the ship. I saw Vivienne going down the gangway followed by Mr. Harbrough. Once she stumbled and almost lost one of her high-heeled shoes, but Mr. Harbrough took her arm and guided her down, though he himself didn't seem too steady.

I ran to Alain's stateroom. His wife stood in the middle of the cabin. The boys were watching her, terror-stricken.

Alain was in his bed, fast asleep. A drawer was open and one could see four or five bottles in there. Alain was fully dressed, except for his tuxedo tie which hung out of his mouth. He snored. There was a champagne bottle beside his pillow. The place smelled like a distillers' plant.

For a terrible moment Alain's wife stood glaring. She seemed ready to walk out on him for good. But then she began shaking him. Perhaps she really loved him.

"Take a good look at him," she shouted. "He's coming with me and he won't be back. Never, *never* will you see him again!!"

We didn't.

F. SCOTT FITZGERALD

The Woman from Twenty-One

Ah, what a day for Raymond Torrence! Once you knew that your roots were safely planted outside megalopolitanism what fun it was to come back—every five years. He and Elizabeth woke up to the frozen music of Fifth Avenue and Fifty-ninth Street, and first thing went down to his publishers on Fifth Avenue. Elizabeth, who was half Javanese and had never been in America before, liked it best of all there because her husband's book was on multiple display in the window. She liked it in the store where she squeezed Ray's hand tensely when people asked for it, and again when they bought it.

They lunched at the Stork Club with Hat Milbank, a pal of Ray's at college and in the war. Of course no one there recognized Ray after these years but a man came in with the Book in his hands, crumpling up the jacket. Afterwards Hat asked them down to Old Westbury to see the polo in which he still performed, but they went to the hotel and rested as they did in Java. Otherwise it would all be a little too much. Elizabeth wrote a letter to the children in Suva and told them "everyone in New York" was reading father's book and admired the photograph which Janice had taken of a girl sick with yaws.

They went alone to a play by William Saroyan. After the curtain had been up five minutes the woman from Twenty-one came in.

She was in the mid-thirties, dark and pretty. As she took her seat beside Ray Torrence she continued her conversation in a voice that was for outside and Elizabeth was a little sorry for her because obviously she did not know she was making herself a nuisance. They were a quartet—two in front. The girl's escort was a tall and good-looking man. The woman leaning forward in her seat and talking to her friend in front, distracted Ray a little, but not overwhelmingly until she said in a conversational voice that must have reached the actors on the stage:

"Let's all go back to Twenty-one."

Her escort replied in a whisper and there was quiet for a moment. Then the woman drew a long, long sigh, culminating in an exhausted groan in which could be distinguished the words "Oh, my God."

Her friend in front turned around so sweetly that Ray thought the woman next to him must be someone very prominent and powerful—an Astor or a Vanderbilt or a Roosevelt.

"See a little bit of it," suggested her friend.

The woman from Twenty-one flopped forward with a dynamic movement and began an audible but indecipherable conversation in which the number of the restaurant occurred again and again. When she shifted restlessly back into her chair with another groaning "My God!" this time directed toward the play, Raymond turned his head sideways and uttered a prayer to her aloud:

"Please."

If Ray had muttered a four-letter word the effect could not have been more catalytic. The woman flashed about and regarded him—her eyes ablaze with the gastric hatred of many dying martinis and with something more. These were the unmistakable eyes of Mrs. Richbitch, that leftist creation as devoid of nuance as Mrs. Jiggs. As they burned with scalding arrogance—the very eyes of the Russian lady who let her coachman freeze outside while she wept at poverty in a play—at this moment Ray recognized a girl with whom he had played Run Sheep Run in Pittsburgh twenty years ago.

The woman did not after all excoriate him but this time her flop forward was so violent that it rocked the row ahead.

"Can you bel*ieve*—can you im*a*gine—"

Her voice raced along in a hoarse whisper. Presently she lunged sideways toward her escort and told him of the outrage. His eye caught Ray's in a flickering embarrassed glance. On the other side of Ray, Elizabeth became disturbed and alarmed.

Ray did not remember the last five minutes of the act—beside him smoldered fury and he knew its name and the shape of its legs. Wanting nothing less than to kill, he hoped her man would speak to him or even look at him in a certain way during the entr'acte—but when it came the party stood up quickly, and the woman said: "We'll go to Twenty-one."

On the crowded sidewalk between the acts Elizabeth talked softly to Ray. She did not seem to think it was of any great importance except for the effect on him. He agreed in theory—but

"Would you tell me how you mixed it? It's got my friend thinking he can't live without me."

when they went inside again the woman from Twenty-one was already in her place, smoking and waving a cigarette.

"I could speak to the usher," Ray muttered.

"Never mind," said Elizabeth quickly. "In France you smoke in the music halls."

"But you have some place to put the butt. She's going to crush it out in my lap!"

In the sequel she spread the butt on the carpet and kept rubbing it in. Since a lady lush moves in mutually exclusive preoccupations just as a gent does, and the woman had passed beyond her preoccupation with Ray, things were tensely quiet.

When the lights went on after the second act, a voice called to Ray from the aisle. It was Hat Milbank.

"Hello, hello there, Ray! Hello, Mrs. Torrence. Do you want to go to Twenty-one after the theatre?"

His glance fell upon the people in between.

"Hello, Jidge," he said to the woman's escort; to the other three, who called him eagerly by name, he answered with an inclusive nod. Ray and Elizabeth crawled out over them. Ray told the story to Hat who seemed to ascribe as little importance to it as Elizabeth did, and wanted to know if he could come out to Fiji this spring.

But the effect upon Ray had been profound. It made him remember why he had left New York in the first place. This woman was what everything was for. She should have been humble, not awful, but she had become confused and thought she should be awful.

So Ray and Elizabeth would go back to Java, unmourned by anyone except Hat. Elizabeth would be a little disappointed at not seeing any more plays and not going to Palm Beach, and wouldn't like having to pack so late at night. But in a silently communicable way she would understand. In a sense she would be glad. She even guessed that it was the children Ray was running to—to save them and shield them from all the walking dead.

When they went back to their seats for the third act the party from Twenty-one were no longer there—nor did they come in later. It had clearly been another game of Run, Sheep, Run.

BRENDAN GILL

The Night Bus to Atlanta

The moment the girl entered the bus, Harry wanted her to sit beside him. There were two other unoccupied seats, one of them next to an old man who was already noisily and untidily asleep, a yellow trickle of tobacco running from his lips, and the other next to a middle-aged woman whose child, torn between nursing and crying, bore on its chin a milky stain oddly similar to that which distinguished the old man. Harry stared at the girl as she made her way down the aisle, focusing his eyes on her impassive face and repeating over and over to himself, "Sit down here. Sit down here." He was not surprised when she sat down beside him, but he felt strangely relieved. He had bought several magazines in the shabby depot while waiting for the bus to arrive from Jackson; he held them fanwise to the girl and said, "Like to look at one?"

She said, without looking at him, "I guess not, thank you."

He pretended to glance through the window at the gathering darkness, but he held in one corner of his eye the image of the girl's hands folded neatly in her lap. He said, "Bus was pretty late, wasn't it?"

"It's 'most always late."

"You take it often?"

"No."

Harry wondered if the etiquette of the occasion demanded more confidence from him. "I'm going as far as Atlanta," he said. "Then I got to take a bus for Spartanburg. I just finished my leave, and the only way I can get back to camp in time is to hop a couple of buses. I've always gone on trains before, but for once I got to hop a couple of buses." The girl remained impassive, neither turning away nor giving any evidence that she had heard him speak. "I don't suppose you're going as far as Atlanta?" Harry asked.

"No, I guess not. I'm going to school—to a sort of school."

The driver of the bus, a fat young man with blond hair, swung into his seat and snapped on the head- and running lights. Harry waited until the first loud coughing sounds of the engine had settled down to a steady racketing, then said, "I never been in this town before. You live here?"

"Yes."

"Well, I guess it wouldn't be so bad if you grew up in it, you know what I mean? I can't figure out these Southern towns, they all look the same to me." Harry hesitated. "Say, didn't I see you in the depot? Weren't you saying good-bye to your folks?"

The girl nodded.

The girl's mother had been crying, and her father had been shifting his weight from foot to foot and turning a soft black hat in his hands. Harry had forgotten the scene completely before speaking of it. He had been waiting in line to buy a ticket to Atlanta, and he had paid less attention to the girl and her father and mother than to the Negroes herded together in the Jim Crow section of the depot, and to the nursing infant which could not seem to keep its mouth closed on its mother's breast. He said, "You must be going away for quite a spell."

The girl said, "Yes, I am." She turned to him, her eyes so close to his that he could see where their blue irises were flecked with pin points of yellow and green. "It's like I was running away," she said. "I'm going over into Georgia to learn to be a nurse, but to hear Mom and Dad talk you'd think I was traveling out to the ends of the earth. That's 'cause they're so used to having me around."

"Yeah, I know," Harry said. "Mine are the same way."

"But I always wanted to be of some help to *some*body, and especially now, with the war, and afterwards, when the wounded ones start coming home—." She bit her lip. "I guess I shouldn't talk to you like that," she said, turning aside. "Could I look at one of your magazines, please?"

"Why, sure, I asked you, didn't I?" She's only a kid, Harry thought, and I bet she figures I'm a regular wolf. That's why she's afraid to talk to me. Why, hell's bells, *I'm* not going to get wounded. The thought of himself as a wolf gave Harry unexpected pleasure, and he tilted his chin and pushed back a lock of hair with his right hand.

The girl chose a magazine on whose glossy cover was printed a photograph, mostly teeth, bodice and legs, of Betty Grable. The girl began to thumb through the pages, but it was plain to Harry that she wasn't reading them. The bus swung away from the soiled and muddy area behind the depot and headed up the main street of the town. Electric lights or kerosene lanterns had been turned on in most of the houses, but no one had bothered yet to draw the shades at the windows. Perhaps it was the kind of town, Harry thought, where, even in winter, no one bothered to draw the shades. He could look inside the small, bare rooms and see men and women seated around their kitchen or dining-room tables, eating and drinking or merely talking. He said, "Funny to think of all those people nice and snug in their houses, and us driving away from them in a rickety old bus and never coming back."

The girl said sharply, "Why did you say that? What do you mean?"

"Why, I only meant that *I* won't ever be coming back. This is my first look at Mississippi, but I guess there won't be any call to look at it again."

As if her body were making the effort against her will, the girl leaned forward and sideways over Harry's knees, staring through the window. Her lips were parted and her hands were pressed together over the small gold cross which hung in the V of her dress. Harry noted that the scent of her body was apparently not that of perfume but of soap. "We're going to pass my house now," she said. "I declare, we're going to pass my house!"

The bus labored up a slight grade, then swung east away from town. At the outskirts, where broken asphalt pavement ran out into the red clay fields, the girl pointed to a bungalow half-hidden behind a row of trees. "There it is," she said. "There's my house."

Harry said, "I don't see any lights."

The girl shook her head. "It must be they're staying in town and going to a movie. They weren't going home to supper tonight. Mother said she just couldn't bear to go home to supper tonight."

As darkness fell, the air inside the bus grew cold. The fat young driver turned on a heater which gave off nothing but an acrid odor of gasoline. Harry had expected that the bus, like a train, would be well enough lighted so that he could read his magazines, but except when they entered a town or made a rest stop at some shanty gas station along the way, the lights were kept off; in the part of the bus where Harry and the girl were sitting there was only the faint glow, reflected from the ceiling, of the two small lights on the instrument panel. The darkness and cold had drawn Harry and the girl together in their seats, so close, in fact, that their arms and knees were joined, and when the girl shifted her legs Harry changed position to accommodate them. The girl had not spoken for nearly an hour, and for all Harry knew she might have been asleep, but now and then as he turned to study her face she would open her eyes and stare ahead of her into the darkness.

The old man, who had fallen asleep on entering the bus at the depot, continued to snore and cough among the shadows, while the nursing infant, instead of crying, made a continuous, dissatisfied, sucking sound with its pursed lips. A couple who had boarded the bus at a previous rest stop were wrapped in each other's arms in the seats behind Harry and the girl. Every few minutes one of them would murmur a word or two drowsily, and the words would be stopped by a kiss; but Harry could not tell whether the girl beside him was aware of the old man, or the infant, or even of the couple. As the bus lumbered on through the night, its headlights devouring the level miles which were Mississippi and Alabama and would soon be Georgia, the cold deepened and Harry slipped lower and lower in the seat. He kept his body turned from the window, his face to the girl, and she, either in sleep or only half waking, had turned to face him as well. Once her jacket fell from her shoulders and Harry reached over and drew it up around her chin and the soft line of her hair against her cheeks. She whispered something to him, but he could not hear what it was; and he guessed that she was dreaming.

He had just fallen asleep when the sound of the bus stopping, or the absence of sound after the bus came to a stop, woke him. He saw that they were at another rest stop, a small lean-to station with a diner attached. Piny woods stretched away on both sides of the road, and the sky overhead was empty of stars. Harry felt stiff, and suddenly and disagreeably restless, as if he needed a ten- or twelve-mile march to take the kinks out of his legs. He saw by the winking light of the sign above the diner that the girl was awake. He said, "Want to get out and grab a cup of coffee?"

To his surprise, the girl said, "All right."

As they stood up, the woman in the seat behind them said, "Eddie, for goodness' sake! Those people can *see* us." The man swore sharply in return, and the woman giggled. Harry felt himself blushing as he walked down the aisle to the door. He followed the girl across the rough clay of the roadside and into the diner. No other passengers had bothered to get out of the bus, and the diner was empty except for the attendant, a toothless old man, and the bus driver. The driver was drinking a cup of coffee. When Harry and the girl came in, he grinned at them in the

"I'd like to put all this in my diary while it's still fresh in my mind."

mirror back of the counter, not lifting his mouth from the rim of the cup. "How you doin', kids?" he asked them.

Harry had said, "All right," before he guessed what the fat young driver had in mind. Then he said quickly to the attendant, "A couple of cups of coffee, please, and some of those doughnuts."

"Yesshur," said the old man, showing his gums.

The girl said, "I don't need to have the doughnuts, thank you."

Harry saw that she was pleased by his having ordered them for her. "Sure, you do," he said, "a couple of those nice big sugar ones." The girl smiled for the first time, and Harry ducked his head foolishly and happily by way of reply. He had never, he thought, seen such a pretty smile. Her teeth were small and even and with the smile lifting the corners of her mouth her cheeks looked rounder and pinker than they really were.

"There you are," the old man said. "Doughnush and coffee."

As they ate their doughnuts, which were stale, and drank their coffee which was hot but bitter, Harry studied the girl's face in the mirror back of the stacked-up cereals and bottles of Dr. Pepper. He was troubled by a thought which seemed all but impossible to fit into words, but he knew that if he waited too long the driver would call them to the bus. He wanted to say, "It's funny us being here like this. It's just like we were husband and wife. And we never even saw each other before!" Probably he decided, the girl would stop smiling if he said that. She would be afraid again that he was nothing but a wolf. At last, risking a part of what he thought, Harry said, "It's funny, us being here like this."

To Harry's delight, the girl said, "It's like—it's like we'd known each other an awful long time."

"And we never even saw each other before."

The girl nodded. "And I guess we'll never see each other again."

Harry said, "No, but we will. We got to. You got to write me when I reach camp; and when I get leave again, maybe—"

The girl interrupted him. "You wouldn't. And we can't write. You don't know where you'll be. You don't know what may happen. We don't even know each other's names."

"That's easy to fix."

The girl's voice sank to a whisper. "We oughtn't to know them. We're not *meant* to like each other that much, meeting like this."

Harry began to stammer, as he always did when he grew excited. "I don't get it," he said. "What do you think I am, a w-wolf?

Is that what all the shooting's for? Are you sore at me because you think I'm trying to pick you up?"

The girl said, "Oh, no, of course not. Oh, no, it's not like that." She looked frightened and bewildered by the reaction she had aroused in Harry, and the small gold cross rose and burned in the light. She put out her hand to touch his sleeve, but at that moment the fat young driver swung off his stool and walked down the length of the diner to speak to them. "Hey, you young lovebirds!" he said. "We got to get that old pile of junk into Atlanta some time this week, you know! Of course, if you'd rather stay on here in this cozy little nest I guess Pop could find you a place to sleep, couldn't you, Pop?"

The old man's face froze. "Thish is a respectable diner," he said. "No place to sleep."

The fat young driver laughed and slapped his palm on the counter. "Good for you, Pop, that's telling 'em. Well, come along, lovebirds. You ain't the first that ever had to make do with a bus."

Harry felt like ramming his fist into the driver's soft pink face; but it was already too late. It was nearly always too late to make a guy shut up by clipping him, because by then the damage had been done. The girl whispered, "Never mind, please never mind." She followed the driver out of the diner and up the two high steps into the bus. Harry took his time about paying the old man for the coffee and doughnuts. When the driver slammed the bus door hard behind Harry and muttered something to him, Harry did not bother to ask him what he had said, or even to tell him to go to hell. He wanted only to talk to the girl.

Because the girl was lying curled on the inside seat, Harry had to clamber over her to reach the seat by the window. He touched one of her hands as he did so, and it felt cold. He fitted himself to her position—like two spoons, he thought, recalling a phrase which he and his brother had used as kids—and drew his heavy Army coat over both of them. They lay face to face in the darkness, silent while the bus gathered speed. Once a car passed the bus and in the glare of its headlights Harry saw that the girl was staring at him. He said, "I wasn't sure you were awake."

"I can't go to sleep."

Harry wondered if this was meant to be a reproach. He said, "I'm sorry I got excited."

"That was my fault."

"No, it was my fault," Harry felt half sick with pleasure at their warmth and nearness to one another; he wanted everything to be his fault. "You certainly look pretty," he said.

The girl laughed softly, "You can't even see me."

"Yes, I can, I can sort of see you." Harry reached out and touched the tip of her nose with his finger. "I can see your nose and your cheeks and your chin." He tapped her cheeks and chin and the gold cross in the faint white line of her throat. "I'm glad you're not asleep or angry or anything like that," Harry said, wondering what made him speak such nonsense.

"I can't go to sleep," the girl said. "I'm supposed to get off pretty soon."

Harry felt the pulse in his wrists hammering in protest. "No," he said. "No, you got to stay on the bus till we get to Atlanta."

She shook her head. "It's like about writing," she said. "We got to act like we never met at all." Then she lifted her hand and touched his forehead and nose and chin. "I can sort of see you, too," she said. "You're nice. Only I have to get off soon. Real soon."

The driver called to them through the darkness, "Hey, you two lovebirds, rise and shine!" Harry was afraid that the driver would wake everyone in the bus, but the old man went on snoring and the infant kept up its steady sucking sound. Even the couple behind him did not stir. "Do you want me to stop at the gate, or do you want to go on into town?"

"I'd like you to stop at the gate," the girl said composedly. "There's always someone up."

Harry said, "You can't go."

"I have to."

"You can't go."

"I *want* to."

"Tell me your name."

The girl did not answer. Slipping out from under his coat, she stood up in the aisle. Harry tried to get up, too, but she pushed him gently back into his seat. "Stay there," she whispered. "Please stay there." To his astonishment, he sensed, through the shadows, the approach of her face, the warmth and smell of her skin and hair. She kissed his cheek, then, after a moment, his mouth, and pressed something into his hand; and the next moment she was walking down the aisle to the door. Harry could hear the fat young driver say, "Well, I guess your boy friend can't follow you in *there*," and afterwards, as the bus slowed down and ran over gravel to the side of the road, "Okay, sister, out you go."

Harry pressed his face against the window as the bus door

opened and shut. In the moon-like wash of the headlights, he saw two high stone pillars with an ornamental iron bracket between them. Worked in iron curlicues inside the bracket were the words, "Saint Anne's Hospital," and a date, "1896." At least, Harry thought, I know the address, I know where she is. As the bus swung back into the middle of the road, Harry caught sight of the girl walking towards the gate. He rapped with his knuckles against the window, feeling the skin of his fingers tighten, then break and bleed, but the girl did not turn. She had just reached the driveway inside the gate when darkness swallowed her up.

Harry fumbled with the object the girl had dropped in his left hand. Though he could not see it, he guessed that it was the cross she had worn around her neck. He turned it over and over in his fingers, touched it to his mouth, and was about to button it into the pocket of his blouse when he was struck by a faint, desperate hope. He got up and walked unsteadily forward. The driver said, "Keep your shirt on, kid, we won't hit Atlanta for hours. In fact, in this tin can it make take years."

Harry said, "I want to look at something." Turning his back on the driver, he held the cross up to one of the lights on the instrument panel. After a moment, he made out, in fine script on the back of the cross, a girl's name. He felt his eyes blinking with pleasure. She had given him her name, after all. She had pretended that they were not to think of each other again, but she had given him her name; she must have wanted him to write. "Listen," he said to the driver, "have you got a pencil?"

"Sure." The driver pulled a yellow stub from over his ear. "But you can't write in this barge."

Harry said, "I can try." He crouched on the top step of the bus, his shoulders against the door, and took from one of his pockets a soiled envelope. He smoothed it on his knee and, with the blunt pencil jumping unpredictably under his fingers, set down the girl's name, the name of the hospital, and the name of the town they were approaching. Then, jaggedly, childishly, but with infinite care, he wrote, "Darling . . ."

The Breaking Point

"WELL, HONEY, they're here all right," Brad said. "I just ran into Fefe in town. Says the fellow he took out yesterday got five sails. We've got a date with those babies in the morning."

Martha looked up from the hotel bed and the magazine she was reading and stared at him. She saw a big man who had once been handsome, who had once been her lover and for a long time now had been her husband. She saw a ruddy complexion that women considered attractive and that derived almost in equal parts from outdoor living and indoor drinking.

"You saw Fefe, and you also saw the bottom of a glass," she said.

"Oh, Christ, are you going to start that again?"

She felt the same way about it, but the pattern that enclosed them would not let her rest. "I'm not starting it. You started it when you broke your neck to get into town to have that first drink. In the hotel twenty minutes, and you can't wait to go into town and get stinking."

She hated that word. She always used it when she felt like this.

"I'm not stinking. Four, five drinks with Fefe—you call that stinking?"

She watched him take his shirt and pants off and stretch out on the bed. "Not stinking," he mumbled. "Uncle Brad doesn't get stinking that easy. Just sleepy. Little sleepy, that's all."

Martha said nothing. She had decided to drop the case. It wasn't the charge she would have liked to convict him on anyway. She knew what the charge really was. It was the fishing in the morning. It was the fact that he never even bothered to ask her if she felt like going fishing in the morning. Their first day back in Acapulco after five years, after the long cruise, maybe she felt like just lounging around the hotel. Maybe she felt like strolling through town, noting the changes, or looking up the people who had been most hospitable to them on their honeymoon. But Brad would never know. Brad would never ask her. Brad would just go on being Brad, the big spoiled boy, the son of the chairman of the board, who never grew up, who thought everything was put there for his amusement—the sailfish, the native ports, Martha . . .

He was lying on his back with his mouth slightly open, his breathing punctuated by the familiar sound of his snoring. If she were to come into a dormitory of a thousand sleeping men, Martha felt sure she would recognize that snoring. How many nights had it disturbed her reading? How many early mornings had its monotonous insistence penetrated sleep? How many nervous hours had she listened to it, and how many mornings had it provided the sound track for her first sight of the new day?

The rhythm of his snoring was broken by a violent snort. He is like a bull, she thought, with no more romance or even human passion in him than the stud bulls we've seen on ranches. He never asks me if I want to make love, he never asks me if I want to go fishing, he never asks me if I want to go to the bullfights; no, he just holds up two tickets—"They soaked me two hundred pesos apiece for these but I've got 'em!" And then, at the bullfights, there was always that business of the horses . . . Oh, she knew her Hemingway; she knew that the business of the horses is neither good nor bad, is not important, is merely a necessary, momentary unpleasantness that should not distract one from the real issue—the integrity with which the *torero* is preparing his bull for death. But Brad there, laughing at the jerky movements of that skinny horse's leg after the bull had refused to take the point of the *pica* for his answer, *laughing* and telling her to take her hands away from her face. My God, how close are sympathy and selfishness, she thought, When I cry for the horse, the innocent bystander crushed to earth, I cry for myself, trembling against the impact of the dark beast.

Once, after a particularly cruel bullfight, she had refused to speak to him for the rest of the afternoon. And up in the hotel room before dressing for dinner, the time he always liked, she would not give herself to him—not so soon after the business of the horse.

He had tossed his head then, with a bull's rage and a bull's stubbornness, and had roared out into the hall, on his way to the bar, with a familiar threat that disgusted her, that made her want to remove herself forever from the path of his charge. She had stood at the window looking down into the great avenue, her mind already hurrying ahead to her suitcase, her clothes, the note she would leave . . . but when he came in several hours later, listing slightly with his overload of tequila, and threw himself down on the bed and began to snore, she was still there, trapped like a bird that has come in through an opening it can no longer find.

As she watched and listened to him sleep that other evening she had wanted to blame her failure to leave him on the rigidity of her Boston family tradition, a background that shrank from scandal and the public charge-and-countercharge that delighted tabloid readers. But she knew herself too well to accept this as any more than the hard outer shell of the frailty of flesh and spirit that would not let her act. It was almost an illness, this passivity. The symptoms went back at least twenty years, for she could still remember coming home from first grade and saying, "Mummy, the girl across the aisle from me holds my hand all the time. The whole recess she holds my hand and I don't want her to." "But, darling, don't give her your hand if you don't like to," Mummy had said; but of course it was never as simple as that, for Martha didn't know how to tell the girl—and so that stronger girl had gone on holding Martha's hand throughout the rest of the term.

It was the same with Brad. She could not get her hand away from his. "Just tell him you've had enough," Martha's one close friend would tell her. But it was always easier to put off the final break, to wait until the trip was over, to make sure she wasn't pregnant . . . and then sometimes when she was sure she was ready, Brad would tap some hidden spring of intuition, and, then for a while he would soften to the man she thought she had married. He would bring her the special flowers she liked and be gentle with her—the way only the very cruel know how to be gentle—and so, for a short time she would forget, wanting so much to forget. And by the time his bogus little courtship had worn thin, her determination, fragile as spun glass, would have shattered.

If only he would perform one final act that could set her off, she thought. Yes, she was like the rusty trigger of a gun he had forgotten was loaded. It would take all his strength to bring the hammer down on the striking point. But even as she feared it, she waited for it.

Next morning they reached the docks at eight instead of seven-thirty because Martha had taken too long in the bathroom. Brad had been needling her with a sharp minute hand from the time he awoke. It was her bitter knowledge that an appointment with a fishing boat was the only thing which he took seriously. He had had his picture in quite a few magazines as a master of giant game fish. It was the best thing he did.

The boat wasn't a clean boat, not even by Mexican standards, and the native skipper merely muttered something without smiling when they came aboard. "He's sore because we're late," Brad said. "They like to get out there before the sun's up too high."

Martha didn't say anything. She really didn't care what effect the extra time had on the moods of his pock-marked Mexican. She was watching the mate. He had a cadaverous face covered by an unkempt beard. Normally he should have been about five feet tall, but a slight hump, or rather a ridge running between his shoulders, bent him over until he was hardly more than four feet high.

They went out past Hornos, the beach that the Acapulquenos frequent at sunset, and Martha could remember her first swim there with Brad when the flaming red sun lit the waters around them with cool fire and the palm trees behind the beach stood out in brilliant silhouette against the purple sky. Had she loved him that evening long ago? She tried to remember: yes, she had, for his Irish good looks, for his gaiety, and for the elaborate charade of romance he had practiced on her.

She looked over at him now, as if to compare the sham she had briefly loved five years ago with this solid reality who was carefully unwrapping his fishing gear—the Hardy reel he had picked up in England and the O'Brien rod bought two seasons ago in Miami, the rod that had conquered yellowtail off Ensenada, tuna near Guaymas, marlin in the Caribbean, and tarpon in the channels through the mangrove swamps that lie off Key West. He was careless about most of his possessions, but not about this rod.

The boat slowed to trolling speed and Brad paid out his line. The hunchback had a pole for Martha and fixed the base of the rod in the socket of her chair.

"Well, *muchacha*," Brad said, "better get the big gaff ready. I feel lucky today."

If the hunchback heard the feminine ending, his face gave no sign. They had spent nearly all their winters in Latin countries, and Martha's Spanish was good enough to cause her to flinch from Brad's linguistic slips. But Brad took pride in his inability to speak foreign languages. And he was in too good a mood at the moment to care whether he called this deformed native a boy or a girl. There were really only a few occasions, Martha was thinking, when Brad's humor was so high—when he was starting to fish, when he came in with a fish bigger and gamer than anyone else's, when he had had more than two drinks but less than six, and when he was undressing for his pleasure before dinner.

"Come on, get on there, baby!" Brad was talking to them somewhere under the sea. "Let's get a big one for Uncle Brad."

When nothing happened for a while, the hunchback threw out some chum, live bait of fairly good size, to draw the larger fish. In a few moments a sea gull appeared, maneuvering in over the wake of the boat to dive for the small fish.

"*Gaviota*," the hunchback muttered. "Damn *gaviota*."

A second gull came in overhead, and then another, coasting or winging easily over the stern. They were a small variety, very white, and Martha enjoyed their grace as they floated overhead.

"Damn *gaviota*," the hunchback muttered again. He reached into a paper bag for a small stone—Martha realized that he must have brought the stones along for that purpose—and tossed it up at them. It fell short of the birds.

"Come on, *muchacha*," Brad laughed. "Where's the old pitching arm?"

The hunchback threw again, but his physical disability limited his throw. "I get hands on *gaviota*"—his English was almost unintelligible—"I—" Instead of a word here, he substituted a terrible cracking sound of tongue against teeth and a quick gesture of snapping down with both fists.

The sudden violence of it, rising out of this wretched little man, made Brad laugh. But it left Martha with a sinking feeling of discomfort.

After a while she felt a tug on her line, pulled her pole back the way Brad had taught her, and then lowered it at the same time she began reeling in.

"You got something there—doesn't look like too much," Brad said. He never liked anyone else to catch the first one.

But as the thing she had caught came closer to the boat, it broke surface, flapping its wings wildly and giving forth a shrill wail.

"Damn *gaviota*," the hunchback said. "Pull in, pull in."

Martha could feel the bird pulling against her line, thrashing the water with its wings as it fought for life.

"Here," she said, quickly handing her rod to the hunchback. "*No me gusta*." She tried not to watch while the bird was pulled into the boat. But she had to listen to its screams; and when they suddenly became louder and more frightened, she knew it was held fast in the hunchback's fierce, sun-blackened little hands. She was imagining what he would do to it—twist its neck or slam it against the side—when she heard the *sound* of what the hunchback was doing to it. It was not too different from the sound he had made with his tongue against his teeth when he had been pantomiming the act before. She kept her eyes away until she was sure it must be over, and then she turned around, just as the limp white body was flung into the sea.

It floated on top of the water with its wings spread out as if it were in flight. Then she saw the bird suddenly bunch forward in a furious effort to rise from itself.

"Brad, it's still living! It's alive! He didn't kill it!"

"Where've you been?" Brad said. "All he did was break its wings and throw it back."

She watched the stern pull away from the crippled bird bobbing in the boat's wake. The gull was silent now. Its silence seemed even more terrible to Martha than its shrieking.

"Why does he do that? Does he *have* to do that?"

Brad laughed. "He hates those things like poison. Says it teaches them a lesson."

The hunchback was setting her line out for her again. Four or five gulls were over the boat now. "I don't think I want to fish any more," she said.

"What do you want to do?" Brad reprimanded. "Let the *muchacha* fish for you?"

It was easier, she felt, just to sit there holding the line than to let him ride her all the way. She prayed she wouldn't catch another one, though. She didn't think could stand another one.

She could not take her eyes from the white speck that bobbed in the distance. She could feel it struggling to rise with its helpless wings.

Suddenly Brad let out a cry of joy—"Sailfish!"—and the boat came to life. The hunchback's face was animated with a gargoyle smile, and even the dark Indian mask that the skipper wore for a face was lit with fisherman's hope and eagerness for the catch.

"I got a good one," Brad called, fighting it happily. "A good one!"

The hunchback was jabbering at Martha, and Brad shot her an anxious glance, his face red with effort. "Damn it, reel in! Reel in, for Christ's sake!" he shouted.

Martha had been watching the drowning gull. The hunchback snatched her line from her and began winding frantically to get it in out of the way. But it was too late. The sailfish had drawn Brad's line across and back under Martha's and their lines were becoming hopelessly tangled.

No longer able to reel in, Brad gave himself to profanity. "Damn it, that's the first thing I ever told you! You goddam nipple-head!"

The tangled lines went slack as Brad's sailfish threw the hook. "He's gone," Brad said tragically. "Would've hit fifty, maybe sixty pounds . . ." And his words were a jumble of profanity again.

Because our lines were crossed, I ruined his day, Martha thought. (Both lines were in the boat now, and the hunchback was working deliberately to loosen the knotted loops.)

It was almost half an hour before they could fish again. The sun was directly overhead, beating down oppressively. A dozen gulls were following them now.

"*Gaviota,*" the hunchback said. "Damn *gaviota.*"

Just then several dove for Brad's line and his pole dipped sharply. "Sonofabitch. Now *I've* hooked one." He was so exasperated that he couldn't even reel in. "Here, *muchacha,* you handle it." In his defeat, he turned on Martha again. "Goddamn it, next time I hook into something big, reel in, reel in like I told you."

The gull that had been hooked left the water and flew up over the boat with the line trailing from its beak. Martha could see it flapping directly overhead, pulling against the hook and crying as the metal point ripped the lining of its throat. As the hunchback reeled it in, it flew around wildly over their heads. Martha screamed, and the gull screamed with her. What a horrible female chorus, she thought.

With a neat gesture, the hunchback reached up and snatched the bird.

"Don't," Martha said. "Please don't"

"Wait a minute," Brad said. "Let me have it."

Thank you, Brad, Martha thought, thank you, thank you. Do it quickly!

Brad took the bird, exactly as he had seen the hunchback do it, snapped its wings in his big hands and tossed it back into the sea.

"That the way you do it, *muchacha?*" he said, laughing.

She watched Brad's gull flounder and then rise in a series of desperate convulsions. He had not even done this as the hunchback had, through hatred of everything more perfect than himself. It was merely something he had never done before.

She put her fingers to her throat to feel the throbbing. She shut her eyes against the glare on the water. Oh God, she thought, seeing in her mind the image of her dead father, the time has come at last, has come. Dear Father, give me strength . . .

ROBERT SWITZER

No End to Anything

"No," SAID WILLS, the American. "There is a beginning to everything and there is an end to everything." He spoke doggedly, his lean, dark face intense. "This should never have had a beginning, but it must have an ending, and the time for that ending is now."

The Cuban, Leon, seated across the table from him, slid farther down in his chair. "Now?" he asked. Huge, dishevelled, a knowing old bull of a man, he slouched in his chair, watching Wills with serious eyes.

"Yes," Wills said. "Now."

"This is tonight. Do you remember last night?"

"Of course."

"Then you remember what you told her?"

"Yes."

On the table was a throbbing oil lamp. It gave little light because it had not been cleaned for a long time. A doorway at the rear of the room was covered by a dirty curtain. The curtain concealed another room from which a staircase led to the second floor. If you pounded on the table, an old woman would come from behind the curtain with a bottle of rum.

"You have a good boat," Leon said suddenly. "The hull is painted white and the cabin is deep blue. The boat is a home and a livelihood and a possession. It is something of which anyone might be proud. Do you know what all that would mean to her?"

"I know what it would mean to me if I took her with me."

"You sound callous; you do not sound convincing."

"That boat is all I have." He looked down, and seeing his long tanned fingers balled into fists—the way he was finding them too often lately—he relaxed them, and watched the blood return to the knuckles. "It is all I ever will have. Do you think I should throw it away?"

"Why would you be throwing it away?"

"There is no need to answer that."

"Yes, there is. Tell me."

"All right. She has Negro blood."

"She loves you." Leon's great bulk was completely still.

"I said she has Negro blood."

"Very little."

"It does not take much."

"She does not look like a Negro."

"Leon, you are talking foolishly. You know what my taking her to the United States would mean."

"It would be no different from Cuba."

"No. Except that here I do not care what men say."

"But you do care what happens to her."

"I care more what happens to me."

The lampwick was burning low. Wills turned it up and for a moment the room seemed bright, then became murky again. It did not matter. It was easier to see in the dark, anyway. The less you saw, the less you had to think about, and everything was easy if you did not think. Stop thinking about the woman upstairs and this matter would be easy too . . .

"It would be madness to take her," Wills said. "You know that."

"Yes. It would be madness, but it would be kind."

"Kind? . . . That is the beauty of words. There are at least two meanings to all of them."

"There are two meanings to the word 'love?' " Leon asked.

"There are a thousand meanings to the word 'love,' " Wills replied.

"A thousand?"

"No," Wills said. "There is only one. I think there is only one, but I do not know what it is."

"Would not kindness be as good a definition as any?"

"You are back to that."

"Yes, I am back to that."

"Why? Are you her father? Is it up to you to give her away?"

"No, it is not up to me," said Leon. "I am only her uncle. But last night you told her you would take her with you. You promised."

"Have you never heard of a broken promise?"

'Yes. I have heard of too many of them. So have you. That is why this is important."

"It was the rum."

"Is it rum that has made her yours for the past month?"

"Well, you know, dear....all things must end."

"Last night it was the rum. Rum is good at making decisions but no good at making plans. Rum is not intelligent."

"Last night you made a promise. That is all there is to it."

"You believe it's as simple as that? Then the solution is just as simple. I cannot take her."

There had been a lot of them, Wills thought . . . The women he had left, some of them beautiful but more of them not, and leaving them at first had been easy and somehow pleasant because it had given him the feeling of change, of passing on to something better. That had been his obsession: to pass on to something better. His horror of repetition had driven him into a life of repetition—a steady procession of different places and people that had been no different—a steady passing on to things that had been no better.

Lately he had looked back a great deal, and whenever he did he looked all the way back. All the way back to the beginning. There had been a beginning, just as there would be an end. And in the beginning there was a girl. Kid stuff. Kid stuff was having a girl. It was taking his girl to the movies or a dance and it was being proud of her because she looked so nice, and being jealous when she smiled at someone else. It was going to her home afterwards and eating pie in the kitchen, and it was kissing her good night and not wanting to let go so that she had to pull his ear to get away, and then both of them laughing. Kid stuff was pressing her young body to his, liking the feel of her, and being content with having her that way.

He wondered why he kept going back to that. There had been nothing to it. She had not been very good looking. Perhaps he went back because he knew he would never go ahead, or perhaps it was because having too many women was lonely, and loneliness was beginning to frighten him . . .

The old woman came frome behind the dirty curtain. The glass in his hand was warm and slimy.

"Well?" he said.

"She is waiting for you—upstairs."

"I know."

The old woman stood there, scowling at him. "It will be well when she has gone. She has been no good since you arrived."

"Go away," he said. "You are very ugly and I am becoming tired of ugliness."

She did not move.

"Go away!" he shouted.

The old woman fled. His forehead was hot, he rubbed his hand over it. Across the table Leon watched him. He emptied his glass.

"I will be back," he said, and went behind the curtain and climbed the stairs. The stairs were poorly lighted but they were solid. He imagined a great many things were like those stairs; things obscured by shadows, but if you had the courage to walk into the darkness after them, you would find they were really firm and dependable.

He opened the door and went in. She was sitting on the bed waiting for him. It was more dignified to have him call for her than for her to go down to meet him. Beside her lay a small wicker bag. The door to the tiny closet was open and the closet was empty. The top of the dressing table was bare. Everything she owned was in that bag. Her movements were beautiful as she stood up and took a step toward him.

"Wait," he said. "Do not speak. You must listen to me. Last night I said I would take you with me. I cannot do that. It is impossible. You understand? It was the rum."

She looked as though someone had reached out of nowhere and whipped her across the face.

"The rum?"

"Yes," he said. "I am sorry."

"You are sorry?"

"Yes. I should not have promised. It was wrong. I am sorry." He could not stand her eyes. "Good-bye," he said.

"But you said you would take me with you."

"I know. But I cannot. You would not be happy." He was more of a coward than he had thought.

"If I were with you I—"

"No."

Quietly she said: "I will die."

"You are young and healthy. You will not die."

"I will kill myself."

"Dying is painful. It is foolish to hurt oneself," said Wills.

She stared at him, not believing he was really saying this. He looked at her carefully now, wanting for some reason to remember her. Her body was superb, there was no doubt of that. The pain started back of his eyes; his old familiar woman pain that throbbed gently now, like the oil lamp, but would soon be an agony. Yes, her body was superb. But his prejudices told him that her lips were a little too thick, her cheekbones a little too prominent, her hair—yes, but her body was magnificent. The pain was sharp, scalpel sharp . . . Once more. Then he could leave her. Just once more . . .

No, you swine, no! The pain went from behind his eyes. He turned from her, and as he walked toward the door she whispered, "Please." As he closed the door behind him he heard her say "please" again.

He went down the dark stairs, pushed the curtain aside and went to the table where Leon was still sitting. The glasses had been refilled.

"It is filthy liquor," Wills said.

Leon moved in his chair. "Did you tell her?"

"Yes," Wills said. "I told her." His sunburned cheeks were drawn tightly.

"What did she say?"

"She said she would kill herself."

Leon breathed deeply. "Do you believe her?"

"No."

"Why not?"

"She has no reason."

"She has no reason?" Leon asked, almost shutting his heavy lidded eyes.

"Do you call me a reason?" he snarled. "Do you?"

"I call you nothing. I only know that she will kill herself, reason or no reason."

"Stop the dramatics. She will not kill herself because she has no reason to and people do not kill themselves for no reason."

"You will not admit that love is cause for suicide," Leon said. "All right. Let us say that she will kill herself through disappointment. She thought she was going to have what she wanted but now she knows that she never will. She is disappointed."

Wills took a sip of the tepid rum. It almost made him sick. The talking was making him sick too.

"If she does kill herself," he said, "it will prove that I am right. There is an end to everything."

"No. It will prove there is no end to anything."

Wills set his glass down on the table.

"You go to hell!" he said, and got up and went out of the place.

PART THREE: *The Lady Speaks Her Mind*

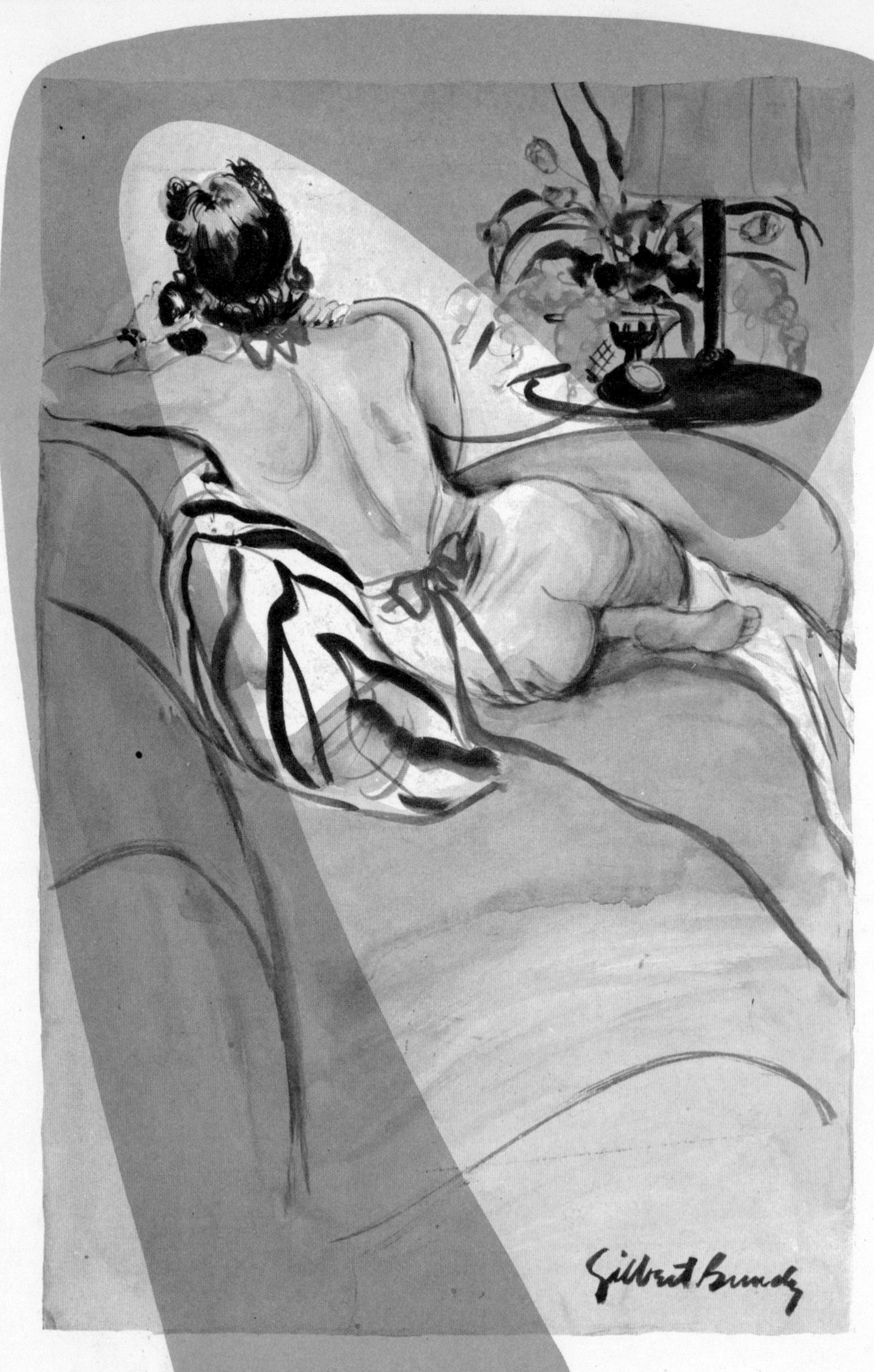

"Why don't you come over here, Mr. Hartman, then I won't have to bother about getting dressed?"

It Was Good Enough for Father

We of the twentieth century like to look back patronizingly at past generations; they, poor souls, did the best they could with the means at hand, but we—let's admit it—are far more advanced. Just consider all the mechanical goodies we have! Everything these days is a great deal bigger and faster than our ancestors ever dreamed of!

Well, we do have bigger things, and certainly faster ones. Better too, in many ways. It would be ridiculous to deny or to decry industrial and scientific advancement, though it's true that, thanks to one or two of our progressive items, we're subjected to forms of torture that former generations (those old stick-in-the-muds) never had to endure. We have, among other so-called advantages, the telephone—an instrument that rings constantly when we crave silence and maintains an infuriating silence when we want it to ring.

In the old days there were no telephones, no cellophane, no indoor plumbing. There weren't any psychonanalysts either; the madhouses were less crowded and the divorce courts weren't jammed to the rafters. Yes, our ancestors may have lacked many modern improvements, but yet, sorry bunglers though they were, they had an insight, a psychological understanding, and an appreciation of human well-being so profound as to make fools of us moderns. They knew, for example, that women need men and men need women and that the interdependence of the sexes must be recognized if a marriage is to succeed.

And so they invented a device known as the double bed.

Today we are more progressive than our forefathers, more sanitary, more civilized. Today we have twin beds—and a self-imposed exile they are, a folly for which there can be no praise. We have but to consider where they are most in use to ask ourselves in horror why we give them house room. Where are they used? They're used in hospitals, in prisons, in insane asylums, that's where! And fifty per cent of the people occupying them there probably wouldn't be in them if they hadn't used them at home.

What has happened to us that we no longer realize the double bed is more thrill-inducing than the airplane, more comforting than steam heat, more engrossing than television? The freedom, the companionship, the moments of lyric tenderness implicit in the double bed rank among life's great experiences. Occupied by two sympathetic members of the opposite sex, the double bed yields the nearest facsimile of complete joy we may reasonably expect on earth.

A close rapport is likely to occur in a double bed—indeed it is to be hoped for—but to think only of sex in this connection is to think of a skeleton, to ignore the glowing flesh and garments of happiness.

Man is an animal. So, fortunately, is woman. Why then, when it is easily obtainable, deprive ourselves of our greatest animal comfort—the proximity, the touch of the creature we love? Curiously enough, this animal instinct in humans is the soil from which evolves the most exquisite bloom we are capable of: love for another. For those who love each other, the spirit and the flesh are inseparably allied, and it seems highly unlikely that, as some moderns claim, connubial desire is kept alive through physical separation. Will a husband and wife seem less familiar, more alluring to one another, if they occupy separate beds? If so, wouldn't separate rooms be even better? And if that's an improvement, how about separate houses? And then maybe separate cities? Different countries? "Darling, how appealing you are when I'm in Saskatchewan and you're in Tanganyika!" Unless the flint strike the steel, whence the spark? What about that?

If the love two people bear each other is a living thing by day, it is fostered and intensified by their sharing a double bed at night.

Many couples, vaguely aware of this, experiment with that unsatisfactory compromise, twin beds side by side, joined by the same headboard. What is the comfort in being joined by a headboard and separated by the covers? This system is perhaps a little better than twin beds separated by the night table, but so little as to make scant difference.

A great attraction of a double bed for the married is its face-saving property. It is kind to one's pride. It is a breach-healer par excellence. Most married differences start out not too seriously—a chip off here, a small dig there, and the first thing you know one partner's feelings are hurt and the other is angry. Suppose this hapless couple is sleeping in twin beds. What happens? The undressing, washing, tooth-brushing routine is gone through, the aggrieved wife flounces to her single pallet and the husband either slams up the window in furious silence or asks savagely if she minds if they get a little fresh air in here to blow away some of this nonsense. He then plunks himself down on the edge of his bed, kicks off his slippers, swings his legs in, draws up the covers, punches his pillow into a knot as unyielding as his mood, and ostentatiously turns his back on the blossom he not so long ago promised to love and cherish until death. The silence is broken only by the click of the light switch as the wife snaps it off and her exasperated exclamation, throbbing with more drama than a three-act play: "Of course! Leave *everything* to me."

Under these circumstances, it is a long time before either of them gets to sleep, though it may be safely said that the husband, a grosser spirit, will eventually get there first. In the meantime the darkness is taut as a fiddle string. Then gradually, as the hours slip by, each one will be thinking. "The hell with this silly business, why don't we kiss and forget?" But each one is damned if he (and the term is used generically) will be first to get up, cross the infinity which is the three-and-a-half feet separating the beds, and snuggle in beside his indubitably erring but still beloved spouse. As a result the couple wakens in the morning after a restive night as out of tune as when they went to bed. By the time the husband gets home in the evening, the wife has had time to think up a lot of other grievances; and the first thing you know, space permitting, one or the other of them has moved out of the nuptial chamber and the rift is widened for fair.

With contiguous beds, the situation is ameliorated but it is still not good, since any move for a rapprochement must be telegraphed, the magnanimous partner (as he will think of himself)—or the crow-eating one (as he thinks he will be considered)—having either to get up and go around the beds or tug at the covers of his own and then of his partner's in order to slip from one to the other. This is a deliberate gesture and takes doing.

But in the double bed! How simple, how natural, how unintentional! The lights are extinguished and tension prevails, but not for long. A tentative toe is stretched toward the center. Quite by accident it touches a leg. Well, even in the heat of battle nothing was said about the other party's being physically repugnant. There is no real need to draw one's toe back again. It stays. One is conscious of a gentle return pressure. A hand, by chance, brushes a shoulder, two heads draw nearer, an arm reaches out . . . It is an endearing arrangement. And even if the reconciliation doesn't happen before going to sleep, where there has been physical contact rest is broken. Two are likely to wake in the deep darkness. Things are different in the dark: those who went to bed as strangers waken as lovers, and pride and bitterness and anger are daylight demons.

The most general objection to the communal couch seems to be that many people feel they cannot sleep in the same bed with another person. This argument is not to be lightly brushed aside. Actually, three-quarter beds and standard doubles are small for two people. There is nothing so restful as kicking space, and nothing more conducive to resentment than the feeling that one must budge only with caution for fear of disturbing another person. Then, too, it is maddening, as one slips into the gauzy borderland of sleep, to have the bed leap under a sudden flounce or to have an arm flop across one's face or to receive a sharp gouge in the ribs from an elbow. Nor does it give rise to gentle thoughts of love to waken chilled to the marrow, exposed to the winds of heaven, while one's unconscious spouse slumbers blissfully at one's side wrapped snug and mummylike in *all* the blankets. Also there is no denying that many wives are prey to peckish morning moods when they have been kept awake at night by that calliope with the cutout open which is a snoring husband. Sometimes he may be throttled without total extinction, or rubber stoppers in wifely ears may mute the racket (there is a nasty rumor afloat that some husbands are driven to them too); but, where such treatment fails, even twin beds won't help. Despite love and longing, separate rooms may be the only answer. Let us turn in sorrow from this insoluble problem and its painful solution.

There are those who complain that double beds tend to sag in the middle and that both occupants are likely to spend their nights rolling downhill to bump into each other at the bottom, getting thoroughly awake as they haul themselves back up the slope, and then repeating the performance all over again. To those who demur on this score we give short shrift. Keep the springs and mattress in good repair, and it won't happen.

In fact, to all objections, barring the noise of snoring, there is a shining answer: the outsize double bed, the jumbo job that anyone can obtain with patience, guile, and some money. A bed seven feet square is a domain of flawless delight. In such a bed one is a property owner roaming the lower forty, solitary if one

CPL. Ned HIL-
TON

wishes it, in easy contact with fellow man or fellow woman when the spirit moves. Either partner may curl into a ball or lie spread-eagle, secure in the knowledge that his spouse is undisturbed, unaware during his most restless gyrations. The feeling of freedom and at the same time of coziness that one experiences in this broad pasturage is delightful. There is so much room that even disciplinarian dog lovers, the kind who say with suspicious firmness, "I'm crazy about dogs, but I do *not* approve of them on beds," may alibi Rover's presence on those very premises with the explanation that they didn't know he was there.

One shocking thing about the movies is that sight of a double bed strikes horror in the heart of the Johnston Office. For a community as concerned about public morals as Hollywood, it's interesting to note that if figures tended to show that fewer divorces occur among couples using double beds than among those occupying twin beds or separate rooms, then Hollywood itself is instrumental in the breakup of countless homes. For Hollywood sets fashions, and many Americans follow slavishly.

Struggling to understand the point of view of the censors, we can't help wondering what is supposed to be "dirty" about a double bed? Or "suggestive"? for countless generations men and women have slept in them, and the children of the household grew up thinking of them—if they thought at all—as symbols of family unity. Father and Mother shared a bed. Why wouldn't they? It was one of the most commonplace and sweetest facts of life. It was the custom in every country of the world and among all classes for hundreds of years. Then came Hollywood and couples in the movies sleep on measly single beds (which, mark you, are separated by two or three feet).

As we have acknowledged, there are arguments against double beds, but they have nothing to do with morals. When the double bed is outsize, they are chiefly economic. Though initial price is steep, it is not prohibitive. The fly drops into the ointment later. Upkeep! That is expensive, because the furnishings for this mammoth cot—mattress pads, sheets, blankets, blanket covers, quilts and spreads—have to be specially made. It takes a lot of goods, blankets, blanket covers, quilts, but, fortunately, an electric blanket does away with layers of wool and down quilts and provides bug-snugness is zero weather. The electric blanket, which seemed originally designed for slow torture, has evolved into the sleeper's boon. And with dual control for double beds, the harmony it creates among married couples is so marked that Nevada will soon be looking for clients. The great he man who spurns comfortable warmth as something effeminate can virtually put his master switch in reverse and manufacture a row of icicles while the little hot dish at his side turns hers on full strength and sizzles cheerily through the night.

It is true that maids are likely to complain when first confronted with the task of making up the mastodon and to mutter that some people are crazy—"that's what, crazy,"—but as a matter of fact the task is not as arduous as it seems, and moving the bed is child's play, since the box springs are set on wheels. That is of no practical importance, of course, because it never occurs to maids to move beds for cleaning purposes in any event; but, should the mistress be fired with enthusiasm, it's a handy device.

The continuing headache is the laundries. They don't complain, laundries don't, but they take one look at those sheets, which are only slightly larger than the movie screen in Radio City Music Hall, and add a few naughts to the bill. It's worth it, though. Such drawbacks as these are far outweighed by the joys, a fact that seems to be dawning on more and more people. One large department store reports a new ratio of more than three double beds sold for every pair of twins.

It is, after all, a simple mathematical computation. Eight hours out of every twenty-four we devote to sleep. Since time flies so quickly, how practical it is—and how delightful—to spend a third of our lives on the double!

The Secret of Love:
Have American Girls Forgotten?

THE ARMY transport was on her way to New York from Bremerhaven. She was loaded with Army officers and their dependents, war-department civilians, G.I.s, alien brides and American children born in Germany.

The voyage was boring. Army transports aren't much fun. The only thing to do to pass the ten or eleven days at sea is to talk. So Julia Norfield and I talked.

"Is your husband still in Germany, Julia, or did he go on home ahead of you?" I asked her.

"I'm one of those fräulein widows," she said.

The look on my face made her smile a little even before I croaked out, "*You?*" It was hard to believe. Julia Norfield had taffy-colored hair. Her face was small and well-made. She was full of sparkle and wit. Her clothes were expensive and smart and fitted her trim figure perfectly.

"You're wondering what she had that I haven't got, aren't you? Well, that's what I'd like to know. And what hundreds of American wives in Germany would like to know. How do you explain it? What do these women have that makes a man like my husband ask me for a divorce?"

Her husband had been an officer in the U.S. Army. They had been married almost thirty years and had two grown children. The son was on assignment with the Occupation Forces in Germany. The daughter was engaged to an Army officer. Captain Norfield was assigned to duty in Germany in 1945.

"I should have thought the military would have kept them from living together."

"The Army condones this thing, Betty. Officers of high rank are doing it. A close friend of my husband's refused to help me. He wouldn't do anything on my behalf, because he is sleeping with a friend of hers himself. The Army doesn't care."

How familiar it sounded. Another American man stationed in Germany, seemingly happily married for years, forsaking country, wife, children, even deserting the Army itself, to live in comfortable sin with a German woman.

I counted all the others I had known about in the three years I had spent with the American Occupation Forces in Germany.

There had been, first, the boss of one of my best friends. He had been sent to Germany in 1945, and lived in happy sin until 1949, when his wife took the bull by the horns and insisted that she join him, for she thought it odd that he did not ask her to come. When she arrived in Germany it did not take her long to discover that he had a young fräulein. She tried everything she knew to win him back, but in the end went back to America, defeated. He had been a colonel in the American Army. They were married twenty-some years and had an attractive daughter, just out of finishing school. His wife and daughter begged him, reasoned with him, ranted at him, wept. But his only thought was how he could get a divorce and stay in Germany with his "Erika."

Then there was the American official who had attained status in the educational field in America. He was a man of intelligence and ability. In 1947 he took his family to Germany, and in 1949 his wife and children returned to the United States because they could no longer bear the humiliation of his open affair with "Hildegard." He was still over there the last I knew.

I remembered a young Army civilian, formerly a combat M.P., who had a wife and two children in the States, but who had never returned from Europe after the war. He was living with a fräulein in a couple of rooms over a cheap tavern. His wife had to take legal action to get child support out of him. He wasn't embarrassed or ashamed. He was concentrating on just one thing: How to stay in Germany with "Ursula."

Of course, I could not forget the day at lunch in the mess hall when the men figured out on the tablecloth the percentage of American personnel in our agency alone in Nürnberg who were "shacked up" with German girls and had already fathered one or two babies. It was 25 per cent of our personnel, and several of them had wives and children at home.

My thoughts went further back, to 1947, when aboard the Orient Express on my way to Prague on leave I met the young wife of a sergeant stationed in Germany. She, too, was going to Prague, on vacation by herself, and because she was lonely and I was a stranger and it didn't matter, she told me the same story. Her man had the fräulein neatly installed as maid in their quarters when she had arrived, and she didn't know for weeks that there was anything between them.

"I'm going back to the States next month," she had said. "But before I go I'm spending some of his money to see Europe."

And there were countless other instances. It was an old story to me after three years. It didn't seem to matter what kind of men they were or what their station. Officers, civilians, educated, ignorant, well-bred, ill-bred—no matter. American marriages in Occupied Germany were collapsing left and right because of the German fräulein.

What *was* their power? What *did* they have that the American women lacked? Was it just a natural evil of any occupation that made the conquered women throw themselves at the conquerors? Or was it really something basic that the American wives failed in that made their men such easy prey to German women?

I had heard it hashed over many times by the American bachelor girls employed by the Occupation Forces. Most of them dismissed it as just out-and-out sex.

"They're whores, that's all," I had heard them comment often.

"No self-respecting American woman would sleep with a man for a carton of cigarettes."

"They'll go to bed with anybody who buys 'em a decent meal. Where could an American man get that at home?"

Of course, this reasoning might have answered for some of the bachelors and confirmed woman-chasers. But it did not solve the problem of the married man who was breaking up his family, or the young Americans who were living quietly, unmarried, with their German girls and helping to raise their own German-born babies. For a carton of cigarettes they had bought family responsibility. Their pay checks were now going for toys and baby milk instead of nylons and lipsticks. And the boys were contented. They were not running out on the girls.

It was not as if there were no American girls there to date, either. Our Occupation Forces employ thousands of American girls. But these same girls who were calling the fräuleins bad names were sitting alone in their billets on week nights, and going to the G.I. movies in crowds of five or six on week ends. It was a rare thing to see an American bachelor out for a night with an American girl.

My thoughts had raced through all this while Julia stood at the porthole watching the green sea hiss and boil away from the side of the moving ship.

"Was she pretty, Julia?"

"I only saw her once. But all the gossips said she wasn't."

"Well, none of the husband-stealers I've seen were great beauties. I guess it's not looks."

"No," she answered, "it's not. Why, some of these women couldn't get to first base in America on their looks or their figures. Have you seen these alien brides on this ship? Do they look like charmers?"

I had to admit that they did not. Yet, Julia had found out that two of them had married divorced Americans. Divorced *after* the men had met the girls.

Julia turned from the porthole.

"I met a colonel in the lounge last night. He's been stationed in Berlin for three years and he's going home to get a divorce and go back and marry his fräulein. Let's ask him in here tonight for a drink. Let's try to get him to give us an American man's viewpoint on these damn fräuleins."

So the colonel came, and he was worth listening to. There was a quiet air of assurance about him that gave one the feeling that he was master of his thoughts.

"I think I can tell you what it is you want to know," he began, after unimportant chitchat had broken the ice, and Julia had put the question squarely before him, telling him in a few words what had happened to her marriage. "Briefly—and actually you can't be brief about it—it's this: European women, not just the German fräulein, but European women in general, make a man feel comfortable. I don't mean just by putting his pipe and his slipper by his chair. My wife always did that in Detroit. She was a good cook, too, and she was interested in my success. I mean something else. They give him a feeling of ease. A man isn't under a strain with a European woman."

"What kind of strain do you mean?" Julia asked. "I never noticed that my husband was strained in my company."

"Perhaps you couldn't see it, Mrs. Norfield. May I speak to you frankly?"

"I want you to," Julia answered eagerly.

"I think it's entirely possible that your husband was under rather a severe strain with you. I've watched you in the lounge. You're an attractive woman. Any man would notice you. You look expensive. But when I first saw you I thought to myself, 'Now there's a gal who can take care of herself. I'll bet none of these jokers fool her.' You see, I didn't have the urge to come over and sit down by you because your air of self-sufficiency scared me out. I was actually afraid you'd think I was a stupid fool trying to make time with you, and you look much too smart to put up with anything like that. I wonder if your self-sufficiency wasn't a little tough on your husband sometimes? I wonder if he didn't feel a lot of the time that he wasn't too important to you? Do you actually think that he thought you needed him?"

"If you mean by that, did I ever put on the clinging-vine act, the answer is 'no.' Is that the secret of the European woman? Does she play it smart and look and act dumb so you great big men will feel more great and big?" Julia's voice was edgy.

"No, that's not it, Mrs. Norfield. She doesn't have to act. She really feels that way. She is dependent on her man. You see, Mrs. Norfield, our highly prized 'American way of life' has made our women aggressive and hard. You are not truly feminine any more. You've lost your *gentleness*. You want to be 'smart' and you've become brittle. You want to 'get somewhere' and you've gotten hard. In your determination to be independent and compete with men you've sacrificed your *womanliness*. When a man is with a woman, he doesn't want to *compete* with her."

"He wants to be lord and master, doesn't he?" The tone of Julia's voice was cutting.

"If you want to put it that way, yes. There is that in the man which must feel that he's dominating a woman. In fact, it's absolutely necessary for most men. Do you find that thought irritating? Certainly after the years of marriage you had this is not a new proposition to you."

"Oh, it's not new. I went through thirty years of it. I practically knocked myself out letting him think he was wearing the pants in the family."

"There. You have touched the center, Mrs. Norfield. You 'let him think' he was boss. You knew all the time that he wasn't. Deep down in his subconscious he felt it. But he didn't realize it until he went to Germany and experienced what it is really like to live with a woman who is content to be just a woman and who thought he was wonderful because he was her man. She did not try to make him over. She took him as he was and built her life around him so that they became like one. Such an experience fills a man with happiness and a sense of importance that he won't give up."

"Won't you admit that these European women are getting plenty out of the American men in exchange for this cozy feeling they're dishing out? You don't think American men are being taken for suckers, do you?"

"Sure, I think some of them are. The same ones would be suckers at home for a clever woman. But these fräuleins don't seem to be clever. It doesn't seem like an act. Their sincerity is natural and deep-seated. It's part of them."

I was ready to chime in by this time. "I think I follow all this lofty talk about our lack of gentleness and femininity. I believe you when you say we're too aggressive. But I want to ask you, man to man, isn't the real reason American men prefer European women to us that they wait on you body and soul? Don't they polish your shoes, run all your errands, make all your bargains on the black market, protect you from chiselers among their own people, cook only for your taste, go only where *you* want to go, pack all the luggage, make the house to please you, and sleep with you when and how you want it? Honestly now, Colonel, isn't that what you really like about these women?"

He thought a moment. "Yes, I suppose that is true, as far as it goes. They spoil us."

"Servants. They're just your servants," Julia spat out. "Do you think any educated American woman in this day and age would kowtow to a man like that?"

He chuckled, but his eyes were wise. "That, Mrs. Norfield, is your answer as to why American men are deserting their wives over here to live with foreign women. Waiting on a man's personal needs is only an outward manifestation of the way they feel about men. *You* get no pleasure out of waiting on a man. *You* think it's out-of-date. You want him to wait on you. That's where your European sister beats your time. She *likes* it. She does not have a false sense of what you call 'self-respect.' She has, rather, a sense of intimacy with her husband, of belonging to him and that he belongs to her. She doesn't feel like his servant—just as much as a person is never a servant to himself. They have a feeling of oneness, a fusion of mood and spirit."

"Don't you feel just a little bit like a heel, asking your wife for a divorce so you can go back to Berlin and marry this girl?" Julia prodded, unimpressed.

"In a way I do, yes," he answered. "But I am forty-nine years old, Mrs. Norfield. Life is truly short. I want what I have found. I never experienced the peace with my wife that I have had with this woman. I have been comfortable and at ease and in love with her for three years, and I like *myself* for the first time I can remember.

I didn't know it was possible to have such a combination of companionship and love and to live so entirely without strain and tension. I have decided I owe it to myself to fight to keep this. I'll pay any price."

"No matter who may get hurt," Julia finished for him.

"Yes."

"And what you've told us is how the rest of these men feel? Is that what makes them ask for a divorce and stay over?"

"That's as near as I can come to telling you why they do it, Mrs. Norfield. I think I've talked too much. Good night. . . ."

MARY JANE SHOUR

Blueprint for a Divorcee

WHEN it first occured to me that divorced women could do with their own very special set of rules, I felt much like Mme. Curie on the day she discovered radium. I was a woman dedicated, a girl with a cause, an author with a message!

Everybody is concerned about the bachelor girl; everyone worries about the widow; thousands of helpful, sympathetic words have been written for *them.* But nobody seems to give a hang what becomes of a lady once the judge intones, "Divorce granted." There she is, poor little Madame Ex, still clutching that same old copy of *How to Get Your Man,* when the rules don't apply to her case any more.

I mean to change all this right now. Who knows better than I the pitfalls, the do's and the don'ts of divorcedom? Consider the research I have done on the subject. Exhaustive. Three ex-husbands' worth. . . .

The first thing a divorcee must learn to cope with is the "gleam." The gleam is that very fancy look that comes over a gentleman's face when he finds out that you're a Mrs. who has shed her Mr. Cats have been known to gaze at canaries with much the same expression. The dream back of the gleam has to do with bed-and-bordello; it makes strong men silly, and it makes married women hate you. The gleam will be there—in somebody's eye—even if you never wear anything more alluring than a Mother Hubbard, drink anything stronger than soda pop, or recount anything racier than the one about the chicken crossing the street.

Once you accustom yourself to the gleam and get used to having all the wives you know clutch at their husbands' sleeves whenever you enter a room, you are ready to pursue your career as a divorcee. The aim of said career is usually to stop being a divorcee and start being a sleeve-clutcher on your own. For that, though, you need a man. And how do you meet a man—an unattached and eligible one, I mean?

Of course, you can go to the Riviera, but just why a trip to faraway places has acquired such a high rating in the boy-meets-girl department escapes me. I have been trainsick, airsick, seasick, en route to much-vaunted glamour spots like Bermuda, Palm Beach, Honolulu, and Beverly Hills; and the best I ever got for my money was a little fellow who sells refrigerators and lives just eight blocks from my home. I have been gleamed at in Majorca and Monte Carlo and Buenos Aires; in Spanish, Italian, French, and even once in Greek—and all the boys were pretty much like the wolves back home, only translated. If an Aly Khan were guaranteed with every ticket abroad, that would *be* something; but romance isn't that easy to find.

Consider the case of Alice:

Alice was always a bride, never a bridesmaid. She had just divorced her fifth husband, with nary a sixth in sight. It seemed as though she had already married all the cute men she knew. Alice went off to seven glamour spots in one season. No dice. Very, very unhappy about the whole thing, she decided to End It All. One dateless night, she wrote and rewrote several farewell notes, swallowed a handful of sleeping pills, and lay down to die in her prettiest pink chiffon nightgown. Next thing she knew, someone was jabbing a hypodermic needle into her arm. The someone was masculine and handsome. He was the house doctor in the hotel where Alice lived alone and hated it. The maid had summoned him when she came in to clean and discovered our Sleeping Beauty. And there he was, beautiful and single and solvent. The doctor and Alice were married six weeks later.

Now, I'll admit, these are pretty drastic methods for a girl to use, and they leave an alarming margin for error, but the case of Alice does go to prove that there are plenty of eligible men right in your own neighborhood. All you have to do is find them.

Some of the other problems a divorcee has to handle are even more difficult than finding a man. How, for instance, do you outfox a wolf? There are several easily discernible kinds of wolf and some time-tested ways of dealing with them. All you need is the diplomacy of an ambassador to Moscow, an iron nerve, and the disposition of a ministering angel. Won't you step up and meet the boys?

Type A. He Has Muscles. . . .

Just FEEL 'em! If you do, beware, though; this lad was on the

"That new man is fast—but how thorough, remains to be seen."

wrestling team at Princeton. Or Yale. Or Michigan State. He's got you confused with Gorgeous George, so watch your step. As he dives in for a headlock, you'd better start to chatter. Talk about anything, everything: your migraine headaches, the price of butter, Harry S. Truman. You don't have to make sense; just make conversation and keep yapping until you *bore* him out of the ring.

Type B. The Healer. . . .

With him, it's all purely medicinal. This lad is doing you a favor. Look at it his way: You're a young, healthy woman and you need a male (he's IT). If you don't follow the laws of nature, who knows what dark neuroses you will be prey to? He'll quote from the Kinsey Report, trot out Freud and the rest of the boys to illustrate. When he gets to Havelock Ellis, just sigh, agree, look wistful, and say that yours is a special case and your analyst forbids. He may think you mad, but he'll probably accept your refusal and come calling another evening all set for a rousing discussion on Modern Marriage—Whither? The rest is up to you.

Type C. The "Let's Audition" Boy. . . .

Certainly he wants to marry you—but! He suggests a rehearsal to make sure this is the real thing. Be firm with this smartie; he's hitting below the belt—and besides, he just *might* be serious. Go all-out Victorian; tell him you'd love to after the preacher has had his say. Corny? Maybe, but this technique has been making husbands out of wolves since great-great-great-great granny used it across the bundling board.

Type D. Your Personal Rudolph Valentino. . . .

The Great Lover who is a real humdinger with the ladies—just listen to him tell all about it. What he lacks in hair and teeth he makes up in verve. He won't paw or claw; he's strictly a palm-of-the-hand kisser, or, at worst, a friendly-pat-on-the-rear boy. But he's murder. Make no mistake about it—especially if he has an interesting accent. Best method with this seasoned campaigner is the reliable, oh-so flattering "I-don't-trust-myself" routine. Tell him you're afraid he'll break your silly little heart. He's heard it before—before you were born—but he'll love every hackneyed syllable and walk out jauntily, humming *Some Enchanted Evening.*

Type E. The Intellectual. . . .

Most dangerous type of all, This yackety-yak Romeo relies on the subtle approach. Wouldn't you feel gauche if you were to slap his hand and holler "Fresh!" in the midst of a discourse on Existentialism? Wisest thing to do is draw him out. Ask rapt, interested questions. One thing the Intellectual cannot resist is an audience.

Keep him well-exercised vocally, and he's liable to forego other kinds of gymnastics. Maybe someday you'll find him explaining the Einstein Theory to you on your tenth wedding anniversary.

Type F. Peter Pan. . . .

He's just an overgrown baby boy. Nobody understands him, he wails, as he backs you onto the sofa. He's so lonely, so forsaken, so unloved. Honey, he's *so* right. Just turn the tables on Junior. *You* get bitsy, wide-eyed, and adolescent. Swipe his act and you steal his effectiveness; he wants a mama, not Baby Snooks. As he begins to pout, ease him out the door. You didn't want him anyway.

The subtle make-him-come-back-for-more technique is wasted on Types A and F—just as it is wasted on characters like the Begrudger, who demands an eye for an eye, a kiss for every canapé he fed you; the Fixer, a by-product of Hollywood, who is "gonna do big things for you, baby"; and the Belligerent Boy, whose irresistible sales talk goes like this: "Why not? You've been married, haven't you?"

Barring undesirable wolves (not husband material), it is best to deal gently with the male sex. Sometimes the sheep in you-know-who's clothing is merely being gallant. He thought you'd be insulted should he fail to make a pass. A good divorcee's maxim to remember is this: Hell hath no fury like a woman scorned—unless it is a man. Act accordingly.

Now let's look, from a divorcee's point of view, at some of the old bromides about how ladies ought to conduct themselves. What may be unseemly for the maiden is often quite *comme il faut* for the divorcee, who has, we presume, lived. Pardon me while I aim at that little old cocked hat.

There is nothing more repulsive than a drunken woman.

Pish! What, may I ask, is so lovely about a lad with a load? True, there is little allure to the lady who gets *sooooo* sad on the third old fashioned or the girl who staggers or the little lassie who throws up. But what of her male counterpart? They have added a few cute tricks of their own. I have yet to meet the lady, however fractured, who insists on leading the band. When the girls get together over a pint or two, they do *not* as a rule raise voices in an off-key rendition of *Down by the Old Mill Stream.*

A lady never sits at a bar alone.

Why not, if she really is a lady, and a thirsty one at that? I am weary of people staring at me as though I were up to no good every time I want a martini and do something about it unescorted. There is absolutely nothing unseemly about a well-mannered gal perched solo at the bar, if she doesn't make it a habit.

Never accept expensive gifts from men.

Now there is a dilly! What expensive gifts from what men? The diamond bracelet coyly tucked in a corsage of rare orchids is a thing of the past. It gets downright tiresome for a girl to find herself forever being warned against gentlemen bearing sables, when said bloke never presents himself. The author is in no position to give advice on this subject. No male, gentleman or otherwise, has ever pursued me waving so much as a mouton jacket from the Thrift Shop. Should he ever turn up, all I can say is —*yippee!*

Don't go out with married men.

Come, now—he just *might* be your lawyer. Actually, having dinner with a married man is exactly like dining with an unmarried wolf, only the food isn't as good. Those hidden little restaurants with the checked tablecloths and dim candlelighting may be quaint, but the food is apt to be pretty quaint also. Just how much *pizza* can a girl digest? I know one divorcee who broke up with her married beau because she broke out in hives.

By this time you should have a fair idea of the problems that confront a divorcee. So, if any girl who reads this is planning to leave her husband, I suggest that she think twice. One far-from-perfect husband is much the same as the next not-so-perfect husband. But, if the die is already cast, if you *are* a divorcee, take heart. A divorcee's life can be fun. Look at the future there is in it. See what happened to Wallis Windsor and Rita Hayworth. Maybe you're next. Just follow the rules, and—who knows?—pretty soon . . .

CYNTHIA HARRIS

Let Him Be Lord and Master

SAD INDEED is the plight of the woman who gets the perfect husband, the man that all her friends wish they had married. If I had not listened so carefully and made a long list of the attributes of the specimen partner, I might have married that truck driver who whistled at me. No doubt I would have been better off.

As it is, for four years I have been married to this man who makes all my friends sigh with envy. It just makes me sigh. He's one of those people described so often as being, "just too good to me. I wish he were more normal." Funny thing, I actually wish that. Of course I appreciate my coffee in bed every morning before getting up to cook breakfast, and nothing is so satisfying as to know that he has also fired the furnace and that I don't have to shiver down to the kitchen. It even gives me time to comb my hair and apply a little make-up, helping me thereby to imitate the cereal ads in the magazines he so thoughtfully brings me several times a week.

He goes out of his way to find my favorite brand of chocolate candy—my weakness. I plead with him not to, that I'm getting fat, but he smiles indulgently and brings me another box a few days later, just as I have determined to go all out for that new reducing course.

When we moved into our house and he scrubbed and waxed floors, I appreciated it, but I told him I would rather do it myself and go walking with him on his afternoons off. His feelings were hurt and I dared not mention it again. It left me lonesome, made me drink too many cocktails before dinner. Like most men who love their wives and were reared by their mothers to think that women were made for waiting on, he overdoes it. This is probably a confession that will ruin my marriage when he reads this and changes his ways. There is no need to say that I don't anticipate the attention, but why does it make me long for someone like Humphrey Bogart? He never waits on anyone.

No woman really appreciates the small details and the housework that men do. Flowers brought home unexpectedly are nice, but a loving man who thinks that it is his duty to scrub his small son and put him to bed while his wife washes dishes can easily become a bore. A survey of wives would show that they preferred that the newspaper be read at that time and put aside when the mother gets the child in bed. Then for a nice game of gin rummy or a discussion of the new people who moved in next door. That is so much more gratifying than having him perform the household tasks and then settle with his paper when she is ready for conversation. How can one feel responsible for the house and children when the man who makes the living is also doing the work? I don't think it fair for him to get credit for everything.

Then the matter of disagreements always makes its appearance when one discusses the perfect spouse. Mine doesn't argue. He lets me talk and talk, then either sulks or goes back to reading. At which latter sign I usually throw something at him. He's the type of man who replaces it on the table if it doesn't break, or gets the broom and sweeps up the pieces if it does. Heaven save me. All I ask is that he throw it back. I would like an occasional shoving around. Anyone who has read at all knows that most women are masochists and delight in being dominated and even hurt once in a while if it is done by a craftsman in the right and artistic manner.

What could be more pleasant than a knock-down drag-out fight and the aftermath, the cowed and disheveled wife pleading with her husband to forgive her, which he should then do? That makes more successful marriages than are openly acknowledged by the great middle class. What joy to be dominated and then petted, rather than the saccharine sweetness of constant attention with no temper to flavor the mediocrity of living in the battered old institution that has been the butt of countless jokes.

Perhaps he is too sophisticated for me. When he is out of town and I make a gala evening of it with a friend of his, does he raise hell? No! He smiles benignly and says he hopes I had fun. Why doesn't he get furious and say the things a truck driver would? I don't believe there are many men who want their wives to have such a good time when they are gone, but why is it necessary in our modern world for them to smile and take it? If I were a man and my wife did any running around, I would be very old-fashioned about it and let her know what I expected and

"For the last time—tell her to stop psychoanalysing me!"

wanted. It would surprise many mild-mannered husbands if they knew the extent to which wives aggravate them just to see what it would take to arouse their anger. It even becomes kind of a game, baiting the man over and over, trying to find out just how much he can stand and just when he will exert his power as lord and master.

If someone would only explain to me why the ideal husband is usually one who never argues about bills, never complains about the food and always moderates his voice when discussing something unpleasant, I would gladly refute each argument. It isn't natural, to begin with, for a man to be that way, and though it is similar to a constant temperature in a greenhouse, it isn't stimulating. Men aren't supposed to wash babies and scrub floors when their wives are healthy, and furthermore, they should get in a tearing rage and occasionally slam out of the house for a night with the boys. They should take their privileges for all they are worth and remember that even an ever-loving wife needs a night alone once in a while to catch up on her fingernails and facial and do that extra bit of ironing. They don't seem to realize that it is more of a nuisance than a blessing for them to be at home seven nights.

Now that I've had the chance to analyze my perfect husband, I have a few suggestions to offer as to the ideal husband. He shoudn't be perfect and his temper must be as violent as mine when aroused. He should demand that his meals be on time and the children quiet by a certain hour. He should expect his wife to look nice when he comes in and the house to be straight. He could tell her that he was going out on Wednesday night and keep two-thirds of his winnings to buy drinks for the boys. He should, of course, have a sense of humor and say something at least once a day that would stimulate her to make an equally witty rejoinder. Laughs stem from laughs and not from seriousness or even consideration. Last and most essential, he should always have a reason, either trivial or important, for giving her a pushing around at least twice a month. Among the lower classes it is supposedly every Saturday night and they seem to make a go of their life together and have numerous progeny.

As long as a man is not too considerate and gives his wife reason to think that he might get bored and leave someday, she will exert herself and make him a good mate; otherwise she will wear his patience thin and both will wonder what became of the lovely days of the honeymoon. Most wives are more satisfied and satisfactory when under the influence of a dominant man.

The clearest sign of a need of brutality is strangely enough ignored by the perfect husband. When a woman nags about details and stays in a bad humor, appearing always dissatisfied, she is only asking for a Saturday night brawl, some rough treatment, a few drinks and the right to be feminine. Give her the chance to ask your forgiveness. She'll love you more for it, and the house will be livable and less trouble to the provider.

HELEN LAWRENSON

What Has Become of the Old-Fashioned Man?

MEN ARE always complaining that women boss them around. They are quite right. But does it ever occur to them that women are sick and tired of this role, that they do not *like* bossing men around, that they wish to God they would meet one, just once, who would say to them, "Woman, hold thy tongue!"—and, most important of all, who would be enough of a man to get away with it?

Of course we boss you around! We shall continue to do so just as long as you let us. But, believe me, it is not what we want.

We are not looking for a bully, or a master. We do not yearn for the rough tough guy who will beat our ears off. Nor do we long for the "autocrat of the breakfast table" type, the Life with Father character whose slightest whim is law and whose wife calls him Mister. What we do want is a man whom we can look up to, whom we respect but do not fear; a man who has dignity and authority in the old-fashioned sense, who will be tender, romantic, protective, but will stand for no monkeyshines. In short, we want a man who in his own home is definitely the head of the family.

Whatever became of this old-fashioned man, anyway? Has he vanished, along with side whiskers? Did he go out of style with the mustache cup and napkin ring? Not at all. He is still around, but not enough of him. The proof of this is that whenever one does show up who looks as if he had the stuff to control a woman without violence, the women of the nation, from bobby-soxers to grandmothers, give vent to one vast communal "Ahhh!" as if they had just sighted an oasis after a long trek in the desert, and then proceed to rush at him with an avidity that, if he has any head for business at all, makes him a very rich man in no time. Gentlemen, I give you Ezio Pinza!

When I saw *South Pacific* it was during a matinee, and the

theatre was jammed almost exclusively with women. When the final curtain came down, there was a curious reaction. Not one of the women made a move. They did not, as is customary at matinees, start pulling out their compacts, fiddling with their lipsticks, putting on their hats, or looking for their gloves. They just sat there, limp, stunned, smitten. Me, too. Every time Pinza, himself, stepped forward to take a bow, it was the zenith. Every woman there knew exactly how Danae felt when Zeus showed up in the form of a shower of gold. Or Leda with the swan. Or Europa with the bull. Or your grandmother with your grandfather.

That Pinza *is* attractive to women is not disputable. You judge a poker player by his chips, and Metro-Goldwyn-Mayer is paying him one-half million dollars to make five pictures in three years. (By this time, he is probably well into the first of them, *Mr. Imperium,* with Lana Turner, which, when released, will make millions of wives go right home and boss their husbands worse than ever, out of rage and frustration.) This is a pretty good start for a grey-haired grandfather who admits to fifty-eight years and has never been in a movie before except to sing one operatic aria in a mediocre picture called *Carnegie Hall.*

It is true that he was, prior to his stage debut in *South Pacific,* known to music lovers as the glamour boy of the Metropolitan Opera House. But it is one thing to be a matinee idol in opera or on the concert stage (take one look at his closest competition: Lawrence Tibbett, Lauritz Melchoir, James Melton!) and it is quite another to make feminine hearts go pitty-pat on the stage or in the movies, where he's up against some mighty photogenic laddies.

He's a big, husky, handsome man, with a devastating smile, but it's not his looks that are the secret of his fabulous popularity. Nor is it his deep and thrilling bass voice, or his Italian accent, or the glamour of his roles. It is simply that women—all women—see him and sense that this is what they've been looking for. Here is a real, honest-to-goodness man. They would never be able to make a fool out of him, or humiliate him in public, or bawl him out, or run his life for him—and they love him for it.

He strikes women as being male in the same old-fashioned way that Clark Gable does, or Spencer Tracy, or Earl Mountbatten (the former Lord Louis Mountbatten), or Bernard M. Baruch, or Prime Minister Nehru of India. Each of these men, in his own way, is almost irresistibly attractive to women. Yet each is also—and this is an important point—a man's man. Women have occasionally reached the swooning stage over someone like Rudolph Valentino, but their husbands have regarded it as one more silly female trait, like a passion for whipped cream on things. The average American man's reaction to a woman's penchant for Charles Boyer or Tyrone Power or Frank Sinatra is, "So what?" But you can't laugh off Gable or Tracy. The very quality of dominant maleness that makes them so alluring to women also makes them outstanding as men among men.

The fact that Pinza, Gable, Tracy, Mountbatten, Baruch and Nehru are all close to or over the age of 50, and that one of them, Baruch, is eighty, may lead some men to the illusion that all they have to do to win a woman's respect is to manage to live long enough. This theory is further bolstered by the amatory victories of elderly beaux like Stokowski, Vice-President Barkley, Ickes, or even Mayor O'Dwyer, all of whom got themselves happily married to pretty women half their ages or less.

I hate to deprive you of the hope that success with women will automatically be yours along about the time you start losing your teeth, but the fact is that just growing old is not enough. For one thing, if you are already married to a woman who has been accustomed to ruling the roost, she is not going to stop merely out of respect for your white hair. The idea of getting rid of her and starting in from scratch with a new young one, although it may have its attractive aspect, is not entirely practical. Besides, it wouldn't necessarily work. Unless you have the inner assurance that has made you the head of your household right from the beginning, the chances are you are not going to develop it out of a blue sky after all those years in the treadmill.

Some psychologists have advanced the theory that the reason girls go for older men is because they are looking for a father. This is a lot of mishmash. Women don't want their husbands to be father-substitutes, any more than they want them to be son-substitutes. They simply want them to be husbands.

Every woman, when she marries, is really looking for the Rock of Gibraltar. What she frequently gets is a stalwart reed. He trembles before her wrath and is swayed by her commands. He may make a few balky attempts at asserting himself from time to time, but for the most part he settles down in a state of perpetual submission. Open that window! Fix that table leaf! Go to the store! You're not leaving this house tonight! Put it down, take it up, lift that load, tote that bale. Get a little drunk and you land in the doghouse.

Your powers of resistance atrophy and your attempts to kick over the traces meet with a stern, "Well, you certainly made a fool of yourself last night!" Your wife regulates your social life. She decides where you're going, what movie you'll see, where you'll go on your vacation. On a party, she'll do the talking. If you start to put in your two cents' worth, she will interrupt you and correct you. "No, dear, that's not the way it was," she'll say, and then *she'll* tell the story and you might as well go off and suck your thumb in a corner. If you wistfully decide to numb your pain with a few drinks, you will soon hear the Voice of Authority telling your host, "No, don't give him any more. He's had enough."

In your home, it's the same. She decides where the furniture goes, what color to paint the walls. You are fortunate if you can wangle one little room for your own and even then she'll probably arrange it for you and call it your "den," as if you were a tamed lion cub. Where the children are concerned, she is the undisputed authority and everybody knows it.

Now this dreary portrait that I have painted would be unthinkable with a man like Pinza or Gable or, again, your grandfather. Why can't you be like them? You don't have to be able to sing or act. You don't have to be as handsome as Nehru or Mountbatten, or as dashing as Gable, or as wise as Baruch. After all, the chances are that your wife married you because she fell in love with you—not just for a meal ticket or your bonny blue eyes. How did you happen to get off on the wrong foot, so that she became the head of the house and not you? Why is it that so many American husbands are, to put it bluntly, henpecked?

The main answer is, as I told you in the beginning, because you put up with it. Oh, you commiserate with each other over your drinks, or you beef in print about it, but I don't notice you *doing* anything about it. Most men don't seem to know anything to do. Occasionally, in desperation, a man will get so fed up with being told off by his wife that he will take a poke at her. Most men, however, simply resort to yelling at their wives, while others, lacking that much courage, go around muttering that one fine day they'll up and walk out on her and *then* won't she be sorry!

None of this ever works. On the stage or in the movies, women may enjoy seeing a Marlon Brando—the animal-type man, or a Humphrey Bogart—whambam! a black eye; but they seldom think they'd like that sort of thing going on around the house all the time. They don't want to be cowed and slapped into submission. They want a man who quite naturally assumes control of the situation, makes the decisions, and lives up to the responsibility of being a male.

I imagine that is what men would like, too, in their wildest daydreams. Why is it that they don't always achieve it? Well, there is one theory bruited around that they get so used to being bossed by their mothers, when they're boys, that they fall into the same role when they grow up and get married. But this explanation doesn't hold water. So were the old-fashioned men bossed by their mothers, even more so than today. So are European and Asiatic men, but when they get married, they become the heads of their families.

To get back to Pinza—a pleasant task, indeed!—he thinks the explanation is because we're still a young, new country and our men have been so busy rushing around that they haven't yet got used to women and how to handle them. He even thinks it may be in part a hang-over from the early pioneer days when the men opened up new territories and women were so scarce that the few on the scene assumed an out-of-proportion importance. I don't quite agree with Pinza, but that's his theory.

"Women," he says, "are given too much freedom here, and they don't really like it. They say they do, but pouf! it is nature for them to want a man to have the authority. I think woman is the greatest thing God ever created. But they need a man to—well, to be a man! They are not happy when they can boss the man around, because it is unnatural!"

Pinza, himself, is married to a girl twenty-five years his junior. They have been married ten years, and, according to all accounts, they are extremely happy. There is absolutely no question about who is the head of the family. Twice, in discussing women and marriage, Pinza used phrases that were revealing. Once he said, "I have forbidden my wife to call me darling or sweetheart in public, because when terms like that are used too much they become meaningless"; and again, in speaking of how she has adapted herself to his ways despite their different backgrounds (she was born in Watertown, New York, the daughter of a dentist; he was the seventh child of a poor carpenter in Rome, Italy), he said: "I have trained her . . ." When I remarked to him that it would scarcely occur to an American husband to use either "forbidden" or "trained," he seemed surprised and nonplussed. "But why?" he asked, innocently. He appeared to think those were the normal words to use when talking of a wife. Naturally!

I don't suppose that any woman has ever been rude to Bernard Baruch in his entire adult life. On the other hand, I cannot imagine him ever being rude to a woman. His method is to handle them with tact, constant courtesy and firmness. When he says, "No," there is no doubt in anyone's mind that he means it. It would never occur to a woman to disobey him or contradict him. This is not just because of his age, his money, or his reputation as a sage.

Women cannot resist Baruch, and for fifty years he has been a magnet for the prettiest, the wittiest, and the gayest, here and abroad. He treats them as if they were uterly delightful little creatures—smart, too, sometimes—whose chief function is to make life more pleasant for men. He believes that they must be protected, guided, pampered, and told what to do. That, according to him, is the proper feminine role; and even self-made, self-reliant women, inwardly as feminine as a meat ax, fall meekly into line when they meet Baruch, developing a docility of which no one had ever believed them capable.

Take Clark Gable. No woman tries to mold *him* to her specifications. On the contrary, they all turn themselves inside out trying to be the kind of a girl they think *he* would like. When Carole Lombard fell in love with him, she gave up parties, night clubs, hi-de-ho and whoop-de-doodle. Almost overnight, she became an Outdoor Girl, a rugged hunting and fishing type who thought nothing of getting up before dawn to spend hours sitting motionless in a damp, cold wild-turkey blind with her own true love.

There is nothing more tractable than a woman, if men only knew it. But too many men don't seem to recognize this. They are afraid of women: afraid of their anger, afraid of their tears, afraid, most of all, of their contempt. They dislike scenes and will do almost anything to maintain peace, not realizing that by seeking to achieve it with this method, they lose it. Because the woman whose man lets her dominate him is driven so frantic with frustration that the more he gives in to her, the more irritated she becomes.

The logical question that occurs is, if women do not really enjoy bossing men, why do they try to do so? The only answer I can think of is that the famed "contrariness" of females is a fact and not a fiction. They will try to impose on a man and at the same time they hope that he won't let them. Perhaps they like the excitement of testing how far they dare go, always happily expecting to be told off.

Then, too, in any relationship between the sexes, *someone* has to be boss, otherwise it becomes an "After you, my dear Alphonse" sort of thing. If the man doesn't assume the role at the outset, the woman does. If you have any trepidation about your ability to master the situation, the only thing to do is to disguise it. Take a deep breath, make your voice firm, and plunge right in. Say to her, "Look! You're my girl and I love you, but you're going to do as I say." You'll be surprised how happy she'll be. But you have to stick to it. Assurance is the thing women love in a man. Not conceit, but calm authority.

Whatever the psychological reasons for it, somewhere along the line the roles got switched and the old-fashioned man who was head of the family went underground. We want him back.

PART FOUR: *Women of the World*

"Then I asked him where he got that illiterate stuff, my mother and father were married."

JOHN DOS PASSOS

Art and Isadora

In san francisco in eighteen seventy-eight Mrs. Isadora O'Gorman Duncan, a high-spirited lady with a taste for the piano, set about divorcing her husband, Mr. Duncan, whose behavior we are led to believe had been grossly indelicate; the whole thing made her so nervous that she declared to her children that she couldn't keep anything on her stomach but a little champagne and oysters: in the midle of the bitterness and recriminations of the family row,

into a world of boardinghouses kept by ruined southern belles and the defalcations of railroad magnates and swinging doors and whiskery men nibbling cloves to hide the whiskey on their breaths and polished brass spittoons and basques and bustles and long ruffled trains,

(in which lecturehall and concertroom, Culture and Art, and readings from Shakespeare and Browning were, under the domination of ladies of culture, the new centers of aspiring life,)

she bore a daughter whom she named after herself, Isadora.

The break with Mr. Duncan and the discovery of his duplicity disgusted Mrs. Duncan. She became a bigoted feminist and atheist, passionately followed Bob Ingersoll's lectures and writings; for God read *Nature;* for duty, beauty, *and only man is vile.*

Poor Mrs. Duncan had a hard struggle to raise her children in the love of beauty and the hatred of corsets and conventions and manmade laws. She gave pianolessons, she did embroidery and knitted scarves and mittens. She lived in the exaltation of revolt against ugliness and materialism and the crass vulgarity of men.

The Duncans were always in debt.

The rent was always overdue.

Isadora's earliest memories were of wheedling grocers and butchers and landlords and selling little things her mother had made from door to door, helping hand valises out of back windows when they had to jump their rent in one shabbygenteel boardinghouse after another in the outskirts of Oakland and San Francisco.

The little Duncans and their mother were a clan; it was the Duncans against the world. The Duncans weren't Catholics any more or Presbyterians or Quakers or Baptists; they were Artists.

When the children were quite young they managed to stir up interest among their neighbors by giving theatrical performances in a barn; the older girl Elizabeth gave lessons in society dancing; Isadora had green eyes and reddish hair and a beautiful neck and arms. She couldn't afford lessons in conventional dancing, so she made up dances of her own.

They moved to Chicago. Isadora got a job dancing to *The Washington Post* at the Masonic Temple Roof Garden for fifty a week. She danced at clubs. She went to see Augustin Daly and told him she'd discovered

the Dance

and went on in New York as a fairy in cheesecloth in a production of *Midsummer Night's Dream* with Ada Rehan.

The family followed her to New York. They rented a big room in Carnegie Hall, put mattresses in the corners, hung drapes on the wall and invented the first Greenwich Village studio.

They were never more than one jump ahead of the sheriff, they were always wheedling the tradespeople out of bills, jumping the rent, getting handouts from rich philistines for Art.

Isadora arranged recitals with Ethelbert Nevin

danced to readings of Omar Khayyam for society women at Newport.

When the Hotel Windsor burned they lost all their trunks and the very long bill they owed and sailed for London on a cattle-boat

to escape the materialism of their native America.

In London at the British Museum

they discovered the Greeks;

the Dance was Greek.

Under the smoky chimneypots of London, in the sootcoated squares they copied poses from black figure vases, went to lectures, art-galleries, concerts, plays, sopped up in a winter fifty years of Victorian culture.

Whenever they were put out of their lodgings for non-payment of rent Isadora led them to the best hotel and engaged a suite and sent the waiters scurrying for lobster and champagne and

R. TAYLOR

fruits out-of-season; nothing was too good for Artists, Greeks

and the nineties London liked her for it.

In Kensington and even in Mayfair she danced at parties in private houses,

the Britishers, Prince Edward down, were carried away by her preraphael-beauty

her lusty American innocence

her California accent.

After London, Paris during the great exposition of nineteen hundred. She danced with Loie Fuller. She was still too lusty California innocent to return the advances of Rodin the great master, to take in the extraordinary behavior of Loie Fuller's circle of crack-brained beauties. The Duncans were arts and crafters vegetarians.

Isadora and her mother and her brother Raymond went about Europe in sandals and fillets and Greek tunics

staying at the best hotels, scorning the philistines, leading the Greek life of nature in a flutter of unpaid bills.

Isadora's first solo recital was at a theatre in Budapest. After that she was the American diva,

had a loveaffair with a leading actor;

in Munich the students took the horses out of her carriage, in Berlin everything was flowers and handclapping and champagne suppers,

with the money she'd made on her German tour she took the Duncans all to Greece. They arrived all of atremble on a fishing-boat from Ithaca. They posed in the Parthenon for photographs and danced in the theatre of Dionysus and trained a chorus of urchins to sing *Aeschylus* and built a temple to live in on a hill overlooking the ruins of ancient Athens but there was no water on the hill and their money ran out before the temple was finished

so they had to stay at the Hotel d'Angleterre and run up a bill there.

When Isadora's credit gave out they took their chorus back to Berlin and put on *The Suppliants* in ancient Greek. Meeting Isadora in her peplum marching through the Tiergarten at the head of her chorus marching in order all in Greek tunics

the kaiserin's horse shied, and her highness was thrown.

Isadora was the vogue all over Europe.

She arrived in St. Petersburg in time to see the night funeral of the marchers shot down in front of the Winter Palace in 1905. It hurt her. She was an American like Walt Whitman; the murdering rulers of the world were not her people; the marchers were her people; the artists were not on the side of the machineguns; in St. Petersburg, still under the spell of the eighteenth century ballet of the court of the Sunking, where the Okhrana ruled

her dancing was considered dangerous by the authorities.

Back in Germany, she founded a school with the help of her sister Elizabeth who did the organizing and had a baby by Gordon Craig.

She went back to America in triumph as she'd always planned and harried the home philistines with a tour; her followers were all the time getting pinched for wearing Greek tunics; there was no freedom for Art in America.

She talked back to the newspaper men; her followers cheered her; it was the top of the world; Art meant Isadora. At the funeral of the Prince de Polignac in Paris she met the mythical millionaire (sewingmachine king) who was to be her backer and to finance her school.

She went off with him in his yacht (whatever Isadora did was Art)

to dance in the Temple at Paestum

only for him

but it rained and the musicians all got drenched and so they got drunk instead.

Art was the millionaire life. Art was whatever Isadora did. She was carrying his child to the great scandal of the old lady clubwomen and spinster art lovers when she danced on her second American tour; it was the top on the world;

she took to drinking too much and stepping to the footlights and bawling out the boxholders.

Isadora was at the height of glory and scandal and power and wealth, her school going, her millionaire was about to build her a theatre in Paris, the Duncans were filleted priests, Art was whatever they did,

when the limousine that was taking her children across Paris

stalled on a bridge across the Seine. Forgetting that he'd left the car in gear the chauffeur got out to crank the motor. The car started, knocked down the chauffeur, plunged off the bridge into the river swollen with the late winter flood.

The children and their nurse were drowned.

The rest of her life moved desperately on

in the clatter of scandalized tongues, among the kidding faces of reporters, the threatening of bailiffs, the expostulations of hotelmanagers bringing overdue bills.

Isadora drank too much, she couldn't keep her hands off good-looking young men, she dyed her hair various shades of bright red, she never took the trouble of make up her face properly, was careless about her dress, couldn't bother to keep her figure in shape, never could keep track of her money

but for all the cheesecloth and the lush music and the dance-cranks and the headlines

a great sense of health

filled the hall

when the pearshaped figure with the beautiful great arms tramped forward slowly from the back of the dim stage.

She was afraid of nothing.

In her own city of San Francisco the politicians wouldn't let her dance in the Greek Theatre they'd built under her influence.

Wherever she went she gave offense.

When the war broke out she danced the *Marseillaise,* but it didn't seem quite respectable and she gave offense by refusing to give up Wagner or to show the proper feelings

of satisfaction at the butchery.

On her South American tour she picked up men everywhere,

A Spanish painter, a couple of prizefighters, a stoker on the boat, a Brazilian poet,

brawled in tangohalls, bawled out the Argentines for a lot of niggers, from the footlights, lushly triumphed in Montevideo and Brazil, but if she had money she coudn't help spending it, hand-outs after the theatre suppers, the generous gesture: No all on my bill. The managers gypped her.

When October split the husk off the old world she remembered the coffins lurching through the silent streets, the white faces, the clenched fists that night in St. Petersburg and danced the *Marche Slave* and the *Marseillaise* with new meaning

and waved red cheesecloth under the noses of the Boston old ladies in Symphony Hall;

but when she went to Russia full of hope of a school and work and a new life in freedom, it was too enormous, it was too difficult; cold, vodka, lice, no service in the hotels, new and old still piled pellmell together, seed bed and scrapheap, she hadn't the patience, her life had been too easy.

She picked up a yellowhaired poet

and brought him back

to Europe and the grand hotels.

Yessenin smashed up a whole floor of the Adlon in Berlin in one drunken party, ruined the upholstery at the Continental in Paris. When he went back to Russia he killed himself. It was too enormous, it was too difficult.

When she couldn't raise any more money to pay for the champagne and oysters the crowds eating and drinking in her hotel suites, the board of her pupils and disciples

Isadora went down to the Riviera to write her memoirs to make some money out of the American public that had awakened after the war to a taste for scandal and art. In America they had money to spend.

She had a studio in Nice, but she could never pay the rent. She'd quarrelled with her millionaire. Her jewels, the famous emerald, the ermine cloak, the words of art presented by the artists had all gone into the pawnshops or been seized by hotelkeepers. All she had was the old blue drapes that had seen her great triumphs, a redleather handbag and an old fur coat that was split down the back.

She couldn't stop drinking or putting her arms round the neck of the nearest young man, if she got any money she threw a party or gave it away.

She tried to drown herself but an English naval officer pulled her out of the moonlit Mediterranean.

One day at a little restaurant at Golfe Juan she picked up a goodlooking young Italian in blue overalls; he kept a garage and drove a little Buggatti racer.

Saying that she might want to buy the car she made him go to her studio to take her out for a ride.

Her friends didn't want her to go, said he was nothing but a wop mechanic; she insisted, she'd had a few drinks; there was nothing left she cared for in the world but a few drinks and a goodlooking young man.

She got into the Buggatti racer beside him and

she threw her heavily fringed scarf round her neck with a big sweep she had and

turned back and said

with the strong California accent her French never lost:

Adieu mes amis je vais à la gloire.

The mechanic put his car in gear and started.

The heavy trailing scarf caught in a wheel, wound tight. Her head was wrenched against the side of the car. The car stopped instantly, her neck was broken, her nose crushed, Isadora was dead.

The Real Ingrid Bergman Story

ONLY a great lady could have thrown her public career away as Ingrid Bergman has done. Think of the dozens of lesser figures who have, by the alchemy of press-agentry, transmuted the dross of sordid affairs into the gilt of romance! Not so with Ingrid Bergman, who overnight turned her shining image of triumph into a sorry, trumpeted tragedy. I wish to write about it: to say here in print how deeply we in Hollywood feel about it.

This girl who, two years ago, could think of nothing save Joan of Arc; who enjoyed the respect and admiration of the world; who could spend weeks with the seminarians of Catholic history; who was constantly in the company of the little priest from Domrémy—Joan's own village; who wanted Monsignor on the set every day she worked on *Joan of Arc;* who was always chosen by the men who run the films to represent whatever causes were fine and true; now this girl had thrown it all away! It has been for me an inexplicable gesture. If there is any explanation of her conduct, any palliation, I should like to set it down here.

Joan of Arc was a killer-film. Victor Fleming, the director, died of exhaustion after it. Joe Valentine, the cameraman, followed him into death. Casey Roberts, who turned himself into a one-man medieval guild to make those wondrous Gothic props, followed them . . . and now Bergman, in a sense, has followed them out of our paths.

I last saw Ingrid Bergman at Victor Fleming's funeral. I stood with the other pallbearers, the veteran stars like Clark Gable and Spencer Tracy, the old-line directors like King Vidor and Clarence Brown. Walking down the aisle of the church after the pall, grieving because no more would I see the great Fleming's lithe figure (his fierce eyes beneath the high forehead and the crest of silver hair) standing behind a camera to control the destiny of a movie set,

I looked into Ingrid Bergman's eyes and thought of Fleming's judgment of her:

"Brother, she is bulletproof. There never has been another figure like her before a camera; you can shoot her any angle, any position. It doesn't make any difference . . . you don't have to protect her. You can bother about the other actors on the set. But Ingrid's like a Notre Dame quarterback. An onlooker can't take his eyes off her!"

The setup of the film was this: Miss Bergman had been the toast of New York in a play by Maxwell Anderson, *Joan of Lorraine*. It was a plum desired by every studio in Hollywood. After much negotiation, it was settled that Walter Wanger, producer, Victor Fleming, director, and Ingrid Bergman, star, would form a triumvirate and make the film. Maxwell Anderson would come out to do the script, and Andrew Solt, a competent scenarist, would ride herd on the continuity. (My part was a modest one: I was supposed to set the battle scenes.) However, as soon as the triumvirate met, it was plain that Miss Bergman was not going to do Anderson's play. She was going to do Ingrid Bergman's play, not yet written, about Joan of Arc.

This was not only a whacking surprise, but a very great pity. Do not think that Miss Bergman was the ordinary run-of-the-mill piece of temperament who wanted to have her own way! On the contrary, she approached the work with the deepest humility, the utmost desire to do the right thing. Soon, there came as many days of debate as there were in Joan's own days. It was like being back in the Middle Ages.

After the actual shooting of the film began, I would sometimes keep long night hours with Victor Fleming. Then, sometimes, I would walk from the set to Ingrid Bergman's dressing rooms, which comprised a bungalow done in cheerful Swedish Modern. There was a little kitchen bar at the end of the salon. Ingrid Bergman, after ridding herself of all that heavy Gothic armor, would appear in a dirndl and kerchief, exhausted. She liked a small drink or two, not too dark. She liked bourbon whiskey, and so did I. Sometimes we would just sit, slowly enjoying the leisure of a cool drink. She was always eager and curious about everything and everyone. She would say:

"Tell me now, Laurence, now that work is over, what will you do?"

I would say that I was going home to my family in Pacific Palisades.

"And what will you do when you get home?"

I would say that, inasmuch as I was tired, I would go back to the children's rooms and see them for a little while, and then I would have a cocktail with my wife. Afterwards when the "studio stomach" subsided, my wife would bring our supper from the electric warmer.

"Then you don't have dinner with your children?"

"Not when working during the shooting of a picture." (It was a question of timing. Children must eat by six-thirty. Often I could not dine so soon after work.)

She would shake her head. "I couldn't do that," Ingrid would say. "I am Swedish. First and last, I am a mother and a wife."

I would find myself studying her as she talked. (As Fleming said, she was bulletproof.) She might never grow to be the great actress Greta Garbo was, but she was a continuously interesting figure. With printed skirt, crepe blouse, kerchief around the mannish Gothic haircut, she was as compelling as sixty minutes before, when armed cap-à-pie in silver harness, white standard in her hand, lights playing about her lustrous face.

I used to wonder why I was so continuously fascinated by her. Any man likes to look long at beautiful women. Any writer in films has worked with dozens of them. Perhaps I remember most vividly the salient personalities of Jean Harlow and Carole Lombard, with Lombard possessed by a flashing wit, a vivid dynamism which this tall, big-boned Scandinavian sitting with her pale bourbon-and-soda did not have. Yet, somehow, she was more compelling.

"No," she would say, "I cannot go home like you do. I would feel lost if I did not go home and preside at table with my husband and child. I must interest myself in everything. I want to know about my child's school, about my husband's medical practice. I want to go into the kitchen and cook."

"But you're cutting it too fine," I told her. "Here you are, a producer and a star, and trying to be a writer into the bargain." I would say she should stop all of it; should arrive on the set and take direction from Fleming, and then get a studio limousine to take her home, instead of driving through the madness of Beverly Hills.

"But I couldn't do it," was always her reply. "I must have my hands in everything. Take a part in everything. I can't be any other way."

I recall a day I had spent with Ingrid and her family at Sam Wood's beach place shortly after I got out of the Pentagon Building. I was writing a script with the late, great, old-line director, Sam Wood (movies killed him, too), and Ingrid Bergman would come

"You whistle the National Anthem and when he stands up I'll hand him his hat!"

down for swimming and sun-bathing. Like Victor Fleming as a director, Wood regarded her as bulletproof. He had made *For Whom the Bell Tolls* with her, and he had also directed her in an enchanting comedy, *Saratoga Trunk.*

One day at the beach, she started swimming straight out in the Catalina Channel. The surf is not too safe off Malibu, and she was swimming farther than ordinary caution would dictate. I asked Sam if he thought we should signal the lifeguard station.

"Ingrid wouldn't like it," Sam said. "Someday," he continued, "Ingrid's going to start swimming and never come back."

"Why?"

"I don't know," Sam Wood said. "But that's Ingrid." He thought a while and then spoke wistfully. "If only I could find another story like *Saratoga Trunk* . . . Remember those opening sequences? All that fire, and yet never for a moment any suggestion of bitchery. Ingrid's the greatest lady I ever saw on the screen. No bitchery at all. You could do scenes with her that, in the hands of someone else, would be vulgar; would be execrable taste."

I said she had been so successful in her first picture (*Intermezzo*) that I doubted she'd ever have to learn to be a great actress. "I'll take her for my next picture," was Wood's answer. "That is, if she decides to swim back this time."

Joan of Arc cost around five million dollars. One night when, dog-weary, Fleming lay on his back on the carpet of his office, he estimated that, for him to have done *Gone With the Wind* at this time, he would have spent eighteen million dollars. Ingrid Bergman, a co-producer and financially in the *Joan* film with Walter Wanger and the director, began to grow acutely cost-conscious. In other words, she had to think of costs in addition to her work in back-breaking costumes, her looks, her lines, her various differences with a man of such integrity as Maxwell Anderson who, out of loyalty to his friend Fleming, wrote and rewrote to adapt his play. The strain must have been great. One night we ran the English film, *Great Expectations.*

Near the opening, there is a magnificent crane shot which carries a small boy up the winding stair and down the hall of an English mansion. It sets a mood, never-to-be-forgotten as the film proceeds. I spoke of Fleming's great take on the carpet of Rhett Butler's stairway, which won Hattie McDaniel an Academy Award.

"But the cost," Ingrid said. "Think of the cost!"

I said an actress should not think of cost; most actresses, when they "co-produce" films, come in and hear the bad news about costs before the picture starts, then leave it to the boys. There must have been some deep feeling about this in Ingrid Bergman's heart. She had not been born with a silver spoon. She told me that, when she tried out for a scholarship in the Royal Dramatic Theatre School in Sweden (Garbo had gone through that mill, too), she blew her lines when her turn came; had to be prompted, and ended her recitation in raging, thwarted tears. Then she ran home to her uncle's shop, only to learn that she had won the prize.

I feel now that Ingrid has forgotten her lines, and has run away in tears. But where is the prize? I read that she wants none, expects none; that she will never compete again. Sam Wood died too soon to learn that Ingrid Bergman had swum out into the blue, not to return, just as he had said she would. It is a hard thing to believe. It is a still harder thing to accept. Her home, her family, those are things not within the province of this piece. But her career, which belonged to all of us, was hardly at its beginning.

There has been no furtive, trumped-up explanation from her. Only a very great lady, as Sam Wood called her, could have thrown it all away in such a fashion. I will never know why. I can only hope that someday she will return to the films; that I will see her before a camera, blonde head on wide shoulders, blue eyes that fire a phrase, high cheekbones that pin-point the light, she who was bulletproof . . . from any angle.

August, 1950

ELLIOT PAUL

Gertrude, Alas, Alas

Two cockneys in a railway car got into an argument as to whether a very respectable-looking man with a clerical collar, sitting at the other end of the car, was or was not the Archbishop of York. They made a bet and one Cockney walked the length of the car, apologized, told the solid-looking citizen about the bet, and waited hopefully for an answer.

The gentleman in question looked severely at the Cockney over the rim of his pince-nez and said: "B—r off, will you!"

The Cockney went back and said to his friend, who had bet that the stranger was *not* the Archbishop of York: "He won't tell us."

I am reminded of that story whenever it is suggested to me that Gertrude Stein has been perpetrating a hoax for the last forty years. A few feature writers have asked her that question point-blank. She has always avoided answering the question.

Her closest companion for more than two decades has been Alice B. Toklas, whom Gertrude has made almost as famous as herself. Gertrude dominates Alice, makes all the decisions, takes all the praise or blame. Throughout their career, Alice has graciously accepted the role of disciple, with no expressed wishes of her own, never questioning Gertrude's judgment or whims. She has never ventured to give advice, or even traffic directions when Gertrude was driving their Model T Ford. When others are present, Alice frequently addresses Gertrude as "Lovey," and if this is not done for effect, it is practically the only thing not done for effect by either of them lo, these many years. They believe in doing things for effect, and that the effect should be mildly provocative and confusing. That is the way Gertrude likes to live.

Having a comfortable income from sources that require no care, Gertrude could have lived almost any way she wanted to. She excelled in philosophy as a favorite student of William James at

Radcliffe, and was one of the most promising students of brain surgery and related sciences at Johns Hopkins. She proved, while still in school, that she could write clearly, convincingly and well and could find a ready market for her works. Any of the careers suggested by those beginnings seemed too easy to Gertrude. She knew there were plenty of conscientious writers and gifted scientists. What she did not see, as a young woman in looking around her, was a single human who seemed to be doing what he or she pleased, without dictation or hindrance. She was not willing to admit that a woman with moderate means, good health and fair intelligence could not live for herself and amuse herself without an illusion that she was essential to society.

"Nothing is meaningless if one likes to do it," she once said.

Wars, depressions, artistic and literary storms, and revolutions come and go. She remains the same—solitary (except for Alice who has practically submerged herself in Gertrude's personality), mysterious, forceful and conspicuous. I doubt if Garbo, Shaw or Einstein has had more publicity. Gertrude frankly loves it. But she has never gone out of her way to get it. Publicists have always come to her. And while they came to scoff, they remained to admire and went away with a haunting feeling that they had been in contact with one of America's most remarkable women of all time. They never knew any more about her writing or her intentions than when they arrived. But she is always so charming, so witty, so kindly and tolerant, so versatile, so unexpectedly diverse in her interests, that it takes a dull person, indeed, not to find some common ground with Miss Stein.

In saying that she was "solitary," I don't mean to suggest that Gertrude has not had plenty of company. Probably she entertained more Americans, from all walks of life, in her Rue de Fleurus studio, between World Wars I and II, than any other American celebrity. And I keep referring to her as "American" in spite of the fact that she has made but one short visit to America in the last forty years. Characteristically, Gertrude remained where she was and let America come to her. She speaks French with an American inflection and a slight flavor of the California she abandoned as a girl. She looks, as Jimmy Cagney remarked, very much like Spencer Tracy and dresses quite as informally.

Not a few of the American "exiles" in the carefree and foolhardy 1920's played the heavy man of letters in the most flamboyant European style. Wherever you found Ludwig Lewisohn, for instance, you would be sure to encounter a flock of writers with various accents, haircuts, and axes to grind. The talk would be of the latest editions or translations of the work of *le maître* (the master) and, in so far as the satellites dared, of the latest editions or translations of their own works, if any. In groups of the advance guard, like the Surrealists, literary talk was taboo. The few timid Americans who were admitted to the circle sat very still and listened to the Gauleiter, who then was André Breton. The talk was of revolution and violence, although Stalin had declined to admit them in a body to the Party. When Gertrude Atherton or chaps like Thornton Wilder disembarked, they saw to it that they were met by reporters of the New York *Herald* and the Chicago *Tribune*, and, if possible, the humbler Paris *Times* and the ultra-British *Daily Mail*. They were listed as "among those present" at the teas and receptions given by the late Mrs. E. Berry Wall, Mrs. Tryphosa Bates-Bachelor and the other prevailing lionesses of the American colony's high society.

Although Gertrude Stein was on speaking terms with almost all the ambitious women who wanted to boost their social standing by giving free handouts to the French, Austrian, Spanish and Russian aristocracy, she never took them seriously and never permitted them to exploit her fame or popularity or amazing conversation. As a matter of fact, Gertrude was on speaking terms with the genuine French old families who seldom, if ever, received Americans. Gertrude endeared herself to these descendants of noblemen who still loved France by her work for the French wounded and later the American wounded in World War I, during which she raised a great deal of money and herself drove an ambulance at the front.

It is almost maddening to think that a writer of her talent should have seen so much so well and should have stubbornly refused to write about it. I have seldom felt sadder than when I read Gertrude's *Wars I Have Seen*. In danger every moment as a famous Jewish fugitive from the Nazis who occupied her province in the east of France, knowing the intimate reactions of the people of the region in which Stendhal found his characters for *The Red and the Black*, Miss Stein, approaching the biblical age, turns out an inconsequential, almost meaningless book which tells us next to nothing. I suppose that is Gertrude's own affair. Anyway, it is consistent with her personal philosophy.

I have never met an intelligent person of either sex, or in any social or economic or artistic bracket, who did not enjoy talking with Gertrude Stein. It is not going too far to class her with Oscar

"We're playing 'Who am I?'—and your wife's got us stumped."

Wilde or Mark Hanna as a conversationalist. She does not bark off wisecracks, like Groucho Marx, or play on words like James Joyce.

Whatever was said to her started an interesting train of associations on which she improvised in a masterful way. She had very few opinions, no zeal about politics, her scientific background was sound and modern but she seldom drew upon that. Sherwood Anderson, Ernest Hemingway, Professor Robert A. Millikan, Josephine Baker, Harold Ickes, Paul Valéry, Doctor Coué, Picasso, Charles Steinmetz, Ponzi, Havelock Ellis, Dean Inge, Frank Harris, Leopold Stokowski, the Sitwells, George Gershwin, Hendrick Van Loon, Oscar Levant, the late Gen. Summerall, Madame Schiaparelli, Helena Rubinstein, Edward G. Robinson—the list is endless—sat at Miss Stein's feet and listened with pleasure. And seldom or never on the special subjects they knew as a trade. Gertrude had no theories about economic or social progress. She pretended not to care for music. The work of other writers held little interest for her, either the classical, the standard or her contemporaries. Her name was constantly being linked with that of James Joyce, as a rampant modernist. Actually, she had never read Joyce, and he told me quite frankly that he hadn't read Gertrude.

Gertrude was at home nearly every afternoon for "tea." It was in those tranquil hours, from four to dinnertime at seven, when the world's intelligentsia flowed through the Rue de Fleurus studio. On the walls were renowned Picassos, the Cézannes, and paintings by Gris, Renoir, Matisse, and Tchelitchev. The guests Gertrude favored were maneuvered by Alice into seats that afforded the best view of Picasso's portrait of Gertrude, and the Cézanne *Woman in the Arm Chair.* These were the No. 1 and No. 2 spots and the initiated knew well that they were to defer for the time being to those who occupied them. A very highranking place was one from which Picasso's *Rose Nude* and *Blue Boy* appeared to best advantage.

Alice, on these occasions, was magnificent. I have never seen such skill as she had in shifting guests for Gertrude's comfort and convenience. Somehow, just before any given person was about to weary Gertrude, Alice had him or her in tow and the seat near the throne was being occupied by someone Alice had chosen and propelled there. The refreshments consisted of tea made and poured by Alice, and the strongest liquor distilled in France and probably anywhere in the world, a special "Marc de Bourgogne," with a handwritten label, about eighty years old. This was a test Gertrude applied to anyone who preferred liquor to tea. The primary sensation, on taking a sip of it, was like swallowing a lighted kerosene lamp. I have seen many accomplished drinkers, and even pronounced alcoholics, gasp, blink, shudder and wipe their eyes. A second later, however, when the rare old flavor asserted itself, the most eloquent looks of appreciation would follow, but no remarks. The sight of Gertrude, placidly sipping hers as if nothing were more natural in the world, discouraged comment.

Somehow, the choice of beverages, the suave, slightly smoky souchong and the ruggedest strong spirits known to man, reveals much about Gertrude's personality. With her, there is no middle ground. The effect was well-calculated, as was everything else in the Stein household, to let Gertrude keep the floor and Alice control the disposition of the guests. I can never remember seeing anyone drunk at one of Gertrude's teas. If a guest arrived with a few too many under his belt, one shot of that phenomenal *Marc* straightened him out. If a guest arrived empty, one drink of Gertrude's potent liquor did not suggest another. Incidentally, Gertrude is a true connoisseur of food and wine. I have known her, while Mathilde, her famous cook, was busy in the kitchen and Alice was dutifully typing such gems as *Nearly All of it to be as a Wife Has a Cow, A Love Story,* to journey by bus all the way across Paris to a certain bakery near La Porte St. Denis to buy exactly the kind of Spanish pastry she wanted for dessert.

It is a legend among Gertrude's friends that Alice has never made an error in typing. I can only testify that in the years I was handling Gertrude's contributions to the magazine, *transition,* every page was letter-perfect. When the first number of *transition* was published, Gertrude complained that the text of her *An Elucidation* had been garbled. We found that a French printer had reversed typewritten pages two and three and none of us had noticed the difference. We were obliged to issue a supplement to *transition* No. 1, containing *An Elucidation* with pages two and three in their proper order. This was commented upon all over England, America, and France, and resulted in a landslide of free publicity. Many of my cynical acquaintances accused me then and still believe that the error was made purposely in order to stir up comment.

Part of Gertrude's tradition was to break off friendships from time to time purely, I think, for variety's sake. Hemingway was banished from Gertrude's presence in 1928 because he had achieved too much financial success by profiting from Gertrude's teachings. Tchelitchev, then a struggling young painter, became *persona non grata,* along with his companion, Allen Tanner, shortly after he had painted a portrait of Alice which accentuated a slight cast in her eye. One young poet who for a time was seen almost daily with Gertrude and Alice was abruptly dismissed when he returned from a two weeks' vacation with a bride of whom Gertrude did not approve. Of course, it always fell to Alice to pronounce these sentences of exile. She would call the disfavored one on the telephone and say sweetly, "I wanted to inquire how you are, because I suppose that Lovey and I will not be seeing you again."

Those who think that only workers should eat have long been indignant about Miss Stein. It is true that nearly half a century of writing has brought her very little money. However, if she had to, Gertrude could earn large sums in several ways. Her art collection, which she bought for a song at the time when others less discerning were ridiculing the Impressionists and Post-Impressionists, is worth well over a million dollars today and is intact. Her lecture tour in the middle thirties in the United States was a financial success. In fact, she was the rage. Her opera, *Four Saints in Three Acts,* to which Virgil Thomson contributed the music, did not do badly. She has lectured and received respectful attention on the subject of English composition and literature at both Oxford and the Sorbonne. I have already said that she reads no fiction except her own, but she has always been an omnivorous reader of autobiographies, biographies, and letters. She insists that only this form of literature is helpful in understanding life, history, and her own "art for art's sake."

Her first book, *Three Lives,* is stark, unadorned, unpretentious realism, and no one should forget that it antedates Dreiser's *American Tragedy.* It appeared, unheralded, when American literary taste was Victorian and "icky" to a degree that now seems nothing short of comical. *Three Lives* won instant praise from the brave and discerning critics who must have long realized that the prevailing brand of corn some day would have to be supplanted by something reflecting modern trends. A fair sample of what readers of books and magazines relished in the period that preceded Miss Stein's little, down-to-earth gem about three servant girls is this quotation, taken from *Barriers Burned Away,* by E. P. Roe.

"Dennis was no faint shadow of a man who had frittered away in numberless flirtations what little heart he originally had. He belonged to the male species, with something of the pristine vigor of the first man, who said of the one woman in the world, 'This is now bone of my bones, and flesh of my flesh;' and one whom he had first seen but a few short months since now seemed to belong to him by the highest and divinest right. But could he ever claim his own?"

Picture the devotees of E. P. Roe suddenly confronted with the following, from Miss Stein's *Tender Buttons.*

"Chicken is a dirty word
Chicken is a dirty third.
Chicken is a dirty bird."

Naturally, the public yelled murder. The bulk of it is still yelling, and Miss Stein is going serenely on. About once every five years, lately, she has put out a book advertised by her publisher as "intelligible." Examples are *The Autobiography of Alice B. Toklas* and *Wars I Have Seen.*

Her best-known story is entitled *Miss Furr and Miss Skeene* and in it she manages to convey a lot about the futile goings-on of a couple of American women abroad by using, repeating, inverting and varying the phrase: "They were gay there."

In her longest book, *The Making of Americans,* which dates back to 1920, she elaborates on a pet idea of hers, namely, that only the middle-class is important. That infuriates the champions of the proletariat, and the aristocrats as well. Also, in this book Miss Stein insists that there are only twenty-six kinds of human faces, and that any face may be definitely classified. When asked to explain a Picasso exhibition of ultra-Cubist paintings she calmly remarked, "There are no feet in nature," as if that settled the whole thing.

Miss Stein is a preposterous woman, the reader will say. She is conceited, overbearing, frivolous, selfish, egotistic, pretentious, exotic, eccentric, unimportant. Her friends will add that she is stimulating, full of common sense, that she has a zest for life and lives it well. Anyone will have to admit that she has held more than her share of the public attention nearly half a century and is still going strong. And whenever a reader is willing to throw away her entire product, he is likely to reconsider when he finds a passage like this, from *Wars I Have Seen.*

"Of course there are a good many times when there is no war just as there are a good many times when there is a war. To be sure when there is a war the years are longer that is to say the days are longer the months are longer are much longer but the weeks are shorter that is what makes a war."

Miss Stein's book for children, entitled *The World Is Round,* contains gems like this.

"Here I am.

When I wish a dish
I wish a dish of ham.
When I wish a little wish
I wish that I was where I am."

In *Geography and Plays* one finds lines like: "Toasted Suzie is my ice cream."

From *Studies in Conversation*:

"A god-mother to her god-mother. A god-father to him, his god-father. A god-father, a god-mother, her god-mother, his god-father, his god-mother, her god-father, her god-mother his god-father. So and so. So and so is his god-father. And so her god-mother, as god-mother. God-mother to whom and when."

She likes oil paintings because "there is no air in them." The motto on her stationery is "A rose is a rose is a rose."

After the fall of Paris, it was a common G.I. experience to encounter Gertrude strolling along a boulevard. The boys could usually recognize her by the queer, dunce-shaped hat she wore. In any event, she was likely to introduce herself, for an American uniform was an open invitation to drop in for a visit at a Gertrude soiree, where Picasso was usually an added attraction. Many a soldier left a Stein session bewildered by an experience that was moving and impressive, yet somehow as confusing as one of Gertrude's more abstruse passages.

Now that World War II is over she is back in Paris, giving sage advice to American veterans. "Boys," she said, recently, "if one of you wants to be a plumber, he doesn't have to be the best plumber. To be a good plumber is enough."

Well. Lots of the boys get plenty of advice that makes less sense than that.

July, 1946

ELAINE GREENE

Tears in the Ladies Room

According to antique tradition, heaven protects the working girl against wicked men—an obsolete defense since we non-antiques can take care of ourselves in that department. True, men still chase ladies around office desks, but modern rules hold that the lady yells, "Yoicks!" first.

Where we do need the help of heaven, hell, Machiavelli, and Margaret Mead is with that horrible harpy of today's working world, the woman executive.

I want it understood at the start that this is not being lisped by one of those "Oooh, you're so big and strong" lassies who doesn't like anything but men. Some of my best friends are women—I can swap recipes, coo over babies, or plan man-eating campaigns with the rest of them. But for one round in the Battle of the Sexes I must step over to the other side.

I offer that there is something sick and dangerous, not to mention occasionally ludicrous, about the woman executive. She is a hypocrite. She is an egotist. She is unprofessional. She plays office the way little girls play house. She forces an intensely unbusinesslike personal relationship on every member of her staff.

As a corollary, I offer that there is something healthy and comfortable, not to mention occasionally exciting, about the male executive. He is at home in his office. He is as objective and honest as a human being can be. He does his job; he expects his staff to do the same. He is friendly but maintains an active disinterest in the personal lives of his employees.

Till a national survey takes over, I submit my own findings, covering the lady behind the desk as she hires, fires, and tends to what goes between. Along the way, we shall give passing pats on the heads of gentlemen executives, when they deserve them.

Except for a blind date, there's nothing as tense as a job interview, where two strangers find themselves in a sudden intimacy—

one examining, the other performing; one with power, the other begging. Given this initial tenseness, watch the woman interviewer worry her prey and feed her hungry ego. This is one of her big scenes—Bette Davis in *Girl Tycoon.* She goes into gear with a once-over I defy any man on the prowl to match in efficiency. That cold, greeting sweep of the eye gets in every speck of dust, off-center seam, last-season look. "Okay, impress me," it says, and then the workout.

I share with my friends and offer to any needy young ladies a self-steeling phrase to be chanted to one's self before stepping into a strange woman's lair. It goes, "Here's a bitch who will try to torture me." I developed it one morning riding down in an elevator with my fist in my quivering mouth. I had just seen a fashion editor, about forty years old, with a beautiful head, slender white hands and bloody nails. She offered no immediate job and the interview was what she had the ironic grace to call a courtesy. Just before dismissing me she spent ten seconds resting the head on the interlaced fingers, staring at me—a mighty long count to be stared at. Then she said, "You know, my dear, that's a really *bad* hat. It has no form. I can't imagine why you wore it."

Another prize pupil of the Marquis de Sade we might call Althea Frothingham Fripp, Mrs., but no wedding ring. A not uncommon setup, the self-important three names and the divorce. The Fripp, after keeping me waiting an hour and a quarter, seated me with a downward flick of her beautiful, weary eyes, ignored my Good Morning, spun her chair around, and read a script. I didn't have the pleasure of hearing her low, cultivated voice until she spun back to me, slapped the papers down and barked, "Tell me why you have come to us." Rosalind Russell, *Lady Director.*

I remember hearing a copy chief boast that she wouldn't hire until she has given her applicants three interviews—even when she knows immediately she can use her. "I want to build her up to a pitch. I want her burning to work for me. I want her utter devotion to the job."

Ah, but dear, sweet, kind men. The important thing about the male when he interviews is that he hates it. For him it's a chore, not a triumphant act of power. He doesn't like to be in a position where someone is performing and begging before him, so, like a person, he tries to put a stranger at ease. To make things even nicer for half of us, there's sex, a little of which, we girls find, goes a long way in business. And in two directions.

Direction one is convention: we're ladies and gentlemen and

"Girls, Miss La Verne is one of our most successful graduates!"

there's coat and chair holding and courteous greetings and no fair torturing. Direction two is biology: we share a potential sex relationship. We will do nothing about it since we're business people conducting business, but it is a fine, friendly potential that we choose to set aside, lending a pleasant glow to the proceedings.

I'm not saying I respect *all* the men I've met. More than one pompous ass has indicated that women belong in offices, if at all, to type and file. And I nearly choked in a session with a callow character who learned all about it from *Front Page*. Feet on desk, thumbs in vest, he said out of the side of his mouth, "You work hard here, friend. No cocktail parties. You eat, sleep, and live this job, friend. You get it in your blood. . . ." with visions of Lee Tracy dancing in his fat head.

Now let's look at the average boss. If it's a man, there are an infinite number of ways he might look and dress. But if the top dog is a lady dog, it's pretty predictable she'll look—as much as nature will allow—like the cover of a high-fashion magazine. Stylish to the teeth, or, more appropriate this season, to the upturned outside corners of her eyes.

She'll wear her hat in the office at all times. Maybe striding around the suburbs where she keeps her husband and her Irish setter she lets her locks stream in the wind, but at work she keeps on her head a symbol of her position, a uniform like the hat on a hotel detective or a butcher. At the drop of an orange velvet pillbox, she'll tell a homemaker, "I admire you so. I'm all thumbs in the house, just can't work with my hands." What she means, of course, is, "I'm not a peasant like you. You peel grapes for your lord and master, sis: I hang 'em over my lovely left eye."

There's even a semihat stage in the hierarchy—not a smaller hat, but a more restricted schedule for wearing it. In one office I know, an assistant was made an associate, or, in the language of the *cognoscenti*, she became a *nouveau bitche*. With the change in title, salary, and duties came a hat, stowed away most of the time in the double drawer of her desk. She isn't ready to wear it typing and phoning, but when some trembling fresh-out-of-college kid is in the interviewing room, on goes the headpiece and the executive lumbers out to patronize the girl all over the air-conditioned place.

Somewhere I said egotistical. Let's make that egomaniacal. Consider Miss D. Daisy Potts. Daisy is a merchandise manager in a fancy department store. She's enjoyed the play on her name all her life—"Give me your answer true . . . Daisy won't tell (good ole Daisy). . . ." And she's made it her trade-mark. In her town house, papered with daisy wallpaper, there are always bowls of fresh daisies, bunches of which she pins at her throat or waist every day before she goes to work. Out at Cape Cod she'll frisk about in a black felt skirt dotted with yellow felt daisies, made for her by a manufacturer (no dope, he) and advertised and promoted enthusiastically by her store staff (no dopier, they). Every year on her birthday her assistants knock themselves out getting a gift based on the trade-mark. One bitter buyer suggested that a shot in the head with a Daisy air rifle might be just the thing.

I have also seen staff members knocking themselves out to find just the right gift for the boss man—something for his hobby or his summer shack—but there it's an honest desire to please a guy they like instead of an economic need to show an understanding of a spectacular personality.

To get along with an executive, either sex, one has to do good work. (I can't subscribe to the popular male notion that a woman executive doesn't know what the score is. She's damned bright, sometimes brighter than her male counterpart because she has to contend with a kind of race prejudice.) In addition, one has to be pleasant. So far, two reasonable requirements. But with an executive, female sex, one must also offer knightly loyalty, everlasting gratitude, and admiration bordering on worship. The lady in the hat does not assume that her employees are working because (1) they need to, (2) like to, (3) or have a talent to express.

She believes that they are there because of the deep personal feeling they have for her. As witness, recent events in the woman's department of a city newspaper. The editor, never very chummy with her second-in-command, moved on to another job. When she announced her resignation to the department, several of the girls wept. The second-in-command, carefully absent from the services, had her secretary prepare a list of the weepers. Naturally they'd go when she took over.

The woman's business world, just like the man's business world, goes round with knifing and climbing over fresh corpses. While men admit it and get a kick out of the race, women cover their competition over with goo. The devotion they affect is codified because if happy in no other way, the top lady is rank happy. Her relations with her staff are dependent on their positions.

With her stenographers and clerks she plays the Rich Aunt with the poor country relation. She corrects grammar and diction, gives advice on grooming and clothing; in short, adopts the proletarian and tries to civilize her.

Up the ladder, with the executive assistant, or career girl, the lady in the hat is a Big Sister. She still patronizes, but is all friendliness to show that she really feels like an equal. "I was just like you once, darling," and she elaborates. Many a long afternoon business girls sit nodding, smiling, gasping, and clucking at the tale of the lady's struggle to success, and they are required to make similar sounds and faces on hearing how wonderful is the current and how horrible was the past husband.

Along with listening goes talking, bestowing confidences that show one's abiding faith in and loyalty to the dame, which professional necessity struck home with me once. I had failed to hide the fact that I was having romantic difficulties (look like a sick calf, that is). At the end of the day, my boss motioned aside the scripts I'd brought her and, with glittering eye, called me a "Poor Lamb." Then she added sweetly, "Tell me all about it." The choice was simple—talk or get off the staff. I knew, too, that sometime when she owed a slice of life to another girl and had nothing else handy she would drag out my story, not bothering to disguise names.

At such a mooning-around period in her life, a friend of mine worked in a man's office. He sent her home one morning saying succinctly, "You look lousy," with that magic male combination of sympathy without curiosity. She got ready to leave, turned on her heel, and flung herself down in a chair, demanding, "What do you think of a cad who . . ." After a happy hour confessing what wouldn't be all over the Men's Grill in two hours, she decided she'd rather stay at work than go home and sulk.

When an executive passes judgment on a staff job, he or she will either like it or not. When the executive is a she, either reaction brings acute discomfort to the staff member. If she likes it, she is doing her protegé a favor. This insidious attitude is usually adopted by the unfortunate protegé so that there is no satisfaction in doing a job well. Instead, the boss demands—and gets—a misty-eyed gratitude and a fresh surge of loyalty. If she doesn't like the work, she has been failed one way, and is failing, as a patron, in another. This mixture of guilt and self-pity is also insidiously felt by all hands. The lady may even lie and say she likes the work, but the top brass doesn't.

There's no doubt that it's deflating being told you did a rotten job, which is precisely what a man will say if that is precisely what you have done. But since it's freely admitted in his office that everyone is human and makes mistakes, even the boss, no intricately balanced dependencies are shaken. If it's a swell job, it's simply and beautifully that.

The promotion scene is similar to the praising one. More gratitude is in order. Just in case I didn't feel deeply enough one time I was given a better berth, my copy chief told me a little story about how there were "women" (no names) who didn't want me to get ahead, about how she had to fight for this for me. "Go to bat," was the way she put it. Then subtly it was suggested that I maintain my loyalty to her, that when I was in the office of number-two woman I report any moves against number one by number two. And unspoken but understood by both of us, if I didn't spy for number one she could and would ruin me with number two in ways I'd never know.

If this sounds complicated, imagine the mess when lady two delicately .hinted that I turn over the goods on number one. At times like this girls sometimes murmur, "It's better than taking in washing," but it gives one pause.

Firing is never done gracefully, except for grudge cases that are rehearsed at length. At ordinary incompetence or staff-cut cannings, the male executive is honestly miserable; the victim has that pleasure. The female executive though, is sometimes not there.

I know an office where mass trembling begins as soon as the top woman takes off for her holiday—because that's when the assistant has to do the ax work for her soft-hearted boss. When a woman executive does her own firing she is in agony, too, but not the truthful masculine kind. It's frenzied lying about people upstairs who ordered the dismissal, frantic promises about help in finding a new job . . . all the loyalty patterns crashing around her. I saw a girl come out of a firing session exhausted. "I had to make *her* stop crying," she said. "I had to keep telling her that I didn't mind, I knew it wasn't her fault. I was *apologizing* to her."

Now we can draw our lace-edged curtain—what better parting shot of the woman executive as seen through the career girls' eyes. Mine own eyes I must turn from the subject while anyone who wants to can figure out the cure for this diseased organism. I have too much else to do, because, goddam it, someday I am going to be a lady in a hat.

RICHARD E. LAUTERBACH

The Legend of Dorothy Parker

THERE is a plump little dark-haired lady now nearing fifty-one who might have been America's greatest woman writer if she had only held her tongue. As it is, her four thin volumes of verse and her three slim collections of short stories are credentials enough for a place close to the pinnacle.

Dorothy Parker, the reluctant wizard of the wonderful wisecrack, has only herself and her friends to blame for her brilliant failure as a literary giant. The things she said and the things they said she said were her undoing. If it had been less easy to talk so well, then perhaps all the rich promise of her quick eye for people, of her tightly tuned ear for language, might have been put on paper, bound into novels, produced as plays. But her skill in fencing with a rapier tongue swept her, too young, to a select literary heaven —whence the bright intellectuals of the gay twenties trumpeted her glib glory.

With such a build-up it was never possible for a fundamentally ease-loving person to cast aside her oral slings and arrows in favor of solid, earthy work. When motivated by love or hunger she penned perfectly cadenced, bitter little verses, or occasional short stories. She became in her heyday the symbol of supersophistication. Describing herself and other female writers of the old "smarty-pants" school, Mrs. Parker observed:

"We were gallant, hardriding and careless of life. We were little black eyes that had gone astray . . . a sort of Ladies' Auxiliary of the Legion of the Damned."

The reputation for the wondrous wisecrack, which changed the course of Dorothy Parker's career before it ever matured, is not entirely her fault. In Hollywood they tell a story about Sam Goldwyn having dinner with Mrs. Parker. During the meal he turned to her and asked, "Do you really say all those things which the papers report that you say?" Dorothy smiled, batted her long black lashes and parried, "Do you?"

In both instances the answer is "No." Any anecdote about a Hollywood producer with a garbled vocabulary and a genius for *non sequitur* is eventually retold about Goldwyn. And for twenty years most quotable *bons mots* emanating from U. S. literary circles were attributed to Dorothy Parker.

The concoction which Alexander Woollcott labeled an odd blend of "Little Nell and Lady Macbeth" was born Dorothy Rothschild on August 22, 1893, at West End, N. J. Her father was Jewish, her mother was Scotch. When Dorothy was very young, her mother died and she was taken to a convent in New York, from which she remembers only that if you spit on a pencil eraser it will erase ink. She was, by her own description, a plain, disagreeable child with stringy hair and a yen to write verse. Her unhappy stay at the convent culminated in her dismissal for writing an essay which the Mother Superior considered horribly unfunny.

Deciding that Dorothy wasn't going to become a teacher, her father did not put her back in school, hoping she would soon marry and therefore not require a complete education. Dorothy beguiled her way into a job writing fashion captions for *Vogue* at the lavish salary of ten dollars a week. On the side she swelled that income by writing and selling light verse and playing the piano for children's dancing class.

While she was struggling along at *Vogue* she married Edwin Parker, a handsome young man from Connecticut whom she had known most of her life. He was a Wall Street broker, serious and correct. They lived together for four or five hilarious days until his division sailed for France. When he came back two years later the Parkers began rollicking down the high, wide and handsome speakeasy road that smashed so many marriages in the twenties.

After the Armistice Mrs. Parker shifted her talents from *Vogue* to *Vanity Fair*. This urbane monthly, under the editorship of Frank Crowninshield, was then publishing the work of such writers as Heywood Broun, Edna St. Vincent Millay, John Dos Passos, Stephen Leacock, Floyd Dell, F. Scott Fitzgerald, Walter Lippmann, James Branch Cabell, Ernest Boyd, John V. A. Weaver, Donald Ogden Stewart and Grantland Rice. Working in almost glorious anonymity, Mrs. Parker earned twenty-five dollars a week, wrote picture captions with an exact count of 14½ which had to have a punch in them, and was friendly with a young pundit named Bob Benchley.

Mrs. Parker soon became the perfect lunching companion for *Vanity Fair* editors. Addicted to plain suits and cute little red hats, she was shy, a good listener and minxy rather than devastating with her modest sense of humor.

In those Prohibition days the bright young people drank their lunches and feasted on dry wit. Mrs. Parker learned fast, both in and out of the office. In a few months she was not only doing all the *Vanity Fair* picture captions but also writing articles under pseudonyms. She became increasingly popular with the staff, especially with Benchley, who was managing editor, and Robert Sherwood, dramatic editor. Mrs. Parker made a practice of calling them "Mr. Benchley" and "Mr. Sherwood," which she still does as a gag.

Mrs. Parker wasn't exactly fired from *Vanity Fair* in 1921. She wrote tartly and with restrained sophistication about most of the New York matters which she examined and reviewed for the magazine. But the storm began to brew almost immediately after she started to grind out sharp play reviews as a pinch hitter for P. G. Wodehouse who was on his summer vacation. She hit too hard. Editor Crowninshield fretted over her biting dissections and lightning really struck when she reviewed Billie Burke's performance in W. Somerset Maugham's *Caesar's Wife,* saying, "Miss Burke, in the role of the young wife, looks charmingly youthful. She is at her best in her more serious moments; in her desire to convey the girlishness of the character, she plays her lighter scenes rather as if she were giving an impersonation of Eva Tanguay." (Miss Tanguay was a vaudeville performer with wild, woolly hair who sang a song called *I Don't Care.*) When Crowninshield received angry letters from Florenz Ziegfeld, David Belasco and Charles Dillingham, he suggested to Benchley that Mrs. Parker be taken off reviews. Benchley next day offered his resignation, hoping that such a decisive action would change the editor's mind. He was quite surprised when Crowninshield shook his hand and said, "Gee, Bob, I'm sorry to see you go." Whereupon Benchley and Parker quit, formed a writing team, opened an "oversized broom closet" office in the Metropolitan Opera building. They called the firm "Utica Drop Forge and Tool Co., Benchley and Parker, Presidents," but never had enough money to pay for having the name lettered on the door. They tried doing a play, but the problem of naming the characters held up that project interminably. Dorothy suggested calling them 1, 2, 3, 4, 5, but found that stage directions like "1 moves upstage while 2 shrinks against backdrop," were more like bad chess than good theatre.

Mrs. Parker, with an office, a typewriter and an appetite, finally starved herself into writing. She did some play reviews for *Ainslee's* and began turning out a little fiction. It took her then, as now, as long as a month to smooth the prose of one very short story. She spent most of her sober hours dreaming up new excuses for not working. A favorite was writing menus on a large mirror of fancy luncheons she'd like to eat. The first two paragraphs of a Parker book review stayed in the typewriter until the paper yellowed and crumpled. The other president of the Utica Drop Forge was no more assiduous. The first line of a Benchley essay beginning, "Now that wages are coming down," stayed in his typewriter so long that wages were going up again before he got around to finishing it. This line became a running gag for Mrs. Parker, who would prefix every remark on the social scene with, "Now that wages are coming down." It invariably made Benchley sick with laughter.

In 1923 they gave up their office and later wangled space at the old humorous weekly, *Life,* edited by Bob Sherwood, who had quit *Vanity Vair* a few weeks before Parker and Benchley.

During these years Mrs. Parker's reputation as a wag began spreading, largely because she had two of New York's brightest circles acting as her personal publicists. One was the Algonquin crowd which included Franklin P. Adams, Alexander Woollcott, Heywood Broun and others. They met at the Algonquin Hotel for lunch, and each day carried away with them the latest and brightest Parkerisms. F.P.A. spread the pointed word in his column and at his regular poker games with Broadway celebrities. Woollcott, who made his reputation out of the conversation of others, delighted in conveying Parker's remarks back to the people they were directed against. This luncheon group, originally self-christened "The S. J. Kaufman Post of the American Legion," grew into what was known as the "Critics' Round Table." The table grew larger, and when curious crowds began to flock to the Algonquin to listen, the regulars went back to eating in speakeasies for privacy.

Another more Bohemian group gathered at the studio of Neysa McMein, a cover artist. Mrs. Parker frequented these alcoholic teas, and finally took an apartment under Neysa's studio, which complicated the Parkers' already confused home life. They were finally divorced in 1928.

Sophisticated magazines were carrying an occasional Dorothy

Parker poem or sketch. In 1924 Elmer Rice suggested they collaborate on dramatizing one of her stories. The play, called *Close Harmony,* ran four weeks. On the fourth Wednesday Mrs. Parker wired Benchley collect: "CLOSE HARMONY DID A COOL NINETY DOLLARS AT THE MATINEE. STOP. ASK THE BOYS IN THE BACK ROOM WHAT THEY WILL HAVE."

The publication of *Enough Rope* in 1926 firmly established Mrs. Parker as a poet. By 1927 the book had gone into eight printings and hit a record high for U.S. poetry sales. It is still selling today.

But most of the smart set were talking about Mrs. Parker's unrhymed witticisms rather than her verses. Woollcott gave the kiss of fame to her bright sayings at a week-end house party which he attended with Mrs. Parker. They were thrown in with a motley group of guests who bathed infrequently. When Woollcott wondered where they came from and where they might be found at other times, Mrs. Parker whispered, "I think that they crawl back into the woodwork."

Inspecting the inadequate washing facilities on that same week end, Woollcott noted an aging toothbrush hanging on the wall above the chipped basin. "What do you suppose our hostess does with that?" Woollcott asked. Mrs. Parker, after a moment's study, answered, "I think she rides it on Hallowe'en."

The upshot of a long series of verbal bull's-eyes was the formation of a group known as "Woollcott's Vigilantes," banded together in self-protection. Anyone who heard a Parker crack about one of the others would report it immediately. It made for some fine fights.

Very early in her career the literary and theatrical crowd liked to be "in the know" by tagging Dorothy Parker's name onto every new crackling gag. Her fame and her stories traveled abroad and came back. Mrs. Parker feels that her act was never as good as her billing. She even indicates that there mightn't have been an act at all if it hadn't been for Benchley. This Benchley stoutly denies. Furthermore, he states categorically that Mrs. Parker, when sober, has never made an unfunny crack. Most of the second-rate ad libs repeated with her by-line are misquotations or not hers at all. Recently columnists, especially Winchell, have been prone to quote Dorothy Parker on topics probably dreamed up by an over-anxious press agent. This is always a source of annoyance to Mrs. Parker.

Even the late Alex Woollcott once wrote a nostalgic story about Mrs. Parker in which he claimed that she had MEN painted on

"He's sort of continental—kisses your hand, orders in French, and gives you the check."

the door of her office just to break the monotony. Actually, Mrs. Parker only talked of doing it.

While hardened to the inferior stories propelled by the magic of her name, Mrs. Parker still winces when something she really authored is credited to another. It was Mrs. Parker who reacted to the news of President Coolidge's death with the cool, "How do they know?" In a magazine piece on Wilson Mizner this tidbit was thrust into his mouth.

Another thing which arouses her ire is a misquotation of:

Men seldom make passes
At girls who wear glasses.

She resents the use of the word "never" instead of "seldom." She often wears glasses herself.

Many of Mrs. Parker's genuine gems are lost to readers because they are too frank to print. Fortunately, her present husband, Alan Campbell, occasionally overhears a good one and repeats it. One example has to do with his wife's comment on a lady politician whose character was being gleefully shredded over martinis. One of the women at the cocktail party said in her defense, "But really, she's awfully kind to her inferiors."

Mrs. Parker quipped, "Where does she find them?"

Until 1925 Mrs. Parker worked on the old *Life* doing articles, stories and reviews. Shortly after the *New Yorker* began publication she moved her acid pen over there, and portioned out her weekly vitriol against the puny efforts of the publishing industry in reviews signed "Constant Reader." Once, at the end of a criticism of A. A. Milne's sugar-saturated whimsy, she recorded the fact that "Tonstant Weader fwowed up."

During the next decade Mrs. Parker did a great deal of traveling abroad, and her interest in things international developed apace. At least one of the periodic European junkets had a higher purpose. In 1937 she went to Spain "without any axe to grind" to see what and wherefore of the bitter Civil War. Writing about her experiences afterward, she said: "I didn't bring messages from anybody. I am not a member of any political party. The only group I have ever been affiliated with is that not especially brave little band that hid its nakedness of heart and mind under the out-of-date garment of a sense of humor. I heard someone say, and so I said it, too, that ridicule is the most effective weapon. . . . Well, now I know . . . ridicule may be a shield, but it is not a weapon."

When she came back, firmly convinced of the Loyalist cause,

she worked hard to arouse U. S. sympathy against the Fascists. All her scorn was turned into this channel, against the isolationists, the fence sitters. At a party given by Leon Henderson in Washington she sat on a piano and pleaded for funds for Spanish children. Her words moved her so she cried. When a photographer tried to get a picture of her misery, Henderson threw him out bodily. At that party Mrs. Parker declared soberly, "A humorist in this world is whistling by the loneliest graveyard and whistling the saddest song. There is nothing funny in the world anymore."

The trip to Spain crystallized a social consciousness which Mrs. Parker had been nicely sublimating since she was a child. Occasionally it cropped up in her short stories or over some dramatic incident. She was arrested in 1927 for "sauntering and loitering" near the scene of the Sacco-Vanzetti trial in Boston, although her active participation was no greater than that of hundreds of liberal intellectuals. She had merely marched in a protest parade.

Mrs. Parker recalls the first incident in her life which caused her to think of humanity in social terms. One wintry day she stood at the window of an apartment on West 72nd Street with her aunt who pointed at the poor, tired old men shoveling the streets clean during a snowstorm. The aunt remarked to her young charge that thanks were due to God for sending the snow as it gave the unemployed an opportunity to work. The child Dorothy thought that the men ought to have the *chance* to work even in good weather.

After Spain Mrs. Parker's writing became more serious but there was little market for it. Editors wanted the charming, sophisticated Dorothy Parker, the old brittle stories, the nostalgic mooncalf poems. This reaction only soured her more completely on humor and light verse. Invited by The Congress of American Writers in 1939 to talk at their poetry session, she entitled her discourse, "Sophisticated Verse and *the Hell with It*."

She turned her old ruthlessness on the glittering adjectives used to describe her own work. "Out in Hollywood where the streets are paved with Goldwyn," she remarked, "the word 'sophisticate' means, very simply, 'obscene.' A sophisticated story is a dirty story. Some of that meaning has wafted eastward and got itself mixed up into the present definition. So that a 'sophisticate' means: one who dwells in a tower made of a DuPont substitute for ivory and holds a glass of flat champagne in one hand and an album of dirty post cards in the other."

With these words Dorothy Parker completely turned her back

on New York, her old hangouts and cronies. She and her second husband buckled down to work in Hollywood. Looking back now on her collections of verse and short stories, Mrs. Parker takes pride only in *Soldiers of the Republic*, a singularly effective story about Spain. But she is far better known than many fine authors who have published a hundred times as much. Her publisher estimates that on a per word basis she is probably the world's highest paid writer. Her poems and stories appear repeatedly in collected volumes and anthologies, and stories are constantly adapted for radio and stage.

Her verse has been all things to all critics: "sly and philosophical" to Russel Crouse, "robust" to Laurence Stallings, "biting and terse" to Henry Hazlitt, and to Woollcott a "potent distillation of nectar and wormwood, of ambrosia and deadly nightshade." Her prose to Robert Sherwood was the "superior of Ernest Hemingway added to Ring Lardner added to Aldous Huxley added to Rebecca West."

But at bridge parties and stag dinners Mrs. Parker is not remembered as the author of the O. Henry prize-winning story, *Big Blonde* or as the dialogue writer for *Pride of the Yankees.* She's the wisecrack artist who summed up Channing Pollock's *The House Beautiful* as "the play lousy," who said of Katherine Hepburn's acting, "she runs the gamut of emotions from A. to B." She's the mistress of the deadly verbal thrust who wired a famous actress when that thespian finally had a baby (after making conspicuous entrances during her prolonged pregnancy) "GOOD WORK WE ALL KNEW YOU HAD IT IN YOU." Dorothy Parker's work has been heavily conditioned by four men in her life. When her early marriage with Edwin Parker floated on the rocks, she fell in love with Charles MacArthur, now married to Helen Hayes. Three years of that bred only frustration and a volume of bitter love poems. The next heart throb was John Garrett, a socialite. The third was John McClain, a reporter, about whose Victor Maturish framework Mrs. Parker made the classic crack, "His body has gone to his head." Her second husband, Alan Campbell, is number four. They were married in 1933 when he was playing juvenile leads in summer stock. While Campbell was touring in Denver, Mrs. Parker received an offer for them to go to Hollywood. They borrowed money to buy a second-hand flivver and drove to the coast. They soon drove a Packard and lived in a mansion.

Up until this second marriage Mrs. Parker's life had been a

series of high plateaus between heartbreaks. She usually crawled out of the pits slowly, pulling herself up by a series of bitter verses, stories and parties. Since she achieved comparative stability with Campbell, the plateaus have leveled out, the bitter verses swell up no more, the stories are so much drudgery and the parties are less frequent. With Campbell in the Army some of her "old friends" hope that the literary output will start again.

After nine years of being one of Hollywood's most highly paid scenarists, Mrs. Parker's scorn for the tinseled town has not abated. She believes one of the troubles with the movies is "that everybody in Hollywood thinks he can write, including the producers. I don't believe the films have anything to do with writing except in a cross-word puzzle kind of way. Writing a script is drawing together a lot of ends which can be worked into a moving picture."

Parker and Campbell have collaborated on tough, realistic pictures like *Mary Burns, Fugitive,* gay, screwball items like *Hands Across the Table* and *The Moon's Our Home,* serious Hollywood self-analysis like *A Star Is Born;* ironically their biggest box-office draw was the saccharine *Sweethearts,* a 1938 musical hit with Nelson Eddy and Jeanette MacDonald. The Campbells sweated out their time in the studios like so many days in purgatory to pay for their earthly bills. The only picture that gave Mrs. Parker any satisfaction "aside from the check every week" was the scenario for Lillian Hellman's *The Little Foxes.*

After the filming of this stage hit had started, she received a frantic phone call in the middle of the night from Producer Sam Goldwyn. "I've seen the rushes," he shouted, "and that picture's communistic, it's communism pure and simple I tell you."

"But, Sam," Mrs. Parker remonstrated gently and with inspiration, "the story is set in the early 1900's. There wasn't any communism *then.*"

"Thank God," Goldwyn exclaimed. He hung up, contented.

While her husband, a lieutenant in the Air Forces, shuttled around for training, Mrs. Parker lived in a dowdy two-room apartment in a New York apartment hotel, which she aptly described as "the kind of a hotel where businessmen install their mothers and then run."

In the Army, Campbell, although he has a solid reputation of his own as a writer, finds most soldiers know of his wife. They refer to her as "a newspaperwoman" and occasionally confuse her with Dorothy Thompson. This confusion, incidentally, is shared by hundreds of others—to the delight of neither Dorothy.

Dorothy Parker still has her old charm. Her conversation is animated, intelligent, not unkindly. She is short, about five feet, with dark hair that bommerbangs over her forehead, large dark eyes and a tired look. She has a nervous, shy, gamin manner relieved by a quick, warm smile. Her voice has an unusual timbre, sometimes throaty, sometimes high. No one has ever heard Mrs. Parker laugh at one of her fabulous wisecracks. She just goes on with the conversation as if she had only said, "How do you do?"

She still likes dachshunds and Hemingway, cries very easily, is extremely generous and intensely self-deprecating, avoids publicity, likes to be lazy.

She is still the center of any room full of people. This, she says, has always upset her. "How would *you* like to walk into a party and have a dozen women look up and say with their eyes, 'So you're Dorothy Parker. I dare you to say something nasty.'" The tragedy is that Mrs. Parker loves being with people, dreads the fact that her reputation precedes and follows her. On one occasion at a first night the woman next to her turned and asked, "Are you Dorothy Parker?" In self-defense, Mrs. Parker said, "Yes, do you mind?"

Mrs. Parker would gladly trade her secured niche as a foremost American wit for one thick, solid, earthy, realistic masterpiece. She would gladly forget her own prediction:

"Three be the things I shall have till I die:
Laughter and hope and a sock in the eye."

She would even hurl mud at her own epitaph, EXCUSE MY DUST. But somehow she can no longer kid herself. Her contribution to the 20th Century Culture, unless she should reverse her field, is the elevation of the wisecrack from the speakeasy barroom to the level of Bartlett's *Familiar Quotations.*

October, 1944

PART FIVE: *Sugar and Spice*

ABNER
DEAN

ROBERT C. RUARK

What Hath God Wrought?

THE AMERICAN woman, by her own admission, is the loveliest, smartest (chicwise), most intelligent, healthiest, richest, tallest, best-fed, best-housed, most-worshiped, most-pampered female on the face of the globe. God and *Good Housekeeping* watch over her home. Santa Claus, Cupid and the Easter bunny are solidly in her corner.

According to her mood, she smells like date night in a harem or a breath of British spring. Nothing she owns ever fades, rips or shrinks. Psychiatrists and agony columnists worship at her feet, to tell her how wonderful she is. All our communications—newspapers, magazines, radio, television, moving pictures—fawn on her. Her marriages are made in heaven, and when a spate of heavenly bliss exhausts itself, special couturières deck her in costumes which blend a maidenly regret at (his) failure with a spicy tinge of harlotry, designed to snare a new candidate for ecstasy. Her sons become Presidents, and her daughters are all Senators and spot-welders. She is never, never wrong, even when she *is* wrong.

Yet she is very possibly the unhappiest creature on the face of the globe at this writing, because she is undecided as to just what and where she is in the scheme. She is on the verge of destroying her basic commodity out of sheer envious ego. As she grasps the gavel and strides toward the rostrum, her lacy handkerchief flutters unnoticed to the floor, and this makes her weep. She is on the way to becoming a definite third sex, having progressed too far to retreat, out of vanity, while simultaneously striving to preserve that which she had and is now in process of losing.

The American woman is finally trapped in a snare of her own devising, and you can read the box score of futility every morning on the third and fifth pages of the tabloids.

Let us dissect this frail creature, victim of her own intolerant ambition, but first let us establish that she has reversed her role.

Sometime back a suburban father eavesdropped a game of House, time-honored sport of the tots, in which his young son, a hearty, sturdy boy in the prime of childhood, was playing hard to get.

"Come on, Jimmy," a little girl neighbor said. "I'll be the mama, you be the papa."

"No," said Jimmy. "I want to be the mama."

"But Jimmy," the little girl said, "mamas is girls. Papas is boys. I'm a girl and you're a boy."

"I don't care," Jimmy replied, stoutly. "Mama is the boss in our house, and I want to be the boss or I won't play."

This particular father went away shaking his head, wondering to what state matrimony had come if even the children were cognizant of the change of status. His wonderment was upheld, the same week, when Miss Bette Davis of the films split for the umpteenth time with the man who was then her husband, William Grant Sherry. It was Mr. Sherry, a retired athlete who paints for fun, who did the wailing.

He said he stayed home all day, doing the housework, while Miss Davis toiled at the studios. He made the beds and swept and washed the dishes, he said, and he even pressed Miss Davis' frocks. He had her slippers ready and a fine dinner, prepared with his own hands, smoking on the stove when Miss Davis came home from the jute mills, and what do you know? Sometimes she didn't even kiss him.

"I am a man who needs lots of affection," Mr. Sherry said, stifling a sob.

But he did not pack his clothes in a huff, and buzz off to a hotel, his club, or the apartment of a friend. Miss Davis moved out, leaving the lorn husband to brood in *both* their houses.

This is complete reversal of form. A short time ago, the lady told the judge the sad story about how she washed and worked and slaved over a hot iron all day, how she never got to the movies, how she was starved for affection, and how that uppercase bum either buried his snoot in the papers, went out with the fellows or fell asleep in his easy chair as soon as supper was finished. Judge grants the divorce, and the old man goes to live outside the nest, until a property settlement is made and it is established who gets custody of the cat. But under the current system Junior has to play Mama in the home. It's the only way he gets to wear the pants, and I largely blame the gentleman for letting the broads get out of hand.

I never bought that old axiom about keeping 'em pregnant and barefooted, in order to insure peace in the dovecote, and even came out, once, in favor of letting women eat at the same table with the menfolk. Time has proved me wrong. The initial mistake was made in treating women like people. We did them no favor when we allowed them the rights and privileges of the male, while subjecting them to few of the penalties of masculinity. Crammed with propaganda and still giddy from political emancipation, Madame Housewife has got entirely too big for her panty girdle. I even recall a note from a couple of years back saying that Ronald Reagan and Jane Wyman had been divorced, after eight years of marriage, for "political" differences. Nowhere in a marriage ceremony will you find a clause which says "love, honor, cherish and vote the straight Democratic and/or Republican ticket."

Misplaced kindness to the female over the last few years has given woman time to think, which is tragic, because womankind has not yet learned to separate thought from intuition. She gets mad at Henry Wallace and burns the eggs. She becomes outraged about Harry Truman and recalls the ancient lipstick smear on Father's collar; she broods of the injustice of stag barrooms and cuffs the kids.

So many labor-saving devices to save her toil have been invented that she greets the cocktail hour as fresh as a sailor on leave. She is the authority on the atom; the FEPC; the Communists and the ECA. She knows everything, and ties her opinion to her own emotions, so that a momentary malaise will set her off onto a witch hunt over the plight of the female Mohammedan. The American male is finding it increasingly difficult to be believably tender to a creature who knows everything and is a little loath to admit it, in a high, shrill voice. He finds it difficult to pat the posterior of a mate who turns his parlor into a debating stand, and who is painfully insistent that she can do everything better than he can—or is mad and broody about the fact that she can't but won't admit it.

It is an unfortunate truth that the American woman continues to regard herself as a willowy sprite, subject to swoon, even though she may be six feet tall, with the muscles of a rassler and the appetite of a goat. One of the greatest ills of matrimony today is the lady's erroneous infatuation with herself as a faery queen, destined to dwell forever in a rosy fog of amorous foolishness.

Anyone who has ever lived with a dame knows women to be generally stronger than mules, with limitless endurance and nerves of wrought steel. Her demands on her husband are generally more economic than romantic, but she is so fattened on soap operas, romantic novels and the cosmetic advertisements that she whimpers with dissatisfaction and brands her husband a lousy lover. She inflicts on her serf a stifling possessiveness that would soak the starch from Don Juan, but she still wants to live in gooey bliss, with her stevedorish qualities unrecognized and her vestigial maidenhood enhanced by imposed delusion.

"Love me, you bum!" she shrieks, scourging him to the connubial cot with a whip. "Love me like Gable, or I will cut off your allowance. Love me or I will quit work. Love me or I will resign from Congress. I am smarter than you are and make more dough than you do and my friends are nicer than your friends, you seedy tramp so kiss me sweet or I will not let you go to the ball game Saturday."

Faced with this interpretation of love's young dream, Father sinks deeper and deeper into the hockey scores and the financial page. Finally, in order to escape a sweeping lecture on the failure of our program in China, he seeks the company of something soft, fluffy and brainless, and they ring up another divorce on the cash register of disenchantment. This leaves one more lonely dame with a fistful of Canasta cards, wondering what she did wrong, and why that ungrateful beast had the unmitigated gall to spurn her charms for a moron who was also her physical inferior.

I submit it is getting tougher and tougher to fondle a female who is apt to be busy in the brain about her career, her clubs, her charity chores (fruit of boredom with what we used to call "woman's lot"), her involvements and her ideological commitments. Speaking for me, if I make a pass at something, I am not reaching for the Heart Fund or the Helen Gahagan-for-Senator Committee. I am reaching for a dame, with all the logical fixtures of same, except a runaway intellect that distracts her from the business at hand.

The capsuling of one of the many salient faults of the female came up a few months back in Congress, when the Senate passed something called Amendment 22 to the Constitution, but with a rider. This was a bill which would bestow on the female Equal Rights. The bill passed the Senate when Senator Carl Hayden stuck a footnote to the effect that woman was granted complete equality before the law, but that nothing in the Amendment would

"Go back to him, Bernice....He needs you!"

"impair any rights, benefits or exemptions now or hereafter conferred by law upon persons of the female sex." It was noted that while half of the female lobby was for full passage of the equality bill, the other half was strongly against it. The negative half reflected a denial of responsibility for legal equality, while wishing to retain all the perquisites of the male. The Senate version clad women with complete legal trousers, but immunized her from a kick in the pants, no matter how well-deserved.

Under complete equality, the chances are there would be no rape. Laws against rape were written into the books in order to protect a weaker sex, which was regarded as chattel, and hence unable to protect itself. Men are not generally receptive, today, to alimony if a marriage turns sour. Under Amendment 22, with no rider, an embittered he-spouse might be able to sue and collect. The same would apply to breach-of-promise suits. You get spurned by a legal equal, boys, and you institute proceedings for heart balm. This the girls don't crave.

So many little treasured feminine prerogatives would go by the board. It would be okay to kiss and tell or even brag, and in the presence of the lady, because you are no longer protecting the good name of a fluffy monopolistic minority. You are merely discussing a business dealing with an equal.

The deadly female weapon of à la carte fainting and ready tears would become obsolescent. The silly business of leaping on chairs at the sight of a mouse would be regarded as no longer amusing or cute. Come down off the chandelier on your own time, Toots. You got up there by yourself. Hatpins and umbrellas in the eye would subject the lady fair to a punch in the snoot. No, sir. They don't really want equality. They want all theirs and all ours, and that is why they are a touch addled at the moment.

A subtle poison spreads among women who have flunked the romance course through their own inability to decide who runs the roost. This is especially noticeable among the middle and upper-middle classes, and is most evident at the female get-together—the hen lunch, the Canasta party, the distaff cocktail fight. You may observe there, to the horror of a masculine eavesdropper, the complete, clinical casualness of the rap against man.

His infidelities are retailed to all the eager hens. The worthlessness of men in general is stressed. Vivid details of his inadequacies in the mattress department are recounted with a lack of delicacy that would shock a commercial traveler. Seldom, except among the coarsest of males, would you hear such a caddish concert of carnal particulars as at a hen luncheon, with the girls' tongues loosened by the third martini. This poison spreads even to the happy, well-adjusted wife or sweetheart, who is contaminated merely by the presence of the cobras who are heartsick at their own failure to hold onto their fellow. Miss Clare Boothe Luce, as I recall, pointed this up a generation ago when she did a play called *The Women.*

End product of this wholesale knock is that the gals who came in happy go away disturbed. Most women are gifted with total recall, and an ability to color said recall according to their mood, so that the husband who comes happily home in the expectancy of a decent meal and a little peace suddenly finds himself set upon by a harridan with hooked fingernails, angered anew at an old and minor transgression that may have been a mutual joke for months or years.

In justice to the woman, it must be said that the husband and lover has been something less than 4.0 in recent years, and has provided plenty of room for a dainty beef. But in justice to the man it also must be said that he has been dealing with a brand-new commodity—the "new" woman—recently, and is honestly baffled. If this makes him something less than an ardent lover and a considerate playmate, you can barely blame him. He courted a maid and watched her turn into a complicated machine—jealous of his masculinity and envious of his immunity from the pangs of childbirth and the heat of the cookstove.

Discontent is the seed which has flowered into the present schism between boy and girl. This discontent was watered and tended by the arm-wavers and the experts, the psychiatrists, authors and agitators who discovered a ripe field for exploitation among the females. Our women are in the analysis stage now—no action is good enough to stand on its own as natural and uncontrived. The unnecessary second-guessing of sex, which has turned it from a thing of simple enjoyment into a clinical horror of deep-rooted complexes and over-expectation and self-questioning and clinical apparatus until the process of climbing into the hay with a lady love resembles a tryst less than an experiment in biochemistry. The agony columns themselves, cluttered with half-baked psychiatric advice by unfrocked chiropractors, are enough to wreck the soundest liaison in the world if taken seriously. The scores of women's magazines have made everything from menstruation to eyebrow-plucking such a vast and complicated mystery, in a big-business sense, and have showered so much expert advice on the female, that she now regards herself as a laboratory of mingled emotion and intricate machinery.

The books that are written by lady authors with definable mustaches and flat bustlines are generally contrived to set up a reaction of self-question, to breed dissatisfaction with that old cliché —woman's lot. In nearly all I have read, the man becomes a sort of villain whose prime purpose is to wreak as much misery upon women in general as he can. This in itself is an evidence of the jealousy of unfulfilled females who were unable to muster up enough allure to snag a provider, and have been shouting sour grapes, clothed in pseudoscientific jargon, ever since. Only trouble is that a vast number of normally handsome, intelligent, sexually attractive women take an old maid's (male or female) rationalizations seriously, and begin to brood about the leanness of their lives. It is comparable to the spoken poison the disenchanted exwives drench their friends with at the tea parties and hen lunches.

Woman's lot, alongside man's is about an even shake, but there has always been a repressed desire in most gals—until they find out how good they got it—to kiss their elbow and turn into a boy. This is maybe because the boy takes the active approach to the girls, while the girls—legend says—were supposed to sit demurely by and be asked. This applies no longer, so now we have a picture of an awkward female who wants to take the masculine initiative while maintaining a maidenly coyness in her life with the opposite sex, and it just don't work. There is a deep-seated shyness in man, bred out of generations of folkway, that turns him out of the path of the aggressive woman. Man has one pride—masculinity. When you encroach on that pride you have lost a lover, and gained a son. Women who discover themselves married to sons shortly find they are living on alimony or sharing a room with another girl friend who made the same mistake.

Pants are a terrific symbol in today's strife between the sexes. Science has shown that there is room for only one person in the same pair of pants. No seat is so voluminous, no legs are so wide, that they will contain a man and wife, a swain and his maid. Womankind, reaching avidly for Pappy's britches, is in process of achieving such a sweeping triumph that she can wear her new splendor in lonely grandeur.

If there is one thing an average (average to mean normal as we know normalcy from a standpoint of sex, economics and personality) man cannot stand from a lass is competition on his own terrain. He will go for tantrums and tears, for a burned dinner and a sloppily kept home, for hysteria and hurled crockery, so long as the lady in question refrains from competition on what he feels is a masculine plane. Competition will curdle the sweetest romance, because competition is what the old boy gets all day long in the trade marts, and what he needs least when he takes off his work clothes and arrays himself in lover's lingerie. When a man pursues a maid, when a man marries a woman, he seeks many things, but competition is the last thing he wants to find beneath the frills. This is why so few minglings of top careers last as marriages except in lip-service, or joke, form.

I would say, too, that man possesses a much more basic morality than modern woman, and is more easily shocked by breaches of same. With the "new" equality has come a flaunting, by the females, of old concepts of copybook morality, and the cockbird finds himself shocked to the gizzard by the naked social unmorality of the emancipated dame who figures she can do *anything* better than he can.

The domination of man by woman in our time has been predicated on gentle deception on the part of the girls, and when they quit leading us down the path we are prone to buck and shy and finally to bolt. The new woman, unless she watches her step, is going to find herself emancipated right out of business, because most of her glamorous mystery has been betrayed in recent years, and she has sacrificed femininity for masculine vanity in fields outside her accepted orbit. Nobody ever comes to see a magician when they know all his tricks.

And it may be said, too, that in the recent frantic rush to top the male animal in his own domain, the she-creature has appeared as something of a fool.

NATHANIEL BENCHLEY

Are Husbands Helpless?

THE OTHER day, while studying the morning paper in order to keep from going to work, I ran across the following item, buried among the end-column blurbs about the length of the Amazon River and the climate of Formosa:

> *Yonkers, N. Y., April 8—Albert Prentiss, 38, of 567 Euclid Avenue, was found dead in the kitchen of his home early this morning. Gas was escaping from the stove, and Prentiss was lying under a pile of empty milk bottles, tin cans and garbage. Police decided he had become trapped in the debris while trying to reach the stove. They notified his wife, Mrs. Dolly Prentiss, 34, who had been visiting her sister, Mrs. Millard Nape, in South Orange, N. J.*

The key to the disaster lies in the phrase, ". . . his wife . . . had been visiting . . ." From the accumulation of junk in the kitchen she obviously had been away at least a week. Prentiss was a victim of Moritz' Law of Nonsurvival, which states: the domesticated American male has one chance in three of surviving any prolonged absence of his mate. If not killed outright, he may either lose his mind or move out of the house and into a hotel, where he will eventually come to no good.

Moritz holds that there are more than three hundred things a wife does around the house of which her husband is ignorant, and their importance is evident only when they are not done. Some of them are mere conveniences, others are vital parts of our social structure. For example: how many married men know where their extra soap, tooth paste and razor blades are kept?

Let us suppose that your wife decides to go away for a couple of weeks, say to take a vacation or have a baby. The first night she is away you look up an old school friend and get middling drunk, and bluster about how you will surprise the little lady when she returns by having the house just as she left it.

You don't really miss her until the next morning, when you

awake at 10:30 and realize that she is the one who has been setting the alarm clock. The morning can be written off as far as work is concerned, so you call your office and say that you are at the doctor's and won't be in until after lunch.

Then there is the matter of eating. The first couple of days you make yourself a full breakfast, but inevitably you get down to canned grapefruit juice and a cracker and coffee, if you can find where the coffee is kept. In my house it is kept in the tin marked "Flour." Eventually you run out of provisions, and the day comes when you find nothing but a bunch of radishes in the icebox, and in the food closet a tin of plum pudding left over from last Christmas. This will require your taking a day off to do the marketing. My marketing makes for about as balanced a diet as you would get on a life raft. I once spent an hour in a self-service market and came out with six cans of chili, a bottle of synthetic lime juice, a dozen apples, some ready-fried potatoes, and a slab of smoked herring wrapped in cellophane.

As for making the beds, you have three choices. You can make your own bed as you get into it every night; you can sleep alternately in every bed in the place and make them all every few days, or you can sleep in your unmade bed. If you pretend you are camping out, this last choice isn't so bad. So bad as camping out, that is. If, however, you elect to make the beds, you will find that a supposedly made-up bed with one wrinkle in it is far less comfortable than one that is pleasantly messed up. Changing the sheets won't occur to you until the man comes around for the laundry, and he usually comes when you are out.

There are any number of tradesmen and peddlers who come to a house during the course of a day, and if you are there to answer the door the odds are five to one you can't tell the milkman from a daring sneakthief. I once let a man wash the windows and wax the floors to the tune of $45 because I understood him to say he had been sent for. Actually, he had just asked me if I wanted it done, but he asked it in an awfully authoritative tone.

My brother had a similarly jarring experience when his wife was away last summer. She told him to pay all bills, but that if something that looked like a bill came from the department store to be sure *not* to pay it, since it would be a credit slip for a rug she had returned. Around the twentieth of the month, when the bills toppled off the desk into his lap, he noticed the one from the department store. Remembering that his wife had stressed this one, he mailed a check on the spot, thereby doubling their credit and throwing the store's accounting department into a daze from which it never recovered.

A man finds that little things tend to accumulate, such as cigarettes in the ash trays, socks under the bed, bottle tops in he sink and, naturally, dust. I am told it is good for a house to open the windows now and then to let in some fresh air, but I have found this only increases the amount of dust and offers a haven for swallows. Now, cleaning a house or apartment is a full-time job, and a professional man has no time to be tramping around with a dust rag and vacuum cleaner.

I once cleaned the kitchen, after I got sick of skidding around on bacon grease. My error was to clean the floor first (an arduous hands-and-knees operation) and then go after the sink and cupboards. The slosh from the sink hit the clean floor, as did the odds and ends I knocked off the cabinets, and I finally did the floor three times, the woodwork twice.

It might be argued that people who have maids or cleaning women will not have this worry, but remember that maids and cleaning women usually work under supervision, and if they are given a full day to themselves when the master is at work, they often use the opportunity to catch up on their movies or drinking. A friend of mine whose wife was away hired a cleaning woman to come in by the day, and it was a week before he noticed there were more cigarettes in the ash trays after she left than there had been before she came. He finally learned from the neighbors that she had been conducting a sort of salon in his absence, and when the grocery bill arrived at the end of the month, it turned out that she and her friends had been quite fond of smörgasbord and tartar steak.

The best way of showing the disorganization that stalks through a wifeless house might be to decribe one day in my life last summer, when my helpmate was in the hospital with a newly completed child. It was a Saturday, about a week after she had left, and I woke up at 9:30 with a good long day of nothing staring me in the face. I arose, went through the motions of shaving with a dull razor, then took a shower and tracked water all over the bedroom looking for a clean bath towel. Owing to my not having sent the laundry there were no clean bath towels, so I was forced to use the cleanest and the least clammy one from the used pile. Something bit me while I was fishing through the pile.

When I looked for the morning paper I found there was none, and had to read one two days old. For the first time I saw a bill pinned in the upper left-hand corner of the paper, with some terse remark about please remitting. I read the paper halfheartedly, while breakfasting on an apple and cold soup.

About 11 the bell rang, so slipping into a sweat shirt and pair of crew pants I answered it, and was handed a towering pile of dresses from the cleaners. These I hung on the back of the hall closet door, where my wife found them a week later and discovered they were not hers . . . Hers were never traced.

I spent the next half-hour searching for a cigarette and finally selected the longest butt I could find in the ash trays. I decided to buy some supplies, which I could do only after I found a pair of socks the holes in which were below the shoe line.

After lunch at the corner drugstore (a peanut butter and jelly sandwich and a vanilla malted), I went to the hospital. My wife was listening to the radio, and looking much better than I was.

"Did you bring the stuff I wanted?" she asked.

"What stuff?" I said.

"The list I gave you yesterday—the sewing kit, make-up box, dressing gown and mules."

"I looked for them," I lied, "but I couldn't find them."

"They're right in plain sight," she said, a little testily. "The sewing kit is in the magazine rack, the make-up box is on your dresser, and the dressing gown and mules are in the closet with the suitcases. Just use your eyes and you'll find them." Then she looked at me closely. "Are you making out all right alone?"

"Fine," I said. "First rate."

"You look awful," she said. "You're thin and need a shave and haircut. Have you been eating?"

"Sure, I've been eating. And I shaved this morning. The razor was dull, that was all."

"Well, the razor blades are right there with the tooth paste, in the linen closet. How long have you been wearing those socks?"

"I put them on this morning."

"If you will remember to bring the sewing kit and all your socks I'll mend them for you."

I left the hospital about an hour later and wandered back to the house. I collected the socks and put them in a pile, and then put the towels on top of them to keep them from blowing away during the night. Feeling the need of a drink, I went into the kitchen for some ice, only to find that the icebox was frozen so solid that I couldn't budge the trays. It was then I recalled having been told to defrost the icebox last week. I split one tray with a screw driver trying to get it out, and upset a bottle of milk on the floor. I had the drink warm, and, since there was no soda, straight.

By five o'clock I was feeling a little gregarious. After considerable phoning I found a friend who was free for dinner, and whipped into the bedroom to change. The only clean shirt left had no top button on it, but undaunted, I tore a button off the bottom of the shirt and affixed it to the neck with a bent paper clip. This, naturally, fell off later in the evening. Taking a last pull at the bottle and humming a gay little tune, I set off into the night.

Although some married men may deny this, there is a certain force which draws them home if they know their wives are there. The wives may not object to their staying out late; yet something tells them when they ought to be getting on home, even if it is only an aversion to being seen coming in with the daylight. If, however, their wives are *not* there, there is an actual force which keeps them *away* from home, because the house seems more empty and there is a strong aversion to coming back to it while it is dark.

When I arrived home this Sunday morning, little children were playing in the streets, and they compared me and Ray Milland. I hurled a milk bottle at the nearest and, missing the tot, it went through the neighboring doctor's car window. I went to the kitchen for a sandwich, and tracked milk from there into the bedroom.

I didn't go to the hospital that day which meant that, among other things, my socks did not get mended. I was terse with the doctor when he called about his car window, but he looked around the house, and the next day two men from the Health Department arrived with orders to fumigate the premises. I started to argue but finally realized it was as good a way as any to get the place cleaned. I moved to a hotel, and when my wife came home at the end of the week and asked what the strange smell was, I said I had heard houses should be sterilized before new babies came into them. I said it so fast I think she believed me.

Heavenly and Earthly Love

EVENING. A soft foggy vapor slowly descends upon the Stephaniestrasse, while the lights from the distant street lanterns glimmer from out the distance. From the city the muffled clatter of wagons sounds as though coming from a heavily carpeted room. Two gentlemen promenade upon the Stephaniestrasse in the middle of the carriage road where the fiacres hastily roll along on a happy, dusty Sunday afternoon.

The First (giving himself credit for being about to say something exceptionally clever): "I am inclined to believe that sensual and spiritual love among women is never equally distributed. Titian is right."

The Second: "Why is Titian right?"

The First: "Because he painted the lovely picture *Heavenly and Earthly Love.* It shows two women. The one is nothing but heavenly joy and peace. The second is nothing but fleshly sensuality. It is thus also in life."

(He puffs deeply upon his cigar as one who has solved a problem. He is proud and happy.)

The Second: "You believe that, really?"

The First: "Yes, I cannot help it. I am a simple fellow and I love luxuriant women. The soulful life is beautiful, as are the pangs of love; yet as far as I am concerned all such folly evaporates from my head when my lips glide over the lips of a woman. Delicately and hot, over a woman's lovely red mouth. At such times I feel as if tiny sparks of electricity were flying from one hot, dry pair of lips to the other."

The Second: "Women train one."

The First: "How so?"

The Second: "A man may be trained for all things. It seems . . . this lady . . . don't be afraid, I'm not the least inquisitive . . . that your lady is a sensuous being. And so you also dream of kisses. My lady . . . don't be afraid, I shall not be indiscreet . . . is very different. I really don't know. Perhaps it is because she is thin; but she somehow managed to train me her way. To recognize spiritual tenderness and joy-bringing friendship as the real basis and meaning of even such sinful relationships."

The First: "Perhaps; yes. A thin woman."

(He resumes smoking, since once more he feels that he has solved the problem upon the basis of natural science. He is well satisfied with himself.)

The Second: "She is refined and timid in love. She has beautiful thoughts. In love, the kiss serves her only as a background for her lovely, delicate thoughts. You will probably think I am just stupid. However, I feel that it is possible to part as brother and sister even after an afternoon spent in the sweetest kind of intimacy. Suffused with a glowing, happy peace and the quiet of an unclouded memory in our hearts."

The First: "There are so many varieties of women! When I leave my lady, I feel like a wild male that goes stalking and bellowing through the forest because some one has torn him from the side of his mate. And she also leaves me as a proper female should. With bleeding lips, a wild longing, an amative hatred and a certain revengeful feeling in her heart. For sensuous love can never be completely satisfied."

(He smokes again for obvious reasons.)

The Second: "My lady could never understand such love making. She should learn to hate and despise me were I to talk in this fashion."

The First: "Mine should laugh at you were she to hear you talk. You know that when you set out to court a woman you try anything. And so I also tried some of those soulful jests. But she stopped me with such vehemence, that I lost all pleasure in that sort of thing for all time to come. Between us two there is never such talk. Kisses, kisses, embraces, burning, seething. To be aroused. To be insatiable! That's it!" (He smokes.)

The Second: "It is astonishing that we two should have met!"

The First: "How so?"

The Second: "Well, because we personify the two extremes. You live the love of the blood while I live the feelings of the soul. Yours is the voluptuous, aroused woman; while mine is the slender, pale woman."

The First: "Well, actually my lady really is not so voluptuous."

The Second: "And mine is not so very slender."

The First: "Mine is rather medium. Not too fat nor too thin. She just appears voluptuous."

The Second: "My lady leans towards the medium. She appears rather slender. Also, she is not pale, but rosy pale."

The First: "Mine also is not exactly chubby-faced. She is rosy. But fiery rosy."

The Second: "It would be great fun to bring these two women together. How would they converse with one another? I have heard of something written by a French dramatist. To go out in a quartet. To dine together!"

The First: "That wouldn't be possible. They may be acquainted already."

The Second: "You . . . The devil! How strange! Perhaps they really know one another?"

The First: "Perhaps they are actually friends."

The Second (with excitement): "Say . . ."

The First: (already half guessing what the other would say): "Well?"

The Second: "Say . . . if you tell me the name of your lady, I'll tell you the name of mine."

(They walk wordlessly alongside of each other for a while and the idea seems to please them both exceedingly. They are at present contemplating whether to reveal the name of the woman in question would be harmless business or base roguery.)

The First (after a long pause): "Give me your hand."

(The Second stretches out his hand.)

(They exchange a long manly handclasp, hard and firm, as their eyes meet in a strange look.)

The First: "Frau Katharine Szabo."

The Second: "How?"

(His eyes stare like those of a mad man.)

The First: "Now it's your turn."

The Second: "How? What? What did you say? What . . . did you say?"

The First: "Frau ... Katharine Szabo."

The Second (grasps him by the arm): "You . . ."

The First: "Well? Well? What's the matter?"

The Second: "That is also the name of my lady!"

(A horrible silence.)

The First: "Tuesday, Thursday and Saturday."

The Second: "Monday, Wednesday and Friday."

(Another pause.)

The First: "And . . . Sunday?"

The Second (with tears in his eyes): "Who knows?"

The First: "And that is your spiritual lady?"

The Second: "Yes. The slender, pale and soulful lady. The heavenly love. The timid virgin."

The First: "And that is the voluptuous, aroused, sensuous lady. The earthly love. The feminine fire. The wild female."

The Second: "I could weep."

The First: "You feel like weeping because you have loved her as a spiritual woman. I could laugh because she has trained me the other way."

(The one who wanted to weep, smiles bitterly. The one who wanted to laugh, makes a tragic face.)

The Second: "What is to become of us?"

The First: "You ask me that? We are wise, modern people and so we shall not kill each other. I don't know what you spiritual people think. We sensual men become stunned at the thought of another man having anything to do with our women. The matter is very simple. I don't need her any more."

(They shake hands.)

The Second: "We spiritual people . . . we spiritual people . . . I also don't need her any more."

The First: "I have an idea."

The Second: "Well?"

The First: "My idea is excellent. In fact I feel as though during the course of my entire life I have not had such a good idea. Listen here. This woman has so skillfully managed to make two distinctly different women of herself, that it seems no more than decent and proper to reward her."

The Second: "Reward her? With what? And how can we—?"

The First: "By both . . . as it seems proper for real gentlemen to do . . . accepting her conception of living. If she therefore desires to be two distinctly different women, let's accept her as two distinctly different personalities. Let's simply believe her. And . . ."

The Second: "And . . .?"

The First: "And all remains as before."

The Second (without reflection): "Good!"

The First: "Are we agreed?"

The Second: "Yes."

The First: "And never . . . never . . . let's mention this affair between us again. In fact let's never speak of any love affair of any sort that concerns ourselves, after this. And she will also notice no difference in our conduct towards her. I will continue to be sensuous and you will lay particular stress upon the spiritual, as before. And we shall both live happily and contentedly. Farewell."

The Second: "Farewell."

(A short, rapid handclasp and they depart to the left and right. Both resolve within themselves to change their conduct and politics with the woman in order to squeeze out the other. Both hearts burn and on the morrow both will make a scene before the woman. And tomorrow the woman will throw them both out and look about for two others to take their place. And the woman will be in the right!)

F. HUGH HERBERT

We Were Just Having Fun

(Affidavit in the case of Emmett Xavier Carter, Plaintiff, versus John Hope Windermore, defendant, and Laura Mae Windermore, co-defendant.)

LAURA MAE WINDERMORE, co-defendant, being first duly sworn, deposes and says: My name is Laura Mae Windermore and I am the wife of John Hope Windermore, defendant in this case. I don't know why there is all this fuss and nonsense. We were just having fun. I was absolutely sober at the time and my husband was sober too. He had had several drinks, but he was sober. I had had one or two drinks myself, but I was completely sober. We were just having fun.

I am forty-one years old and my husband is forty-six and I absolutely deny that we were not sober. I have read the affidavit of Mr. Emmett Xavier Carter, the plaintiff in this case, and it is a pack of lies. Mr. Carter says we were not sober and that is a barefaced lie. I have three children growing up and I would never be seen in a public place if I were not absolutely sober. I read in Mr. Carter's affidavit where he says my husband was three sheets to the wind. I have never heard this vulgar phrase, but if it means that my husband was not sober then it is another lie. He was having a good time and that is all. We were just having fun, and I would like to know what anyone can object to in a person's having fun.

This is exactly what happened and, since I am making this statement under oath, it is absolutely true. I always tell the truth and teach my children to tell the truth at all times; and when I am under oath I am particularly careful to tell the absolute truth, which some people who shall be nameless are *not*, even when making an affidavit.

I have been told that I can take all the time I want to explain what happened, so I will start at about five p.m. on

December 31st, which is when the whole thing really started.

At about five p.m. on December 31st, I was engaged with my three children in our apartment in dismantling our Christmas tree and putting away the ornaments for next year. This is something we always do on the evening of New Year's Eve, and we try to get it done before my husband gets home from his office because he always tries to help, but is not very helpful, being sort of clumsy and careless and breaking the ornaments the way a man is often apt to do.

I was low and depressed while we were doing this because my three children, who are growing up quickly, all had different dates for New Year's Eve parties and I sort of wished they were still small so that they would all be home at midnight when the New Year came in and we could let them hear the bells ring and give them a sip of wine and then put them safely to bed like we always had done.

My oldest child, Henry, who is eighteen-and-a-half and very much like his father the way he smashes Christmas-tree bulbs, asked me what we were going to do for New Year's Eve, meaning me and my husband, and I told him we had no plans and would probably stay home and listen to the radio or something. I probably sounded kind of low because my daughter Edie, who is seventeen, said that sounded terribly dull and my daughter, Pat, who will be sixteen next month, said that was a crime and they would absolutely make their father take me to a night club where we could throw serpentines, make noise and have lots of fun.

Well, of course, I told them they were crazy and I would never let their father fling his hard-earned salary around in such a silly way, but I could not help thinking that it was very sweet of my children to be thinking of our having fun, meaning me and my husband, and I remember thinking that maybe it would be sort of fun going to a night club instead of just sitting at home listening to our radio, particularly because it has been practically impossible to tune in one station at a time since my husband tried to fix our radio to take out a loud hum.

So then my children got busy on the telephone and spoke to their father at his office and they told him that I was feeling sort of depressed because we were not going to any party or anything and they told him he had to take me to a night club for New Year's Eve or they would be simply furious with him, and he seems to have said okay. I did not actually hear him. My children would not let me get to the telephone.

They told me, however, that he, meaning my husband, thought it was a terrific idea and that he would be home presently raring to go and that I should not be surprised if he came home lit up like a Christmas tree. This last is a phrase which my husband has never used and, in fact, I had never heard it and did not know what it meant.

I am merely quoting my children, who assured me repeatedly that this is what he said.

So then my son Henry said that I must get into a gay and festive mood and he went into the kitchen and brought out a bottle of cooking brandy that I had used most of to make the hard sauce for our Christmas pudding for Christmas. I would say there were about three tablespoonsful left in the bottle, or maybe a little more. Not more than four tablespoonsful anyway.

So then my children insisted that we must divide this brandy up among us and drink a toast to the New Year before my husband got home so that I would be in the right mood for him. I do not approve of children taking hard liquor at any time, but when they had divided up the brandy into four glasses there really seemed to be so little in their glasses that I said it would be all right and we all drank a toast and I must say it tasted very nice. So then my children insisted they must drink a toast to me and I was very touched. I have the best children in the world, bar none. So I told them I thought they were very sweet but we should have to drink this toast in Cokes because we didn't have any more brandy. Then Edie got busy on the telephone again in the bedroom, and presently she came out and said that her father had just told her there was a bottle of Scotch behind the Encyclopedia Britannica in the bookshelves. I thought she was making this up, but they insisted I must look and much to my surprise there was a bottle of Scotch right behind the volume *Mushr-Ozon*. I had no idea it was there before because I am much too busy with my housework to look things up in the Britannica, although I always try to keep the books dusted in the living room.

So my children opened this bottle and insisted I must have a little drink and they must have a sip each for themselves. Theirs was really only a sip because my daughter Pat said I measured it out like out of an eye dropper. Mine was just a small drink. I poured it myself. I would say there was about a tablespoonful. There was ice in the glass and soda water because my children insisted it had to be a regular highball, but I am quite sure it was only a heaping tablespoonful.

So then my children insisted I must get all dressed up and my son walked to the florist's and bought me a beautiful orchid. It was just as big and lovely as the orchid he had already bought to give to his girl whom he was taking to a New Year's Eve party. I was very deeply touched. My son Henry is a fine, good boy.

So then, about seven p.m., my husband came home from the office. He is usually much earlier because he is an executive, but on New Year's Eve they have a party at the office for all the employees and, of course, he was there being an executive.

My husband said it was a wonderful party and I guess it must have been because he laughed happily telling us the amusing things that had happened like kissing the pretty stenographers and harmless jokes of that nature, and he was in a perfectly wonderful mood from the very moment he got home until about three a.m. when he became indisposed and went to sleep. He was gay, happy and gentle and not, as the plaintiff, Emmett Xavier Carter, said in his affidavit, which I have just read again, "surly, truculent, abusive and violent." It is just too ridiculous for words. He was in a wonderful mood.

Anyway, I told my husband how dear the children had been and showed him the orchid my son Henry had bought for me and my husband was even more deeply touched than me because he broke down completely and cried. I was really amazed and touched because my husband is not usually emotional or demonstrative like that. So then my children insisted that we, meaning me and my husband, must drink a toast to each other before my husband took a shower and got dressed. I explained to my husband that I had already had two little drinks and he told me that he might have had one or two at this party at the office, but that he could not remember for certain. He explained that being an executive he was sort of host to the others and naturally he would drink to their health and so forth. Anyway, he thought it was a good idea for us to have another little drink, meaning me and him, so we had one. I would say it was about a tablespoonful.

So then my son Henry helped his father to get dressed in his tux and one of the girls phoned for a cab and my husband and I set out for New Year's Eve at exactly six minutes past eight. I am positive of the time because the little clock in the hall stopped at this exact time when it fell over as we were leaving, and it has remained at this time ever since. I did not see it fall, I only heard the crash. It is a miniature grandfather's clock about twelve inches in height, very beautifully made. It keeps accurate time and was given to us as a wedding present, more years ago than I like to think about. My husband said his hat was hanging over a corner of the clock and that is how it fell when he was getting his hat. My husband told me what had happened in the taxi and he was very sweet, and very upset. He brought the clock along to show me the case was not damaged—only the crystal and the hands sort of bent and probably the works, because it would not tick. I told my husband he should have left the clock at home, but he seemed to want to have it with him and he kept on saying how sorry he was and that he would buy me fifty clocks to make up for it. He was so upset that he actually cried again, but I cheered him up and by the time we got to the Purple Slipper he was once more laughing and full of jokes. I mention this just to show what a wonderful mood he was in and nothing even resembling all those adjectives to be found in the plaintiff's affidavit, which is a pack of wicked lies.

So anyway we had a wonderful ringside table at the Purple Slipper and I was really very proud of my husband that he was able to get it so late on New Year's Eve. He told me he got it because he is an executive with a fine concern and has plenty of drag and I was really very proud of him. Not just because he got a reservation on New Year's Eve, of course. I was proud because he is a wonderful man and still very good-looking. Some people might think that a man with very little hair is no longer good-looking, but I agree with my children that their father is good-looking even though practically bald.

My husband ordered drinks for us directly we sat down. I told him I did not think we needed any because of the little drinks we had already had at home. However, my husband explained that in a place like the Purple Slipper on New Year's Eve the highballs were practically pure ginger ale and no liquor at all hardly. He said it was just a genteel racket and that nobody ever kicked because on New Year's Eve people just want to have fun without really getting drunk. And I must say I could only taste ginger ale in ours, so I am sure he was right. I never did taste any liquor in any of the drinks we had.

There was a floor show which was very enjoyable. My husband has always been very partial to pretty girls and these were very pretty, and the one my husband pinched was very polite and gracious when he apologized like I made him. She stopped at our table to admire the miniature clock which my husband insisted had to be on our table, and that is when he pinched her.

After the floor show we danced. My husband is usually a pretty fair dancer, but he was not in very good form on this occasion. He said the music was too slow for him, and after he had caused a little upset at one of the tables by almost falling over it, I suggested that we should not try to dance any more and my husband said okay and went back to try and fix the clock. He was most upset when he could not get it to strike the chimes, but I pointed out to him that he would just have to get it to tick again and I finally got him to quit tinkering with it.

So we just sat and listened to the music and we put on those paper hats, and my husband held my hand with one hand and threw paper serpentines at all the pretty girls with the other hand and it was all very silly and noisy, but we were just having fun. And my husband told me I was prettier than any girl there, which of course was ridiculous, but I still liked hearing him say it. He also told me that when he was kissing all the young pretty stenographers at the office party he would much rather have been kissing me, and that when he pinched that girl in the floor show it was really meant for me. And we both laughed and he leaned over the table and kissed me in public and people at other tables watched us and laughed and even clapped their hands and we did not mind at all.

And then the New Year came in and they lowered the lights and a pretty girl with very few clothes on stepped out of a cellophane egg with a spotlight on her and they played *Auld Lang Syne* and my husband, who has a fine baritone voice, sang louder than anyone and kept on singing after everyone else had stopped.

It was shortly after this that the plaintiff, Emmett Xavier Carter, came over to our table. I had seen the plaintiff once or twice during the evening. He was at another table and several times he had smiled at us and I had smiled at him like you do on New Year's Eve when everybody is having fun. He came to our table and asked my husband to stop singing *Auld Lang Syne*. He said the people he was with had elected him a committee of one to ask my husband to cut it out. He said it depressed his friends and depressed him. My husband said it was one of his favorite tunes and that he would sing it as long as he liked. He said this might be for several hours yet. He was kidding, of course, because anyone could have told him his voice would not hold out much longer.

But he was very friendly, meaning my husband, and he invited the plaintiff to have a drink with us. This invitation the plaintiff declined in a very rude and unfriendly fashion. I can remember his exact words and I will state them. The plaintiff said, "Look, grandpa—you're tighter than a tick right now. Take the young lady home and take your silly clock home and go to bed."

My husband very properly resented the plaintiff's attitude. He said to the plaintiff, "The young lady happens to be my wife, you silly so-and-so." Since I am giving this affidavit under oath, I should state that my husband did not actually use the words "so-and-so." He used a phrase which I cannot bring myself to use even in an affidavit and which I very much dislike hearing anyone use, even my husband, but I could not really blame him because the plaintiff's manner and bearing were so rude and unfriendly.

The plaintiff then made a definite threat. The plaintiff said to my husband: "If you were twenty years younger and not absolutely stinko I would sock you right in the puss."

Again my husband very properly resented the plaintiff's remark. My husband is rather touchy about being very nearly bald, and while he does not mind being teased about it by me and by our children, or at least never seems to mind very much, he does resent it from strangers like the plaintiff.

I did not want any trouble and I immediately advised my husband to ignore the plaintiff entirely. My husband took my advice and started to sing *Auld Lang Syne* again louder than ever. Furthermore, in order to show that he bore the plaintiff no ill-will for his boorish behavior he said to the plaintiff, "Sing with me—if you know how to sing—you silly-looking so-and-so."

During this unpleasant incident, my husband was clasping the clock with both hands so that it would not be damaged any further. I then said to the plaintiff, "Please go away. We are just having fun. Please don't annoy us."

The plaintiff would not take this friendly, well-meant advice. The plaintiff said to me, "Cutie-pie—take the old so-and-so home and get him to bed."

Now my husband is still extremely jealous and he very properly resented this stranger's familiarity. I resented it too, of course, but I realized the plaintiff was disgustingly drunk, and I did not wish to make any sort of scene. Some people cannot celebrate New Year's Eve without becoming intoxicated. Others prefer to remain sober and just have fun. I suppose it is a matter of a person's breeding and of good taste. I see by the plaintiff's affidavit that he describes himself as a broker. I venture to say that if he were an executive in a fine concern, like my husband is, he would not have behaved as he did.

My husband, infuriated by the plaintiff's familiarity, said to the plaintiff, "No silly so-and-so can call my wife 'cutie-pie' and get away with it." He went on to tell the plaintiff that I was a fine wife and a fine mother who had raised three fine childern. He drew the plaintiff's attention to the orchid my son Henry had given to me and he showed the plaintiff the damaged clock which he was still holding, meaning my husband. During all this, my husband was so deeply affected and properly indignant at the plaintiff's manner that he broke down again. He was unable to sing and he cried. The plaintiff them made a number of very rude and uncalled-for remarks about the clock, which my husband very properly resented. He explained, or attempted to explain, to the plaintiff the circumstances under which the clock had been given to us so many years ago, and when the plaintiff continued his derisive and horrible remarks my husband raised the clock slightly and seemed to sort of try and wave the plaintiff away from our table. The plaintiff still remained at our table and appears to have leaned forward, striking his left temple against said clock and causing the little scratch referred to in the plaintiff's affidavit as "deep laceration and surrounding contusion." I never read such nonsense in my life. It hardly bled at all. There was some blood on the tablecloth, but this came from the plaintiff's nose, which he must have hit when he fell drunkenly across the table.

My husband said the following after this unfortunate accident and these are his exact words. My husband said, "The clock struck one." My husband's attitude was not, as the plaintiff states in his so-called affidavit, "surly, truculent, abusive and violent." As a matter of strict fact, my husband was smiling at the plaintiff as he said it. He was in a perfectly good mood and he laughed very pleasantly. Then my husband turned to me and said, "Did you get that, Laura? I said, 'The clock struck one,'" and he laughed again to show there was no ill feeling. I mention this to show that he was in a wonderful mood and perfectly sober. I mean he knew exactly what he was saying and doing. My husband has always had a fine sense of humor.

It was at this stage that the plaintiff threw the remains of a steak sandwich still on its plate at my husband, and in defense of my husband, who had fallen off of his chair, I struck the plaintiff across the shoulders with said clock. The plaintiff claims that he was struck on the head, but I did not aim at the head. I also deny emphatically that I said "Strike two!" as the plaintiff alleges. I was too excited and indignant to say anything.

I do not remember exactly what happened after the waiters all came and interfered and so I will not say anything under oath. I know that shortly afterwards my husband was indisposed and fell asleep, as I have already said. I think this was in the taxi going home, but I cannot be sure.

I hope that my husband will be well enough tomorrow to make his affidavit and I know that he will bear out all that I have said. We were both perfectly sober and we were just having fun and I think the whole thing is an outrage. We were just having fun.

Signed:
Laura Mae Windermore

LELAND STOWE

What's Wrong with Our Women?

"I GIVE you: the American woman." My friend Jacques raised his glass, pausing just enough to emphasize the slight touch of arsenic in his voice. He smiled a double-edged smile, and then added with just a shade more emphasis: "You can have her."

"But, Jacques," I protested. "But really, Jacques. The best-looking woman in the world—the most modern—the most intelligent. The most beautiful legs—the best figure. Why, you Europeans are the first to admit it."

"I know," said Jacques. "I know. We're the first to be fascinated —and, after a little experience, the first to get cured. Of course your women have wonderful figures. Of course they look superb—providing one doesn't look too closely, you understand. But let's be fair. As a novelty, the American woman is incomparable. For a brief flirtation, or perhaps for a week-end excursion, she has much charm. She can be amusing and decorative. All that is quite evident. But don't take her seriously. You mustn't make that mistake. Your women, they are much too spoiled. Marry one of them? No, thanks. You can have them."

One thing about Jacques. He had not merely sampled the wine; he was a connoisseur of it. Yet he was announcing his withdrawal from competition on this side of the Atlantic. For observant, cosmopolitan males, that has become a pretty common occurrence. Our renowned American Eve may still boast of a rather fabulous collection of superlatives, but a lot of the lure and polish seem to have vanished from her original apple. In more discerning masculine circles today, men constantly conduct a sort of unofficial, nonstop Gallup poll on the relative merits of women. And our star-spangled contestant has come a cropper. Even though she is generally recognized as the most glamorous of the world's women, her rating in this quality poll has been declining steadily for a number of years. Maybe men are getting around more, and getting a bit more perceptive as they get around. Anyhow, the more that men get around (outside the U.S.A. as well as in it), the less importance they attach to the good looks and other superficial assets of American women.

A famous French masculine film star, sailing for home after two years in Hollywood, exclaimed with unconcealed relief: "At last! At last I shall have the pleasure of being together with a *homely* woman." His sardonic comment obviously intimated his anxiety to get somewhere where women are chiefly interesting for considerably more than their looks. There are, it seems, many different ways for women to be appealing.

Of course, the American woman thinks of herself as "different." She glories in her difference. America's Eve has been indiscriminately praised and pampered by her men ever since she first became conscious that she was developing curves where females benefit by them. Our enraptured Adams have showered their attentions upon her and made her the most ballyhooed female in the world. In the process, they have hoisted her on a pedestal—from which it is every male's privilege to try to bribe her into sneaking off, once in a while. Our Eve has scarcely needed to polish her apple. Any guy, she thinks, is a cinch to take a bite, if he gets half a chance.

It's doubtful whether any other nation's women have ever been so idolized. The first objective of the average young American male is to corral a personal Eve for his private pedestal. That not having been too difficult, the bewitched and bedazzled captor-turned-captive waves his hand toward the stunning creature on her elevated perch and exclaims: "There she is—our American woman! There's nothing like her in the world. Venus de Milo couldn't hold a candle to her. Isn't she wonderful?"

Being American, naturally she has to be wonderful.

And, admittedly, she does look the part. On a pedestal, I mean.

But our American woman can't stay on a pedestal all the time. She's got too much vitality, too many ideas, and too many wants. Being a dream girl—a symbol of the ultimate in womanhood—can get monotonous, both for her and the fellow who worships her. After all, except for the art-lovers, who in hell is interested in a woman on a pedestal? America's Eve is an extremely practical female. None, certainly, has done any better for herself. Whatever the attitude of her symbolic perch, you will notice that she always keeps her feet quite solidly on the ground. Everyone admits that she is well worth looking at. Enough, then, of dream-girl concepts. Let's look at her *as a woman.*

A clinical, down-to-earth inspection of America's Eve is long overdue. What Mr. Average American still does not perceive about his native-grown "deadlier of the species" is little short of astonishing. If few women care to be seen without their make-up on, most American men are even more anxious to preserve their illusions. In their minds, apparently, the American woman is *—American.* What more need be said? Yet there does exist a serious, sociological need to get a much more balanced and rounded assortment of facts about her—especially since she's becoming, as I've pointed out, the subject of increasing criticism.

During twenty years as a foreign correspondent, I've lived and traveled on five continents. I've naturally got in the habit of comparing men and women of other nationalities with our own; and I've come to some interesting conclusions. One of them is that my friend Jacques knows what he's talking about. Professional experts and amateur globe-trotters agree our Eve is neither all she thinks she is nor much that American men assume she is. Compared with her overseas sisters, she doesn't, they find, score as many top points as might be expected. She has become the victim of too much ballyhoo. The pedestal pose, encouraged by her men, has thrown her out of focus. In short, she has been looked at too much—but *looked into* far too little. You can't blame Eve for that. It's the American Adams who cling to their rose-tinted spectacles.

At this point, gentlemen, can you take it?

Kindly sit on your emotions. Try to relax into the judicious mood of lordly males who are accustomed to a calm weighing of evidence. Bear in mind that objectivity was never more necessary. Dismiss the personal, and seek the common denominator. For present purposes, you are entitled to make any exceptions you choose. Here, I am concerned only with what some regard as the average characteristics of the supposedly average American woman, since there's no way of making an investigation of our woman except in terms of the majority of their sex. And let's rule out patriotic prejudice. This is to be no dance of adoration around a symbolic pedestal. It's a quest for facts. Let's begin, then, with a simple question —a question so simple that Mr. Average American rarely asks it:

What are our women like?

Almost everyone knows the obvious half of the answer. Certain orchids unquestionably belong to America's Eve, and there's astonishingly little disagreement about them. By something approaching general consent, she is described as:

The best-looking woman in the world.

The most modern woman in the world.

Among the world's best-dressed women.

Also, she has a remarkably fine figure; she is exceptionally intelligent; she is the most independent and free of women anywhere; she has more power over her men then do women of other nations; she enjoys the most privileges of any women anywhere; on the whole, she has more legal rights than women elsewhere; she has more initiative than most; and, finally, she owns more property and wealth—both collectively and individually—than women have held in any other country, at any time in history.

That's as brilliant an assortment of orchids as anybody's Eve might hope to win. In addition, the American woman wears this handsome corsage with befitting gestures and with few intimations of embarrassment. If false modesty ill befits a queen, she prefers to act the queen. But the trouble is that our Eve's orchids, however unique, do not begin to supply a complete answer to what—exactly—she is like. Probing, cold-blooded realists, not overly impressed by her flattering corsage, are likely to unwrap a supplementary bouquet for the American woman; and the bouquet looks suspiciously like poison ivy. Each branch bears a precise label, something like this: "Our woman is also—"

The most spoiled and self-centered woman in the world.

The most aggressive.

The most unhappy and dissatisfied.

She is less feminine and less interested in men than are women of other lands; she is less interested in husband, home and family; she is the world's most expensive woman; she is more restless and bored than other women; she is, in general, less spiritual and she possesses less individuality.

"Who says so?" roars a chorus of indignant American males.

Please, gentlemen. Your seats! These are the conclusions of a distinguished array of psychologists, psychoanalysts, sociologists, and such. Lined up behind them are most foreigners (male or female) who have spent much time in the United States—and also an increasing number of traveled Americans. You may prefer to dismiss the amateurs; but the experts are specialists. Experience has made them prudent fellows: they shy clear of public forums where they might be lynched. But the scientific urge compels them to examine all kinds of evidence and to publish the results of their researches in such weighty volumes as *Modern Woman: The Lost Sex*. What they reveal may be embarrassing or annoying, but you can't ignore or underestimate their accumulated facts. The specialists can't be accused of malice. Nor can their findings be waved lightly aside.

On the evidence, one fundamental fact should be plain. Something pretty awful has happened to our good-looking headstrong, self-satisfied American Eve. She has fallen off her pedestal!

As yet, she herself and a host of her unanalytical admirers may be only dimly aware of it, but the question has long ceased to be whether something, just possibly, might be amiss with her. Today the question is phrased only in one way: "What's wrong with our women?" When that becomes a dominant query, danger signals are flying, helter-skelter, all over our social landscape.

Mr. Average American is an incurable idealist about women—especially about "our women." But if millions of American Adams are still unprepared for the realists' candid portrait, millions of our Eves are caught in a more desperate plight. Suppose their men begin to open their eyes, for a change? Suppose they begin to look closely and listen attentively? Obviously, women can't change years of habit in a few weeks or months. What, if anything, could be expected to blast American females out of being themselves?

Well, it has happened—if only to a degree. For a brief period during the war, America's Eves succumbed to a revolutionary change, both out-of-character and significant. Suddenly they lost their long-established habit of playing "hard to get." When I came home from China, Burma, India, and Russia at the end of 1942, I could scarcely believe my eyes. In one year of war an amazing thing had happened. American women, right out in public, were walking the main streets of our cities *holding hands* with their men in uniform. In restaurants, on trains, almost anywhere, you saw American Eves—completely off pedestal, publicly showing affection for their husbands or boy friends. The entire American scene had taken on an unaccustomed warmth and humanness. The change was so tremendous that it was wryly amusing—but also decidedly ironic. Never, before or since, have I seen American women demonstrate *en masse* so unabashed an interest in mere man.

Of course they reverted swiftly to normal, once the war ended. Within a year after V-J Day, Eve was back in the saddle, pushing toward whatever she thought she wanted and dragging her unprotesting male after her. In most foreign countries women do not need a national draft act or mobilization to prompt or excuse a natural show of affection toward the men of their choice. But it will probably take another world war to blast the American woman into treating her man publicly as anything more than a convenient door opener or check payer.

The war had another upsetting effect on American women. And, from their viewpoint, this one was truly menacing. Millions of American men got a once-in-a-lifetime opportunity to compare their women with those of other nations. For the first time in U.S. history, the American female encountered large-scale competition from foreign women; and the competition proved almost as deadly as it was real. If vast numbers of our men had been kept overseas for another two or three years, heaven knows what inferiority complexes and neuroses America's vaunted Eves might have developed. They were caught completely off base. They were thrown on the defensive—a situation that simply wasn't in their book. Most alarmingly, a very considerable percentage of American males abroad indicated plainly that what they discovered both intrigued and pleased them.

This is where America's Eves began to wobble visibly on their previously unthreatened pedestals. Those foreign creatures were shamelessly without scruples. They gave every evidence that they recognized a good thing when they saw it. As for our boys overseas, whether in Australia, the Orient, the Near East, or Europe, they were pretty well embarked on learning new things about women—or was it more things about a different kind of women?

It wasn't the women of easy virtue who made a lasting impression on them, either. The vast majority of American boys who married foreign girls fell in love with decent, respectable persons—girls or women who represented the average in their country and community. Among the Americans, the percentage of those who were free to marry and *did* marry foreign girls was impressively high. They took the vows with 55,000 British women alone. Tens of thousands more married women from all parts of Europe, the Far East and Australia. The Yankee Lochinvars brought their war brides home with great pride; and most of these supposedly rash ventures appear to be working out very satisfactorily.

"I'll take my dishonorable discharge and get out of my own country if they send my girl back to Italy," declared a corporal recently. When a girl puts a guy in that frame of mind, she must have something. What made so many American youths fall so hard for the women they met overseas? The answer to that question should be highly educational for many of the girls they left behind—and left. Talking about their non-American fiancées,

Americans overseas have been heard to make the following remarks:

"You oughta see how my French gal can cook and sew."

"Say, these Australian women are really okay. They're so natural and unspoiled. They appreciate any little thing you do for them."

"You know—my girl can do everything. Every time I see her, she's fixing my socks or my uniform or something."

"I'll say these women over here are different. Why, they're always asking what *you* want to do. Imagine that!"

"They don't expect you to spend a lot of money on them. They know how to have a good time."

I remember an Air Forces lieutenant, reassigned from England to a special training job in Texas. Somehow he managed to have his English bride join him. "You ought to see how my wife has got our quarters in the barracks fixed up," he told me. "It takes a British girl to make a place cozy with next to nothing. The American wives at camp can't hold a candle to her. Most of them are griping and complaining. They're all jealous of her, too. Betty just buckles down with what she's got, and shows them up. British girls really know how to make a home. For one thing they're not spoiled dolls."

The war brides' husbands fairly oozed with glowing testimonials. Sex appeal and the mating technique did not seem to be major elements in their happy state of mind—at any rate, not what aroused most comment. One conclusion was inescapable: by and large, these foreign women possessed a lot of qualities that the average American girl apparently lacked, either *in toto* or to a noticeable degree. You can sum the whole situation up pretty accurately in this fashion: *most women of non-American background and nationality are brought up to please men.* And most males, including Americans, are so egotistical or perverse as to greatly relish being pleased.

Our servicemen merely discovered overseas what almost all cosmopolitan, traveled observers have long known. They learned that, on the average, the women of other continents are considerably more interested than American girls—1) in men as men; 2) in their own personal lifetime jobs of being successful as women, wives, and homemakers. As a result, foreign women know a good deal more about cooking, sewing, and housekeeping than the cocksure, somewhat willful, and much more self-promoting American women do. The overseas woman attaches at least as much importance to what she can do in her feminine sphere as she does to how she looks. She grows up with an acute consciousness that her chief asset is her femininity; the more intrinsically feminine she is, the better. In her different civilization, culture and code, it is an accepted axiom that the woman demands less and gives more. She regards this as natural. All she needs to do is to understand that her own feminine weapons are unbeatable. The more she sticks to her own ground, to her own weapons and instincts, the greater are her prospects of genuine fulfillment as a woman. These things are ABC's for most women throughout the world—except in the United States.

The most important differences between foreign and American women are those you hear the least about. There's a popular idea that foreign women excel in such items as greater vivacity of expression, more exotic complexions, and more zestful performance after the lights are out. All of which is sometimes true. But to assume that these are their chief distinctions is unsophisticated, inaccurate, and beside the point.

The basic ways in which majority of foreign women differ from Americans are—1) in their attitude and mentality; 2) in their acceptance of woman's position in society; 3) in their essential femininity. And so America's Eve is left in a rather lonely place of her own. Why, she wonders, do these foreign women rate so highly anyhow? They are not nearly so independent. They do not have so many varieties of careers. Their lives are narrower. On the whole they possess far fewer legal rights. Even if they give more, they get less—so far as the eye can see. Yet the experts now hand these women a suprising number of laurels—and at the expense of the very females who have collected more fancy adjectives and adulation than any others on earth.

At this critical point, many American pedestal-worshippers are doubtless being blown off their chairs by their patriotic emotions. These are mere generalities, they say wrathfully. If the psychologists and the rest of these so-called, self-designated "experts" wish to level a wholesale indictment against our American women, let them be specific. What facts can they produce to back up their unchivalrous, uncalled-for accusations? Probably most of these professional "detractors of American womanhood" are frustrated intellectuals, namby-pamby professors, or shameless ex-patriots. Let them put up, or shut up!

Which is reason enough to get down to cases. So let's consider the main charges that the realists bring against America's Eve when they attempt to balance the picture and put her in perspective.

"Let's keep out of it—he probably has a very good reason."

1. *Our women,* they say, *are the most spoiled and self-centered in the world.*

That reminds me of Mary Garden's classical comment: "American women don't worship their men. They merely skin them." (Now really, Mary. Aren't you carrying it to extremes?) Being a reporter by training, I would prefer to let American women speak for themselves. I wonder if you've heard very much of what they've been saying, from coast to coast, for a good many years?

"I just adore Robert Taylor," says Mrs. Smith, "so Bill and I went to the movies."

"Dick really wanted a Buick, but I *had* to have a Packard," explains Mrs. Johnson brightly.

"I can't stand Chinese food. *You* can go there some other time."

"I've found a wonderful place for our vacation. We always go to the mountains. You know, *I* like them much the best."

"And really," says Mrs. Perry (just as if her husband hadn't the remotest connection with the matter), "they offered $30,000 for *my* house. But of course, *I* wouldn't consider selling it for that."

In the United States, the over-all feminine chant emphasizes the perpendicular pronoun. Our women betray themselves when they talk about what they prefer, what they want, what they've got, or what they are out to get. Listen for a while and you can't escape the impression that it's the men's first obligation to please their women in practically everything—and that this is an operation which should be reversed only under exceptional circumstances. There is no other country in the world where women wait so presumptuously for some male to light their cigarette. And this is the only country where obliging males frequently get not so much as a slight nod for their pains. America's Eve takes most of the daily little courtesies as her imperial due. She parades her feminine priorities and often ignores the existence of any masculine priorities. In general, she exudes a deeply entrenched conviction that woman comes first and goes through life much as she goes through a doorway. No women are more waited upon. Yet no women anywhere are more indifferent or oblivious to what reciprocal graciousness can mean.

2. *Our women are exceptionally aggressive.*

Spend an hour or two trying to get near bargain counters in your local department store. Watch the "lady" shoppers pushing into commuters' trains or city busses. Observe how they capitalize on the "women-first" tradition—in railroad stations, elevators, or anywhere. In American ticket lines or queues, notice how, almost invariably, it is some female who pushes callously ahead of dozens of waiting people.

In the New York subway the other day a determined Amazon nearly knocked a man off his feet as she barged into a train. In any foreign city, the woman would have excused herself graciously—certainly, if she were as well-dressed as this female was. Did she turn around? Did she beg the fellow's pardon? Not she! For all she cared, the man she had crashed into might have been a bag of meal. The venom in his eyes was really something. It is only in America that it is woman's special prerogative to be rude. We have more female pushers, shovers, grabbers, and go-getters than any other section of the globe. There remain only a minority of exceptions, ladies who are nobly aware that "aggressive" is not synonymous with "lady-like." But the only place for our average Eve is out in front. She gets there.

3. *Our women are the most unhappy and dissatisfied.*

The realists waste few words on this question. "Look at their faces," they say.

That's pertinent advice. The faces of American women tell a great deal. They merit much study and more reflection. Negatively, they are very interesting. I say negatively because our women's faces, on the average, are unusual for what they do *not* have rather than for what they have. In general, they lack mobility and expression. They also lack the range of individuality that differentiates the features of most women abroad. In the American woman's countenance, as in her voice, it is exceptional to discern something truly distinctive, a real personality. And her face too often mirrors discontent; in repose it is likely to be metallic, without inner light.

When American women are alone and not called upon to put on a social act, their faces reveal a great deal. Traces of contentment, let alone happiness are rarely to be observed. But the evidence of widespread unhappiness among our women is not only written in their faces. They themselves are the first to admit the depths of their discontent. By the frankness of their confessions they continue to appall and alarm psychiatrists and other doctors. In no other country do women reveal their spiritual uneasiness so publicly as in the United States. By scores of thousands, their letters are published yearly in "advice to the lovelorn" columns and read by millions of other women—who presumably are interested for similar reasons. Dorothy Dix, Beatrice Fairfax, and many other confessional columnists are assured of handsome, lifelong incomes simply because such a great percentage of their fellow countrywomen are excessively unhappy.

An eminent psychiatrist, backed by many of his colleagues, says American women "have gone *too far too fast* . . . They haven't developed emotionally in keeping with their economic and social advancement." Pearl Buck offers an extremely perceptive observation. She says: "I have never seen in any country . . . such unsatisfactory relationship between men and women as there is in America. No, not even in Japan, where women as a class are depressed as women never were."

That's straight from the shoulder, and fundamental. The American woman may enjoy remarkable privileges and exceptional power. Nevertheless, and by and large, she confesses herself to be spiritually and emotionally adrift. In her actions, as in her face, she reveals an unparalleled inner hunger and uncertainty.

4. *Our women are less feminine and less interested in men.*

It's notorious that women "wear the pants" in the average American household. But it's equally evident that the trousers chafe them sorely. America's Eve is the undisputed boss in nine out of ten of our homes, and equally so in virtually all our elementary and secondary schools. European observers have no doubt (and neither should any half-conscious American male) that women run almost everything in the U.S.A.—except, occasionally, their husband's offices. That demonstrates the pronounced ability of American women. But it also greatly reduces the field in which men are essential to them. American husbands intrude upon or share in only a minor portion of their wives' major activities. Maybe this makes it inevitable that our women show a limited and minimum interest in men.

As a minor test, try this one. Walk along Fifth Avenue or any comparable thoroughfare in any larger American city at any time between mid-morning and night-fall. Watch the steady procession of women. The majority of them would not see Clark Gable or the handsomest man in the world if he passed by, or even if they almost bumped into him. It couldn't happen in Stockholm, Paris, Rome, Rio—or Geneva, Switzerland. Not that "honest" women in other lands actually invite sidewalk flirtations. They don't. But wherever foreign women go, they carry with them a subtle awareness of men as *men*. They are too feminine to be capable of spending several hours in public places without occasionally noticing a man who has some quality that, however fleetingly, focuses their attention. In similar circumstances, most American women simply do not see men at all. They have more important things to think about. Men are reserved for certain times and places—a matter of the women's own convenience. At other times and places, men do not, as a rule, exist for them. In no other part of the world have I observed this phenomenon to a like degree.

This brings up a paradox. Certainly no other women spend such enormous amounts of money on beauty treatments, coiffeurs, "uplifts," and other paraphernalia to enhance either appearance or sex appeal. You might think this expensive ritual demonstrates the American woman's interest in males. In males as a convenience to have around? Or males *as such*? Or is she chiefly interested in attracting attention and admiration for herself? I leave it to you to figure out the percentages on this delicate subject. But this much is sure: femininity is a quality which cannot be measured by what a woman puts on. Femininity is what any woman has got on the inside—what she *is*. Could it, by any chance, be true that the more feminine a woman is on the inside, the less she feels the need of excessive indulgence in make-up rituals, "slenderizers," and innumerable other "come-on" devices? Could it be that when women strain so desperately to create a romantic appeal they admit subconsciously that what femininity they possess rather badly needs bolstering? . . . I'm just a chap who looks—and wonders.

Most of the world's women have precious little cash to spend on beauty treatments. But there's no discernible shortage of femininity among them. If they believe in enhancing their appearance, they seldom go to the American extremes. Where sex appeal is concerned, they do not confuse artificial accessories with the fundamental article. As for being feminine, it remains for America's Eve to assume that what goes on the outside can be quivalent to the quality of femininity itself. Judged by their efforts and actions, our women desperately want to be more feminine. They gild the lily—and how! But if they were not essentially less feminine than they ought to be, would they feel the need of making such efforts to get that way?

Femininity also means staying on women's ground. This is the last thing most of our women seem satisfied to do—and the last thing many of their men will let them do. Our superindustrialized civilization demands that women compete with men in many of their own fields. They have done it, aggressively and with ability. More and more they have had to compete with men—as a result of which they have taken to aping men and acting like men. In the process, they have become increasingly less feminine—in their habits and actions, in their minds and instincts. No cosmetic house will ever invent a formula or penetrating cream that will come within a billion light-years of the seat of the dislocation.

5. *Our women are less interested in their husbands, home, and family.*

Why waste space on the obvious? Close to 100,000 American war grooms have already brought home the vital evidence and testimony. They fell for foreign women chiefly because these unfamiliar creatures were surprisingly interested in woman's job and woman's sphere.

6. *Our women are excessively expensive.*

When foreign men start squiring almost any star-spangled Eve, they reach this conclusion promptly. In our near-matriarchy, the female customarily does the choosing, and she is rarely reticent about her tastes and preferences. After a brief exposure to our female tourists in prewar Paris, many a European ruefully made the comment that it's largely the American woman's fault she is losing her power over men. The idea is getting around that women want a lot for what they give. When our boys went overseas, they discovered the same thing, by comparison.

Of course many of our women manage to keep their demands within reason. But the notion has nevertheless got around that the American feminine article is, on the whole, about the most expensive known to man. It isn't merely because of what she expects for entertainment and clothes. It's because of *what she expects*—namely, plenty. Maybe masculine overindulgence and false pride are partly responsible. It's human for the girls to take what they can get. The emphasis on material things and comforts in our society is certainly another factor. In any case, the upshot is that America's Eves are pretty demanding darlings. Far more hard cash is spent on their material comfort, adornment, pleasure, or whims than on those of any other women. American men make a cult of encouraging this situation. Why blame the women? Here we merely recognize a fact.

7. *Our women are more restless and bored.*

In general, they have more leisure than women elsewhere. Timesaving inventions, from electric washing machines to God knows what, have conspired to leave an increasing vacuum in the daily routine of most of our middle- or upper-middle-class women. A great many have gone into women's clubs and other social or charitable activities. Even so, they often have more time than they know what to do with, or are bored with the uses to which they put their time.

This may apply specifically only to a minority. But this minority sets the pattern and exercises an influence much beyond its numerical size. Man or woman, we Americans are restless animals. But the restlessness of American women, according to psychiatrists, goes much deeper than that of men. America's average Eve seems always to be seeking desperately, but not finding. She is the antithesis of the relatively fulfilled, inwardly secure woman who exists in impressive numbers in most foreign lands.

8. *Our women are less spiritual and have less individuality.*

Here again perhaps our assembly-line civilization is largely to blame. Something is criminally responsible for the terrible standardization of American women. Anyone with a slight degree of artistic discrimination must be aware of the deplorable sameness of females from one end of the U.S.A. to the other. The majority of our women look the same, dress the same, act the same, and sound much the same. Any real incentive to make new acquaintanceships with women is lower in this country, I believe, than in any other. An intelligent Chinese writer, Helena Kuo, says (in *The American Mercury*): "American city women, with their standardized faces, legs, shoes, and figures, seem so uniform that we of the East cannot recognize them individually . . . They seem to come off the production line so rapidly that they look like members of a Rockette dancing chorus."

In most countries women aspire to be distinctive, in personality and appearance. The opposite is true here. America's Eve has the naive idea that she should ape her sister-competitors as much as possible. The fashion magazines, the beauticians, and Hollywood exert a diabolical influence. The combined result levels down our women of all ages. The conception of a woman *being herself* is regarded as outlandish. Only the most discriminating and strong-minded succeed in resisting terrific pressures toward conformity.

If our women are not even a fraction as interesting as they could be and ought to be, they themselves are largely to blame. They refuse to grasp a simple fact—*when a woman is different she has really got something.* The element of the unsuspected, the unlike, or the mysterious is totally absent in most American women. If you meet them in Boston or Atlanta, the odds are that you've already met them in Chicago or Seattle. Whatever the labels on the bottle, the wine is much the same. What a wasted opportunity! What a neglect of fine material!

With the loss of her individuality, the American woman inevitably loses a certain indefinable spiritual spark as well. For some reason, the humble American waitress is a notable exception. But good repartee, the skillful art of fencing with words, is too rarely the forte of the American Eve. Perhaps our civilization overstresses the exterior and sadly neglects what is interior and personal. Individuality comes from the inside and feeds on spiritual fires within. But this, precisely, is what most of our women seem determined to have as little of as possible. It is our great loss as well as theirs.

By this time is must be apparent that the orchids collected by our American Eves do not stand up well under a Klieg-light inspection. The glamour and the beautiful (standardized) figure may suit her posture well, but they are only one aspect of a rounded-out composite portrait. The American woman's attention and efforts have been recklessly concentrated on appearances—on what she can get, have, or use—on externals. Far too many years, she has occupied herself feverishly with almost everything except those things that would most develop her femininity and would give her the deepest satisfactions that women can have. It is small wonder that, on the average, she gives every indication of not knowing what she wants. How can she know what she wants, when, in our mechanized and extroverted civilization, she does not know where she belongs?

Have American men been of any real, intuitive help to her in her confusion, perplexity, and frustration? Far from it. They keep pushing her deeper into the squirrel cage of her quandary. If there is one song that all the women in the United States of America ought to sing in chorus, it is this: "You made me what I am today—I hope you're satisfied."*

The odd thing is that an amazing proportion of America's males actually seem to be fairly well satisfied. It doesn't make sense, and it's no tribute either to their awareness or their intelligence. After all, the specialists agree that there is a good deal which has gone haywire in our women; and the reason isn't simply that those cantankerous, feminine creatures really wanted to go haywire. They never could have succeeded without a lot of unconscious or intentional help from their men.

But that's another problem, and it requires another investigation. If you don't know what or how much has gone wrong with your women, Mr. Average American, it's time to take a long look in your mirror—whether before or after shaving is of minor importance.

**Copyright 1913. Copyright renewal 1941, Leo Feist, Inc. Used by special permission, Copyright Proprietor.*

PAUL GALLICO

The Savage Beast in Us

WHAT with a show yanked off the Broadway boards, the producers thereof plunked into durance vile, and others quaking beneath the basilisk eye of the censor, it behooves this forward-looking and inspired hack to examine some of the facets of sex at $4.40 per, and the so-called lure of the female form divine. My purpose is to reveal the stuff as a combination of fraud and abysmal ignorance. For the most part, the female flesh as exposed on Broadway is a blight and a bore. We are trying to Save The Boys Some Trouble.

Since the flesh show on Broadway has the same basic philosophy as other legitimate business ventures such as the manufacture of eyelets for lace shoes, or the making of paper boxes, namely, to create a profit on the books, it is rather startling to find at this late date that the entrepreneurs of such displays have failed to give the same careful study to the organization, display and sale of their product as has the average proprietor of any similar purely business enterprise. In fact, the first casual consideration of their operations leads me to the conclusion that they don't know what the Hell it's all about.

Let us, for instance, consider that absurd accident of human anatomy known to science as the umbilicus, which is presented nightly as a treat to the public eye at prices varying from four dollars and forty cents for an orchestra seat to blanket inclusion among the benefits covered by the two-dollar *couvert* charge in cafés and night spots.

Who told those congenital nitwits there is anything stimulating, or mildy entertaining about this ridiculous wrinkle staring like a blind eye from the center of an expanse of otherwise not too revolting epidermis?

I have yet to hear of a single instance where any average male, having been confronted with this tidbit, has rushed panting into the night to seek assuagement for the fires kindled in his circulatory system. If anything, this abdominal replica of Polyphemus has the chilling effect of examining a fine piece of velvet and finding a cigarette hole in the middle of it. Yet, costumers are encouraged to expose this silly scar on the theory that men and women will queue up at the box office or night club gates to get a peek at it.

Forced to conceal more arresting areas, the business man involved in the presentation of ladies set to music, finding nothing on the statute books involving the midriff, orders it exposed on the theory that it is better than nothing. It won't work, boys, and why don't you get wise and hide the damn thing for good and all?

Let us continue the expansion of our thesis with an examination into the esthetic or entertainment value of the "grind" and the "bump," two cultural manifestations of the theatre frequently featured in indecency trials.

The "bump" appears to be a violent twitch whereby the artiste gathers up all of the area immediately south of the chest and hurls it in the general direction of the audience, aimed at hitting some man, in the fifth row, right between the eyes.

The gesture is held to be fraught with aphrodisiac significance, a sure-fire yank on the hair trigger that is supposed to control the beast in us. Oh, yeah?

Outside of the fact that the movement is awkward, unrhythmic, and hideous to behold, even when backed by an orchestra of symphonic proportions, it just won't work as a beast-rouser. What it makes me think is that some gent in the company, having somehow achieved invisibility, has stolen up behind the danseuse and administered a good swift kick *à derrière*. The sight of an entire stageful of coryphees performing this gesture, as is sometimes arranged by dance directors under the impression that it is Hot Stuff and will Sell Tickets, is enough to ruin the *après-midi* of any faun.

The supposedly sultry "grind," in which the performer revolves her hips in time to music while the rest of her stands still, may have practical value as a slimming exercise, but performed in public and by herself, I must report that from the viewpoint of the average susceptible male, the results are negative. On the contrary, it has undeniable comic aspects. A lady engrossed in delivering herself of these revolutions, her face transfixed with the curious far-off stare resulting from the muscular effort, reminds me of nothing so much as a gal who has backed herself up against a tree or a wall and is attempting to scratch an itch she can't reach.

I read not long ago, in these very pages, the interesting sugges-

"All right, everybody now—sing!"

tion that behind the plague of cockeyed and farcical female hats of recent years lay a psychological conspiracy on the part of the pixies who concocted them to make women look grotesque and silly. One suspects a plot of even vaster proportions to present the female figure on the stage in its most ridiculous, rather than its most attractive and undeniably seductive light.

It is probably more a reflection upon the innate vulgarity and complete lack of sophisticated education on the part of the gents who invest their dough in the type of musical that has replaced the banished burlesques.

The perefectly-proportioned female figure is a joy to behold, but there is only one in every hundred thousand worth looking at from an esthetic point of view. Show shop proprietors are not concerned with esthetics. They still fall for that oldie that men go to the theatre for the purpose of seeing a girl without her clothes on. The gent who goes to the beach or attends the average dinner party today gets more of an eyeful under pleasanter and more stimulating circumstances than can be afforded by any six girl shows you want to name, always excepting, respectfully, the undeniable jolt of the public disrobing of the Misses Lee, Hart and sisters.

Since one man's meat is another man's yawn, the entrepreneur, when engaging the supernumeraries who are to carry aloft the red oriflamme of s-x during the evening's performance, takes care to mix them up as to types, shapes, styles, and coloring. As a kid, you will remember wondering how that fat dame with the back porch of a hippopotamus ever got into the burleycue chorus. Later you learned that she was put there for the guys who liked fat dames.

But the net result of such a chorus line of please-alls is to release upon the boards the damndest horde of swaybacks, thick-hips, spindle-legs, flat-chests, string-necks, high-bosoms, bean-poles, short-torsos, bony-arms, and round-shoulders. Granted that with some study a guy will find a little number concealed in the gang who will set him to reflecting over the possibility of getting her telephone number, the mass effect upon the average male member of the audience is to cause him to mutter: "Where the Hell did they ever collect that bunch of dames!" As a stimulus to sin it's a washout.

The late Mr. Ziegfeld was intelligent at his profession of beast-rousing. He engaged girls of uniform chassis, with the loveliest faces in the world, merely varying the color of their hair, and then loaded them down with clothes. They came in wearing practically everything that could be scraped together from the costumer's ateliers, or was lying around backstage, and what they couldn't wear around their torsos, or drape over their shoulders, they carried on their heads. He knew what few of his contemporaries know: the more clothes you put on a woman the more exciting she becomes. Conversely, the more you take off, the closer you approach to the rind, the more ridiculous she looks unless God has been very kind with his endowments.

It is long since woman has had the sensory appeal she reveled in during the Victorian era when her form was concealed from chin to toe, warmly and invitingly buried beneath layers of petticoats, excitingly battened beneath corsets, corset-covers, and something thrillingly known as a chemise. Where is the gent who can keep a gleam out of his eye at the enchanting sound of the word "chemise"? All that is accomplished, conversely, by "bra" or "panty" is to make us more than a little bit ill.

The habilimentary liberation of woman has cost her a lot in attraction and desirability, and nowhere is this quite so patent as on the stage. She, or the nitwits she permits to set the styles for her, have robbed us of all imagination. The male eye instead of being titillated with mystery, is shocked with epidermal *faits accomplis.* One swish of Florodora's long skirt, to show a gleam of white underfrock and a smidgin of ankle, was sufficient to purple every bald dome in the audience in those dear departed days. Today the boys snooze gustily though the allegedly carnal moments of the revue until those happier minutes when those poor, dull, naked freaks are replaced by the comedian, or somebody who can sing.

The strip tease of the burleque chains, lately elevated to a national industry, is nothing more than a physical projection of a facet of the *psychologie érotique* of the average male. To put it in terms that even I can understand, when a gent sees a pretty girl concealed by a lot of clothes, he immediately wonders what dwells beneath them, and mentally eliminates the garments, one by one. This harmless practice often puts him into the mood to part with diamond bracelets, emerald clips, sable coats, or even proffers of marriage which lead to happy homes in the suburbs, and little kiddies pushed about in prams.

The strip tease as a public exhibition is vulgar, and belongs to the more private environs of the lupanar, to which place the licensing authorities will eventually relegate it. And all because the dizzards who cater as a business venture to the b. in u. are too thick-witted to realize that every guy worthy of the name is his own stripper. Turn loose on the stage a bevy of gals with pretty faces and ankles, who can sing a little and dance a little, and who are wearing pretty clothes and plenty of them, and we'll have a wonderful time.

I remember the first time I saw ladies on the stage without any clothes on at all, and I do not recall that I was forced to utter muffled cries for smelling salts or that I went out from the theatre and began knocking out the cornerstones of churches. It was at a visit to the *Folies Bergère* in Paris, *circa* 1926, when I had a younger, moister eye. The girls were presented nude, in great masses, draped over properties, hanging from the chandeliers, and stowed six-deep around the scenery in *poses plastiques*. They looked like a group of amiable pink pigs. The French run more to upholstery in their preferences than we do, so in some groupings there were sufficient curves to suggest a vague pass had been made at art. But I'll be damned if anything else was suggested. I came away neither a worse nor a better man.

At least the French managed to maintain some standards for the forms they exhibited, and did not expose ladies modeled on the classic lines of giraffes, or whose legs, instead of proceeding from their torsos in a reasonably correct manner, are set at odd angles to the corners of their trunks.

Our revue costumers either have no eye for the faintly comic anatomy of a lady, or, as has been suggested before, they are deliberately avenging themselves on the whole tribe. Otherwise they would not send them forth into the glare of spotlights looking like plucked chickens. The beauty of woman's line lies in the sweep from the curve of her bust to her ankles. The Empire style was one of the most graceful ever worn by woman.

The silliest joke played by nature on the girls, though unquestionably utilitarian, was the widening of the hips to make them look like ambulating hour-glasses. Night after night these hips, rimmed with feathers, electric lights or assorted tinsel and rhinestones, are presented to audiences as the acme of erotic sophistication. It's all hooey, along with the chest cups, fringes, diadems, and other paraphernalia used to outline territory deemed illegal. The girls look just plain ridiculous, and guys who are supposed to be entertained are plain bored.

It is bad enough when these poor, chilly-looking monkeys are marching about, or merely trying to sing a song in unison. I will not touch upon the caricatures that occur when thus clad they engage in tap dances or acrobatic numbers which result in a girl's rear end, clad in white satin, suddenly appearing behind her ear, like a winter moon, when she tears herself in two in what is graphically termed a split, or ties herself into knots that resemble the confused physique of a clam. These performances may have merit as *Grand Guignol,* but where sex is concerned, it's a laugh.

Another type of pseudo-excitement long passé is the high kick. It had some value when its enactment revealed a flash of silken leg emerging from skirts. Performed by any of those stork-legged, knob-kneed chorus babes clad in the limit of the law, it has all the sex appeal of a pair of calipers.

I trust that I have faithfully exposed my argument: that if Broadway flesh-peddlers think they're putting on hot shows, they have another guess coming, and if guardians of the public morals are worried about me and the other guys becoming corrupted by those dull, imbecilic, puerile, gyrations over which they are currently exercised, they can quit worrying, because it just ain't so.

Seven Moments of Love

AN UN-SONNET SEQUENCE IN BLUES

1 *Twilight Reverie*

Here I set with a bitter ole thought,
Something in my mind better I forgot.
Setting here thinking feeling sad.
Keep feeling like this I'm gonna start acting bad.
Gonna go get my pistol, I said forty-four
Make you walk like a ghost if you bother me any more.
Gonna go get my pistol, I mean thirty-two,
And shoot all kinds o' shells into you.
Yal, here I set thinking—a bitter ole thought
About two kinds o' pistols that I ain't got.
If I just had a Owl Head, ole Owl Head would do,
Cause I'd take that Owl Head and fire on you.
But I ain't got no Owl Head and you done left town
And here I set thinking with a bitter ole frown.
It's dark on this stoop, Lawd! The sun's gone down!

2 *Supper Time*

I look in the kettle, the kettle is dry.
Look in the bread box, nothing but a fly.
Turn on the light and look real good!
I would make a fire but there ain't no wood.
Look at that water dripping in the sink.
Listen at my heartbeats trying to think.
Listen at my footprints walking on the floor.
That place where your trunk was, ain't no trunk no more.
Place where your clothes hung's empty and bare.
Stay away if you want to, and see if I care!
If I had a fire I'd make me some tea
And set down and drink it, myself and me.

Lawd! I got to find me a woman for the WPA—
Cause if I don't they'll cut down my pay.

3 Bed Time

If this radio was good I'd get KDQ
And see what Count Basie's playing new.
If I had some money I'd stroll down the street
And jive some old broad I might meet.
Or if I wasn't so drowsy I'd look up Joe
And start a skin game with some chumps I know.
Or if it wasn't so late I might take a walk
And find somebody to kid and talk.
But since I got to get up at day,
I might as well put it on in the hay.
I can sleep *so* good with you away!
House is *so* quiet! . . . Listen at them mice.
Do I see a couple? Or did I count twice?
Dog-gone little mouses! I wish I was you!
A human gets lonesome if there ain't two.

4 Daybreak

Big Ben, I'm gonna bust you bang up side the wall!
Gonna hit you in the face and let you fall!
Alarm clock here ringing so damn loud
You must think you got to wake up a crowd!
You ain't got to wake up *no* body but me.
I'm the only one's got to pile out in the cold,
Make this early morning time to keep body and soul
Together in my big ole down-home frame.
Say! You know I believe I'll change my name,
Change my color, change my ways,
And be a white man the rest of my days!
I wonder if white folks ever feel bad,
Getting up in the morning lonesome and sad?

5 Sunday

All day Sunday didn't even dress up.
Here by myself, I do as I please.
Don't have to go to church.

Don't have to go nowhere.
I wish I could tell you how much I DON'T care
How far you go, nor how long you stay—
Cause I'm sure enjoying myself today!
Set on the front porch as long as I please.
I wouldn't take you back if you come on your knees.
But this house is mighty quiet!
They ought to be some noise . . .
I'm gonna get up a poker game and invite the boys.
But the boys is all married! Pshaw!
Ain't that too bad?
They ought to be like me setting here—feeling glad!

6 Pay Day

This here whole pay check's just for me.
Don't have to share it a-tall.
Don't have to hear nobody say,
"This week I need it all."
I'm gonna get it cashed,
Buy me a few things.
Ain't gonna pay a cent on that radio
Nor them two diamond rings
We bought for the wedding that's
Turned out so bad.
I'm gonna tell the furniture man to come
And take back all them things we had
That's been keeping my nose to the grindstone.
I never did like the installment plan
And I won't need no furniture living alone—
Cause I'm going back to rooming and be a free man.
I'm gonna rent me a cubby with a single bed.
Ain't even gonna dream 'bout the womens I had.
Women's abominations! Just like a curse!
You was the best—but you THE WORST.

7 Letter

Dear Cassie: Yes, I got your letter.
It come last night.
What do you mean, why I didn't write?
What do you mean, just a little spat?

"Where to now, Madam?"

How did I know where you done gone at?
And even if I did, I was mad—
Left me by myself in a double bed.
Sure, I missed your trunk—but I didn't miss you.
Yal, come on back—I *know* you want to.
I might NOT forget and I might NOT forgive,
But you just as well be here where you due to live.
And if you think I been too mean before,
I'll try not to be that mean no more.
I can't get along with you, I can't get along without—
So let's just forget what this fuss was about.
Come on home here and bake some corn bread,
And crochet a quilt for our double bed,
And wake me up gentle when the dawn appears
Cause that ole alarm clock sho hurts my ears.
Here's Five Dollars, Cassie. Buy a ticket back.
I'll meet you at the bus station.

Your baby,

Jack.

PART SIX: *Science and Sex*

"The way the news is these days one might as well stay in bed."

LAWRENCE GOULD

Marriage Makes Strange Bedfellows

At the marriage of a cousin of mine when I was a boy, a lady in the congregation wiped her eyes, and whispered to my mother: "I do think a wedding's so much sadder than a funeral, don't you?"

No doubt she was thinking of the "terrible experience" the innocent and unsuspecting bride would shortly have to go through, as well as the hard lot of a woman who had to live with one of the dreadful creatures she thought men were. But, Victorian as her viewpoint was, I thought then and still think the old girl had something. To induce a man and woman to promise to live together "until death do them part" may perhaps be rated Nature's most ironical achievement. For despite their irresistible attraction for each other, any man and any woman are still on the whole so alien in mind and spirit, and instinctively so hostile and suspicious that no permanent relationship between them can help meaning undeclared or open warfare a good deal of the time.

Indeed, hard as many of us still cling to the fairy-tale picture of the prince and princess "living happily ever after," the improbability of such an ending to romance has long been recognized by both law and religion. For example, in a recent divorce suit before the High Court of London, Mr. Justice Alfred Buckhill ruled: "We cannot assume marriage a state to which the word 'happy' can properly be applied. It is enough if the spouse can say it was normal. It may then be understood that 'normal' means there is nothing much to complain about. And that is quite enough for anybody." And not only do most religious bodies hold that mere unhappiness of either or both parties to a marriage is no valid ground for divorce, but it has often been frankly stated that the real purpose of marriage is "spiritual discipline," not mutual enjoyment.

This is much like the position of those who regard war as the normal state of human existence: indeed, the same forces that produce war operate in marriage almost as inevitably. The relations of a man and woman are a microphotograph of those of two adjoining nations which, because of differences in culture and tradition, don't become "one" by signing a treaty of alliance, and even when they have signed it, may still wind up fighting one another. Let's picture the average married couple as a Romeo and Juliet who've escaped the harsh fate the dramatist had in store for them and feel that their troubles are now over. No matter how much in love they may be, the time will still come eventually when they will discover that their apparent interests and aims in life are in hopeless conflict.

The trouble may begin with the family income, which is seldom big enough to cover everything they both want. What there is of it must clearly be saved for the things that really matter, but there's likely to be quite a difference of opinion as to which things these are. Who shall have the new coat this year, since they can't both have one? Shall they buy new furniture, or insurance? Shall they join the country club, or save for taxes? Shall they spend their vacation in the woods where Romeo can relax and rough it, or go to a summer hotel where Juliet will get away from housework and have a chance to show off her wardrobe—such as it is?

Admitting that these are trivial matters which could be disposed of by using a little common sense and good will, the *feeling* that they embody is *not* trivial. To each of us, his own needs and desires seem self-evidently more important than anyone else's, and he feels whoever cannot see this is deliberately stubborn and thick-headed. From Romeo's standpoint, because he is the bread-winner, his mental and physical requirements mean the family welfare, while to Juliet it is too clear to be arguable that the home must come first and that she as the home-maker has the first claim to consideration. Both may be much too polite to press the issue—or at first, to admit its existence—but it's just as real as the feeling of each of the present warring nations that its claim to supplies and munitions should be met before all others.

Then there's the eternal problem of the children. If Juliet is typical of her sex, she feels they are her God-given life work, and can't understand why Romeo should get the idea he's neglected if she's too preoccupied with them to give him much attention. Does not he keep dinner waiting when—as he claims—he can't get away from the office? But if Romeo in self-defense begins to take an interest in his offspring, that creates new grounds for disagreement. For not only do both he and Juliet have a full set of the fears and prejudices which we like to dignify as ideals, but each feels the children must be brought up by his or her special pattern because this is "right" and all the others are "wrong." Romeo wants Junior brought up a "real Montague"—a he-man; while Juliet says all the Capulets have been known for their polished manners and she doesn't want her relatives to think her son a roughneck.

So much for the matrimonial *casus belli* which everyone who has thought about the subject seriously recognizes. There are others that go deeper, and are generally more or less unconscious. To begin with, there's the basic impulse that makes people marry at all—and I'll be surprised if you are thinking of the same thing I am. The impulse I'm thinking of is not sex, even though the idea that sexual desire ought to lead to marriage has been so deeply impressed on most of us that it seems part of the nature of things. Animals have sexual desires, but if they "marry" (that is, stay together longer than the moment of coition) it is not for sexual reasons: it is to make ready and care for their offspring, and once these are able to go on their own, the parents show no further interest in them or in one another.

Man's almost unique idea of mating for life seems to be largely an outgrowth of the fact that immaturity and helplessness last so much longer with the human species than with any other—so long, in fact, that they grow to be a habit which we are unwilling wholly to relinquish. As a result, when we are no longer able to live with—or "on"—our parents, we yearn for "a home of our own," in which among other things (if not beyond all other) we hope to recapture the sense of security and permanence the original home gave us. Whatever the sentimentalists may say, I doubt if anybody ever married mainly "for love" in the sexual or the romantic sense. We marry to find a substitute for our fathers and mothers —or perhaps hoping to "make up to ourselves" for all we wanted from them which they didn't give us. The devoted son and previously confirmed bachelor who marries a few months after his mother's death is an extreme case, but his obvious need to replace a relationship he cannot live without is also a factor in the willingness of any man to settle down to domesticity once his adolescent appetite for wild oats has been appeased.

The chances are, anyhow, that Romeo would not have married Juliet except for the hope that she would "be a mother to him"—give him more or less the sort of treatment that he learned to love from his own mother. All his feelings are unconsciously conditioned by this secret craving. Whether he is willing to admit it or not, he wants Juliet always to admire him, make allowances for his shortcomings, and keep her arms open to serve as his refuge from the struggle with the harsh world outside. If she lets him get away with it, he'll also have her doing many of the small things mother did when he was little—"pick up after him," provide the things he likes best to eat, and fuss over him when he is ill. The fury of jealousy into which her interest in another man will throw him is again based to no small degree on his little-boy desire to have mother all to himself.

But Juliet had her own more or less unconscious reason for feeling that getting married was the most important thing in the world. It isn't mere laziness that makes a girl look forward to the day when she'll be able to "stop working"; it's the fact that once she has a husband to support her, the responsibility for her life will be shifted to somebody else's shoulders. Even before they were married, Gladys' earning power was twice her husband's, and she thoroughly enjoyed the luxuries it brought her. But once she was Jim's wife, she forgot the dress-designing business completely. And when Jim lost his job and was months finding another, the suggestion that she might pitch in and help with the family finances threw her into a hysteria of rage. "I'm Jim's wife," she stormed, "and it's his business to support me. If he couldn't do it, he had no right to get married."

The trouble some wives have with the family check book isn't because they are stupid about money matters, though they like to give that impression. It grows out of their insistence that the man who's taken father's place must "provide" for them and free them from financial worries. For while every normal woman has her share of the maternal instinct, and gets a kick out of mothering her husband when she's in the mood to do so, with another side of her she wants a father for herself as well as her children, and woe to the husband who won't play the role when she demands it!

So while impulses rising out of the need of a home lead to marriage, they also wreck it when they clash, as they are almost certain to do. For both husband and wife can't be "baby" at the same time. The day comes when Romeo's need of sympathy over the fight he has just had with the boss runs head on into Juliet's feeling that he must keep his job somehow because "What will become of her if he doesn't?" Or Romeo comes home feeling lousy with a fresh cold and finds Juliet has a headache: if she is indifferent to his sufferings, his heart is outraged, while if she nobly forgets her troubles in solicitude for his, she will hate him inwardly.

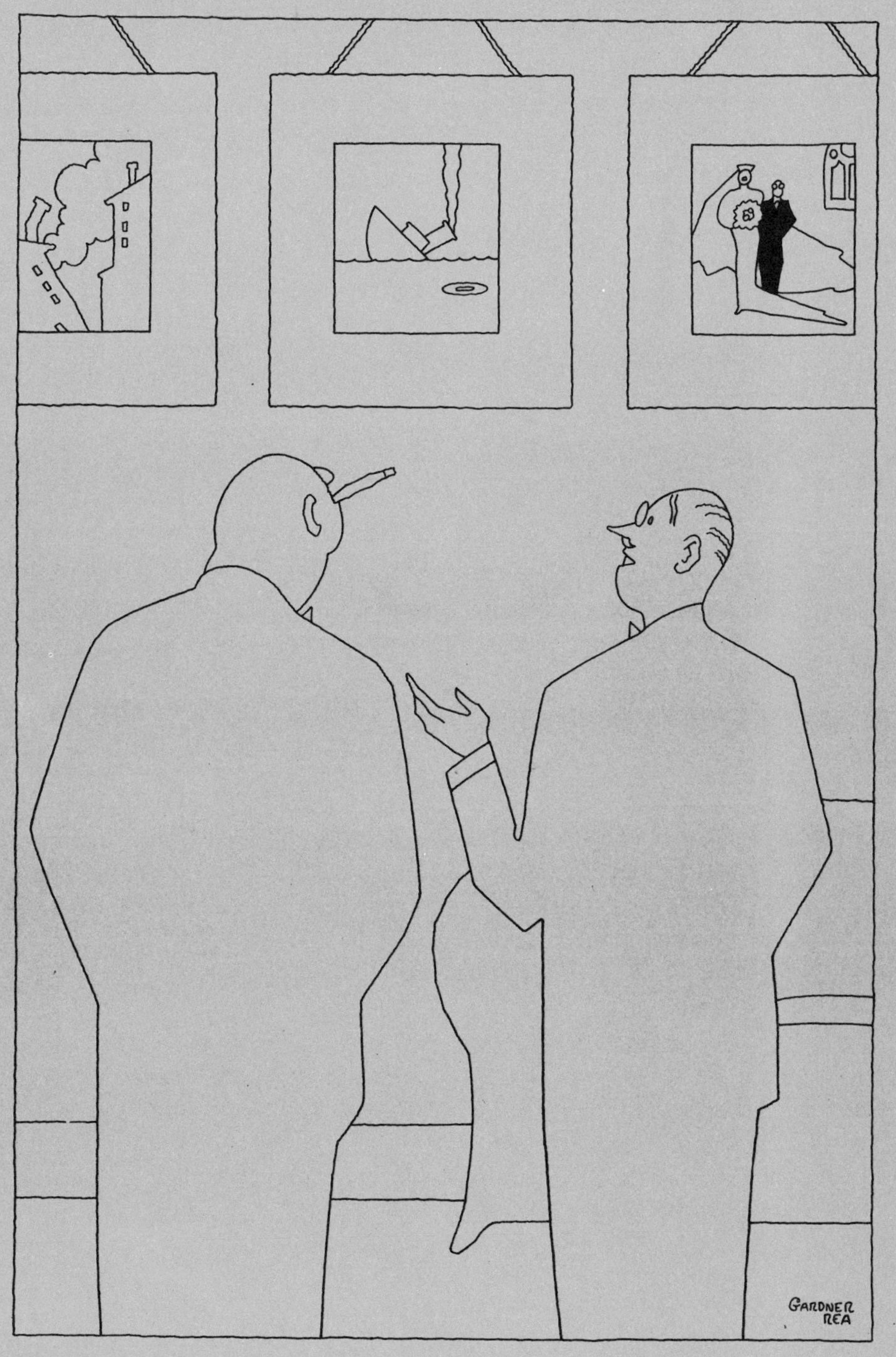

"The Chicago Fire, the sinking of the Titanic, *and my marriage."*

For that matter, Juliet is pre-disposed to look for grievances where her husband is concerned, because she grew up with a strong prejudice againt the "alien" male sex. She may have heard all her life what untrustworthy creatures men are. While Romeo heard before he got into long trousers that you've got to keep a woman in her place or you will not be able to call your soul your own when she's around.

Mutual suspicion and hostility between men and women have the basis of jealousy on one side and fear on the other. As we grow up, most of us accept from sheer necessity the fact that there are other people who are physically bigger and stronger than we are. We soften the blow, perhaps, by trying to reassure ourselves that brains and character are in the long run more important than mere brute strength. The president of the college debating club develops a fine scorn for football players, and the fight promoter sneers at the poor dumb ox who takes all the beatings but has to go fifty-fifty on the money he gets for them. But the mockery is always just a little hollow, and it's an unusual member of the male sex who doesn't take more pride in his successes in athletics than in business or artistic triumphs. I have heard that in his younger days Fritz Kreisler responded to compliments about his tennis far more warmly than to good words for his violin playing.

But if men feel that way, think how it must strike a girl to realize that she is irretrievably a member of the "weaker sex" in the primal sense. Especially during the age when her interest in romance is latent, she sees that her brothers are not only allowed to do many things that are forbidden to her, but able to do most of the things she'd like to try, like playing ball, better than she can, without apparent effort. Even before this she had realized another instance of Nature's discrimination: they've been endowed with a mysterious completeness which they are inordinately proud of, and which she does not have. Finally, as she grows up, she finds that to be a man carries the privilege of seeking pleasure where he pleases without severe moral reprobation, while the tiniest slip on her part causes her to be regarded by others as second-hand merchandise.

Dr. Alfred Adler summed up the effect of these facts on the average girl or woman in the phrase, "masculine protest." And with at least part of her emotions, she reacts as any human being does to unfair treatment: she develops an intense urge to get even. In rare cases this takes the constructive form of proving she's "as good as any man" by doing a man's work—becoming a doctor, or a scientist, for instance. But mostly a woman gets square with the favored male by taking a man down a peg or two whenever opportunity is offered, and this naturally happens oftenest with her husband. Granted, Juliet has all the chance in the world to realize that Romeo is no hero; still, the glee with which she's apt to rub the fact in doesn't do much to preserve the romance.

Most, though not all women will admit having some trace of masculine protest, but there's an emotion nearly all men feel to which few of them will plead guilty. This is fear of women, and above all, of the woman they love. At one stage of his life—when he was a baby—every man's life hung upon a woman's willingness to feed him and care for him: and deep down in his unconscious mind, no man ever entirely forgets this. So when his wife or his sweetheart isn't in the mood to be made love to, or perhaps to listen to his troubles, something of the panic of the helpless infant who is left alone and hungry because "mother doesn't care" is stirred in his heart. Outwardly, indeed, "Hell hath no fury like a woman scorned," but inwardly a man whose hungers are denied may react with a rage which is all the more devastating because his pride usually will not let him admit the real reason for it.

The sources of conflict of which I've been speaking not only make trouble between married people in their own right; they often affect the sexual relation. For while sexual desire is rooted in a physical need, complete satisfaction of desire is dependent on the momentary state of mind of both partners, especially on how they feel toward each other. The relation between mental attitude and physical desire may get badly twisted—I knew one man whose wife stirred no passion in him except when they'd had a violent quarrel—but with normal people, it's impossible to be thrilled sexually by someone of whom you're fundamentally distrustful, or against whom you cherish a deep, unsatisfied grudge. So if you find your wife unresponsive, it need not mean she's a human iceberg: quite as probably she's thinking of how you went out and played golf when she wanted to be driven to the beach. And if your husband kisses you as if you were his old-maid aunt, it's not because you're losing your looks, but because you didn't show sufficient interest when he told you about the new customer from Pittsburgh.

Marriage, in a word, is like an automobile: when you think of all the things that can go wrong with it, the wonder is it's ever able to keep going. And yet cars do run; and nowadays (or at least until war stopped pleasure-car production) it would be a poor sort of man who wouldn't own one because of probability that he'd have trouble with it. And the same has always been true about marriage, which, with all its difficulties, is the oldest of all human institutions, and the likeliest to survive, no matter what changes war or social revolution may bring.

The reason for this, of course, is that a man's emotional need of a woman of his own, and a woman's corresponding need of a man, are stronger and deeper than their mutual antagonisms. It outweighs the frequently observed "polygamous instinct" of both sexes, and it can't be satisfied by merely casual contacts. If it has its infantile or childish elements, these have to be "sublimated." Even in countries where there's practically complete sexual freedom (for instance, the Trobriand Islands as described by Dr. Bronislav Malinowski in "The Sexual Life of Savages") men and women end by pairing off and settling down in a comparatively permanent and exclusive union. The person who dodges marriage, either by the undue prolongation of the adolescent period of experimentation or by the unnatural expedient of celibacy, is trying to solve the biggest problem of life by denying its existence. He is—to put it politely—as unrealistic as the isolationist or pacifist who denies the facts of international relations because he can't see any answer to them.

Yet marriage can bring both peace and happiness—at least, most of the time—and the formula is much the same as that for peace between one nation and another. The first and in some ways hardest step is mutual understanding, based on the fact that beneath all differences in language and viewpoint, both parties are more alike than they are alien to each other. I noticed in France during the last war that with few exceptions, American soldiers who could speak French came home(as I did myself) with new affection and respect for their then allies, while too many non-French-speaking doughboys never got beyond the stage of talking about "dam' Frogs." There is no good reason why a man can't learn to understand if not to speak a woman's language, or a woman, a man's. Equally absurd is the idea that there's any fundamental contrast between their aims in life. Both want to be loved, to feel important, and to be safe; and the fact that they've been trained to satisfy these wants by rather different methods is no more a hopeless barrier between them than the fact that a Frenchman's idea of a good breakfast is the liquid he calls coffee plus a croissant or two is a hopeless barrier between him and the fellow who demands real coffee, ham and eggs, and trimmings. The Frenchman will make it up at lunch time, and why is that anything against him?

Besides realizing that they want essentially the same things, a husband and wife must recognize that they can get these better by co-operation, than by competition. If you and your wife will really play ball, you can achieve love, and a feeling of security from one another more easily and effectually than you possibly can get them elsewhere. And if you can't get them from the man or woman to whom you are married, the idea that they'll come any more easily with another member of the sex you've not learned to get on with is—at least nine times in ten—sheer wishful thinking.

Once you've seen this, the last step becomes comparatively easy. It is mutual allowance and concession, based not on "unselfishness" (which kills a marriage more quickly than anything else I know of), but on the fact that each of you gets more from them than he or she loses. You can't run a marriage on a cash-and-carry basis any more than you can a big business or an international alliance. Just as you take a chance when you marry, the one way to make a go of marriage is to keep on taking chances in the sense of each partner trusting the other to recognize what is in the long run to their mutual advantage. Right now, we of the United States are forced to trust a curious assortment of allies because all of us will be ruined if we do not; and the same necessity applies to a husband and wife in their alliance against life's problems and dangers. The idea that if you do not hang together you'll hang separately may not sound romantic, but it is the bedrock of reality on which alone romance can endure.

FRED C. KELLY

Have You a Mistress?

As THE result of my own little survey, conducted largely by telephone calls to my more adventurous and informed friends, plus some meditative looking out of the window, I am ready to report at this juncture that the practice of mistress-keeping in the U. S. is on the downgrade. My conclusions may not upset Dr. Kinsey or cause any hurried changes in his forthcoming report dealing with the American female, but they seem to me sound.

A mistress, it appears, is of much interest to every man who is honest with himself—particularly if it is someone else's mistress, about whose existence he doesn't need to be secretive. I'm using the commonly accepted definition of a "mistress," that the relationship must have a semblance of permanence; a lady is not a mistress if she merely grants special favors now and then with no expectation that they are to continue.

I have no exact figures, but have been making some estimates. In doing so, I have consulted the epochal work of Dr. Kinsey on a phase of the habits of the American male. It seems that about one-half of all married men in the United States explore new pastures at one time or another. Their behavior varies according to educational level. Those who have not been to college are likely to do their roaming during the early years of marriage. The odds seem to be against any permanent alliance as a result of this experimenting. Maintaining a mistress doesn't quite pay off.

As I conceded, my report is based largely upon my own investigations. It so happens, though, that I'm an attentive listener, and both men and women have been known to confide in old Uncle Fred. From what evidence I can gather—with a little conjecture added—it appears that the man who seeks a mistress is most likely to be one getting along toward middle age, of college education, whose wife's book learning is less than his own. He is apt to be fairly successful—not tied too closely to office hours, and not obliged to use most of his earnings to meet his household budgets. The percentage of men who fulfill all these qualifications is doubtless fairly small. It is further reduced by the problem of geographical location. If a man lives on a farm or in a village, his opportunities are not too good. Mistresses are to be found mostly in a few large cities. In New York, quite suitable for anonymity, one does not need to look far to find interesting specimens. Washington, too, with its considerable semi-leisure class and shifting population of well-to-do people, may be expected to have its full quota.

I know a man who happened to go to a cocktail party in Washington, where he was holding down a temporary war job, and soon afterward found himself with a mistress. He expected to return to a more routine life when the war was over; but when his job was ended, he discovered that it was not quite so simple to drop such an alliance as to start it. He received hints that if he became too forgetful perhaps his wife might hear a piece of news. He found it necessary to make fairly frequent trips to Washington, as a result, and though nothing has yet happened to break the pattern, he devotes much time to worrying.

I have said nothing about unmarried men who den-up with women out of wedlock. Since most men get married, the number of bachelors with love nests could not much affect the statistical average. My observation is, though, that bachelors have even more troubles with their mistresses than married men do. When the relationship seems too good to give up and yet not good enough to keep, it is convenient to have a marriage in the background as a deterrent to going further than one or the other wants to go. Bachelors and their mistresses seem much given to violent quarrels.

It is because the mistress plan is exceptional that it stirs our curiosity. What causes a man to lead a double life? If his wife doesn't suit him, why doesn't he get a divorce? I know one man who says getting a divorce would mean too much bother—too much red tape. Then, there's my friend Edwards. His wife is older than he, and he would be hard put to explain why he married her, except that she showed him great affection when he was a youngster working at a humble job. Since then she has given him constant devotion and lives but to serve him. He doesn't want to break her heart and, besides, they have two children. But she has aged rapidly and he feels almost as if he were living with an aunt. So once or twice a month he makes an airplane trip to Chicago, where he has a comely friend he has known since school days. She is widowed, works for an advertising agency, and is too businesslike to favor one client over another; in the office she is known as cold and aloof. Her arrangement with a man from out of town is exactly to her taste. Both like the arrangement so well that it has gone on for some time, and both try to think that the wife is not really being deprived of anything. I doubt that she would agree, if she knew all the facts, but at any rate that is the way they have chosen to rationalize a selfish situation.

Then there's the idealist—the man who is looking for something special, or thinks he is. That's why he picked the wife he did. I have in mind a man whom I shall call Jim. A long time ago, Jim fell in love with a girl he scarcely knew. Now it must be kept in mind that falling in love is by no means the same as *being* in love, as feeling genuine affection. Falling in love might be generally accepted as a form of insanity if it weren't so common, if it didn't occur in all walks of life to people who in other respects seem sensible enough. Well, anyhow, Jim met this girl and at once began to act the way people do. The slightest expression of her face could make him supremely happy or throw him into despair. No sinful imaginings regarding her entered his head, because he thought of her as an angel, as a creature out of this world. He had not the remotest idea why she was his ideal. Possibly, without his being conscious of it, she reminded him of his mother. They got married and then he became better acquainted with her. He found that she had been raised in so sheltered a way that she thought sex wicked. She insisted that lovemaking be limited to one night a week; and even then it was all too self-conscious and hedged-in to be beautiful.

Jim had not enjoyed wide experience with girls and supposed that he had married one typical of the general run. He accepted his situation, and it was some time before he began to glance at the fruit on other trees. Then, one day, he went on business to New York, where he attended a cocktail party and met several young women willing to go look at etchings. One invited him to her apartment. Soon his horizons broadened. He now makes business trips to New York several times a year. The young woman and he like each other, but the last I heard of the affair she was growing restless, not content with these occasional meetings. I fear he's going to face complications. And to make matters worse, it looks as though Jim has a touch of delayed adolescence coming to the surface these days, since he's still afflicted with the wandering eye of the "idealist" and it probably won't be long before he'll be seeking just a little more perfection—and a little more trouble.

"His wife wanted to know what I had that she didn't have, so he took me over and showed her."

A main cause of a steady, though limited, demand for mistresses is the puritanical background that most of us in this country have known. From childhood, in most families, sex is hush-hush, not to be discussed openly. Sex codes and moral codes are jumbled together. For that reason, even in the privacy of many homes, nudity is frowned upon. Doctors, psychiatrists, social workers, and the Kinsey report all say that an astonishing number of husbands lack precise knowledge of how their wives would look undraped. More married women than you'd think would feel shocked even to look into a full-length mirror without the protection of at least a nightie; and they shy from lovemaking except in darkness. The husband, who has to depend on imagination and guesswork, may begin speculating on how entertaining he might be in the right company, or at least thinking that a change of scene might offer a nice diversion.

The husband himself may be inhibited or diffident, particularly when first associated in an intimate way with a well-bred young woman whom he has kept on a pedestal. Without quite understanding why, he may feel the need of surroundings where he could feel more at ease and more playful. Maupassant doubtless knew his psychology when he wrote a short story about the man who, on his wedding night, first visited a bagnio to get himself into the right frame of mind.

Our puritanical background often creates an interest in outside talent for a quite different reason. Since sex is taboo, it is forbidden fruit, and the pursuit of it is adventure. Where nothing is illicit—as in wedlock, with the supposedly neat combination of temptation and opportunity that G. B. Shaw has mentioned—part of the adventure is lacking. If a husband is at heart a romanticist with an inquiring mind, he may think it jolly to see what he could find in another orchard.

For most people, though, a necessity for secrecy has its disadvantages. There's not only the danger of being discovered and stirring up a ruckus; we simply do not like the idea that something questionable about us could be found out. These matters are handled in a more matter-of-fact way in Europe. In France, partly for economic reasons, it used to be fairly common practice —and I supose still is—for a young man to join with a girl, known as his little friend, in setting up housekeeping on a modest scale, with a sharing of costs and responsibilities. Perhaps both are employed; he pays the rent and part of the grocery bill, and she does the cooking. Thus there is a money saving, and any other advantages are sort of thrown in. Usually the male of the duo felt no obligation to take his little friend about with him socially as if she were his wife. A kind of unwritten rule, however, was that she could expect him to take her to a good restaurant or give her a pleasant outing at least one night a week. When the arrangement was known to their friends, no one seemed inclined to make any fuss about it.

What is true in France is possibly because the French have achieved a uniquely sophisticated point of view on sex relations which few Americans can even understand, much less follow. One never hears of "affairs" in Milwaukee or Kansas City or Los Angeles or St. Louis in which the wife demurely puts up with another woman in her husband's life and even encourages a certain social relationship in which the jolly little trio meets for drinks or supper, as in a Noel Coward comedy. Just as apocryphal as the Design-For-Living tête-à-tête seems to be the wise and tolerant wife who understands that a little fling with a mistress will bring her John (still a boy at heart) back to her more loving and contented than ever. It doesn't often happen that way.

One man I know decided to have a bit of adventure and still not run any chances. He pursuaded his wife that it would be a lark if they spent a week end at a hotel under an assumed name, pretending to be in mischief. He bought her flowers, an expensive negligee, and champagne. The affair took a turn more realistic than planned. She went out on an errand, leaving him in the room. Then she couldn't remember the name they had registered under and was not quite sure of the room number. She had to rap at three different doors before she found the right one. At one of the other rooms, the young man who came to the door tried to persuade her to tarry. So alarmed was she that when she rejoined her husband she was glad to see him. From hints he gave me, I judged that they had a pleasant time.

The most serious problem about having a mistress, I gather, is that the very things that make her desirable also make her dangerous. You cling to her because she is fond of you, genuinely interested in your welfare, always striving to chase away your worries and give you a sense of well-being. But, being fond of you, she comes to resent sharing you with a wife. She feels sure that the wife isn't doing right by you; that she doesn't even look after your home properly. I know of one mistress who said, "When I love a man as much as I do you, I'm not content to enjoy him only in my bedroom. We ought to be sharing a greater variety of interests." Little by little, she nudged him toward a divorce court. Then, after he had married her, he didn't like her nearly so well as before. As he explained to me, "The price was too high—I mean, in making another woman unhappy and all the emotional disturbances I suffered. We never like what costs too much, do we?"

Another friend told me of his problem. "It seemed ideal at first, our arrangement. What I liked best about it was that she had no interest in matrimony. She had been married once and seemed to prefer her freedom. She used to say, 'You're a wonderful friend, but you'd be a dreadful husband.' So I felt that our relations were on a high plane, with no ulterior motive on either side—just a nice exchange of courtesies. Little by little, though, I could see a sordid element coming in. She began to refer to the sad lack of permanence of our situation. Having observed that I was sober and industrious, with good earning power, she began asking herself, 'Why not a marriage certificate to hang over my bed?' She wanted me to do something I didn't want to do. That spoiled everything. She was like a drug that I hated to give up; and yet I knew I had to."

A most serious point against the whole idea of a mistress is, of course, the problem of the children at home. A man weary of his wife or simply in a frolicsome frame of mind may well think twice before exposing his children to the humiliation of learning the results of papa's roving eye; perhaps he risks losing their love, something he might consider most precious of all.

The headaches from mistresses greatly exceed the joys. But when we sum up all of the reasons why the number of mistresses is probably less than one might suspect—considering the romantic way many of the famous ones have been portrayed—we still haven't stumbled on the one true reason why this is so. Despite the divorce figures, marriage is still the most popular arrangement. Although it may sometimes seem prosaic, marriage has its points. Perhaps in France there are many mistresses because of the number of marriages of convenience; and a husband who has married for position or because all had been "arranged" may have his reasons for straying a bit. But American men as a group still seem "unsophisticated" enough to marry for love, and even with all the well-stressed failures, American women can do right well at keeping the home fires burning. With marriage there is at least the hope and expectation of permanence and emotional security. Marriage is still the best solution to a puzzling problem. As for beautiful mistresses, it will be prudent to let the other lads have them.

J. B. RICE, M.D.

Do You Know Your Women?

NOT LONG ago, a righteous young bridegroom sought a divorce because his wife "wiggled her hips" in a provocative fashion whenever she walked down the street. Not only did this unseemly conduct excite the gleeful applause of the boys in front of the cigar store, but their ribald comments caused him "intolerable mental suffering." To the delighted judge's question regarding the tail-wagging bride's manner of locomotion during their courtship, the young man sadly replied that it had been the same. But he (and his outraged lawyer) felt that after marriage a more dignified and matronly gait might have been assumed. The judge concurred in this upright attitude and granted the divorce.

If either the bridegroom or the judge had had the gumption to consult an anatomy textbook, they might have been easier in their judgment of the tearful young bride. Women and men walk differently because they are built differently. A woman's pelvis is much wider than a man's; and her thighs are hooked onto her trunk at a different angle. Since her thighs are further apart and her legs shorter, many women have to "swing it" to walk; although there is a rumor among medical students that some gals are not above improving on Nature a little under the stimulus of an appreciative audience.

Jacques Loeb, one of America's greatest medical scientists, once said that "Physiologically, men and women are different species." He might have added with equal truth that mentally and structurally they are different species also. They are much less alike than ducks and geese, for example, or even dogs and wolves.

The current rate of divorce as compared with the current rate of American marriage is in one-to-three ratio, and everybody cluck-clucks in dismay. But the real surprise is that you can confine two bellicose animals like a man and a woman in closer quarters than is usually allotted to animals in the zoo, with so little mayhem. No one expects wolves and leopards to get along together, or even highly domesticated cats and dogs, for that matter. A married man's best bet of escaping both the electric chair and the insane asylum is to learn something about the physical and mental traits that make women a different species of animal. Although science hasn't finished the job of explaining women yet, it has made some progress. But you have to dig it out for yourself; don't run to your wife for help—she thinks she's normal. One of the few things you don't have to bother with is ribs; she has the same number that you do.

Up until recently psychologists thought that women were feminine and men masculine mostly because of training. Little girls played with dolls, they said, because they were encouraged to imitate their mothers. They were better behaved than their brothers because they were taught to be gentle and ladylike, whereas boys were permitted and even encouraged to develop into little toughs because it was manly. People assumed that a girl raised like a boy would act like one; but when the experiment was tried she fooled them. Girls treated like boys from birth still reacted to most psychological tests as girls.

As a result of this unsuspected fact biologists were prevailed upon to stop dissecting frogs long enough to look into this troublesome sex business. And it was eventually demonstrated that women "were that way" not only because of environment and training, but because their bodies and minds were feminine from the very beginning. Every one of the billions of cells that go to make up a woman are different from a man's—so different that they can be distinguished as being female under the microscope. And recently two scientists showed that the chemical make-up of a woman's brain was not the same as that of a man. The implications of this discovery are not entirely clear. Women's brains contain more phosphorus, for example. However, the fact that blobs of phosphorus are also present in the heads of matches does not necessarily mean that women's ideas burn more brightly, even when they scratch their heads.

The underlying cause of much squabbling between the sexes is physical. Although only about one-fifth smaller than men (six per cent shorter, and twenty per cent lighter in weight), women have only a little more than half the muscular strength. As they use their muscles less, their food requirements are smaller. A very active man needs about fifty per cent more vittles than a very active woman; and his tastes naturally run to proteins and other energy-building foods. Since most homes cannot afford two menus, different dietary requirements constitute an important, although unrecognized, source of friction. Frequently a man requires a steak for dinner, whereas his wife needs only a salad. Either one of them grudgingly gives in and eats the other's diet, with unpleasant effects on his disposition; or they compromise on a diet suited to neither—and both gripe. No doubt much after-dinner surliness in men can be traced to not receiving the kind and amount of food they need; and much logy indifference and downright stupidity in women results from a dinner of pork chops and potatoes when what she wanted was a fruit salad and a cup of tea. A man's diet may ruin a woman's disposition in another way. The growing fear of slimmer competition while she steadily loses ground in the battle of the bulge may make a jealous shrew of the sweetest tempered wife.

Physical weakness accounts for many irritating feminine traits. No woman, with only half the muscle power of a man, could possibly have survived in this rowdy world if she were as ready to put up her dukes as a man. The near certainty of getting the worst of it in physical combat has taught her to avoid situations characterized by flying fists or beer bottles. Casting around for some other means of defense, she found a powerful weapon in a very unlikely place . . . her mouth!

Most women have sharp tongues—they have to. It's their way of fighting. Whereas a man is inclined to take a poke at his adversary, a woman prefers to stand off, with hands on hips, and bawl him out. And she gets just as much kick out of a verbal victory as a man does from being on the gratifying end of a haymaker.

Try telling any woman that her sex is, by Nature, inclined to be deceitful, underhanded and tricky. Then top it off by calling women the most shameless liars unhung. You're lucky if all you get is the "hands on hips" stance with a sarcastic reference to Schopenhauer. Nevertheless, the accusation does contain a grain of truth. The gangster's credo, "Never trust a moll," was founded on bitter experience. Her physical inferiority, with the economic dependence which accompanies it, has made it impossible for most women to fight "like a gentleman" with any hope of success. Few wives can say to their husbands, "Do this," with the implication, "Or I'll pin your ears back," and get away with it. She is, therefore, forced to resort to subterfuge and circuitous methods to hold her own in the "Battle of the Sexes." Her rubber-band muscles account also for "nagging." She has no hope of taking what she wants by direct assault, so she is forced to resort to a war of nerves and win her ends by attrition.

Marriage might have a better chance for success if men and women didn't try to sleep in one bed. However, at the present writing there seems little prospect of abolishing this vicious practice. In the first place, it is difficult for both to be comfortable under the same weight of covers. The layer of fat which lies just under a woman's skin protects her from the cold and enables her to be comfortable at temperatures that rattle the teeth of her husband.

And in summer she takes another mean advantage, for she has an exclusive way of cooling herself without sweating. When the surrounding temperature gets too high, she simply adjusts her built-in thermostat and produces less body heat than before—as much as twelve per cent less! It's simple, but effective; and no man ever born can do it. Scientists, with scant regard for the proprieties, have placed a nude man and woman in the same room and then gradually turned on the heat. The woman's skin remained cool and dry at a temperature two full degrees above that required to wring beads of sweat and profanity from the man. Because men and women are physically adapted to different temperatures, battles of the thermostat and window-wranglings are inevitable.

Difference in the amount and kind of sleep required by the two animals is apt to add a more ominous strain to peaceful relations. The average man, because of his heavier work, needs more sleep per night than the average woman. Many men are secretly convinced that the reason their wives are wide-awake and ready to go places and ring doorbells at night is because they lie around the house and sleep all day.

In most families the "sluggish" male must retire earlier than his spouse, or sleep later in the morning. The daily sight of a sprawling, unshaven, snoring husband in the merciless grey light of morning has rubbed the star dust off many a romance. There may be something touching about a sleeping child, or tenderly provocative about a sleeping woman, but a sleeping man had best be left unseen—and, above all, unheard.

Snoring is by no means an exclusive male accomplishment; but the greater depth of relaxation which men achieve during sleep allows their noisily flapping soft palates to rival the vocal attainments of a healthy sea lion. Although a good virile sea lion may have just what it takes to send a sea lioness, there is no instance in zoo records where a human female has broken out in goose-pimples over one.

A very difficult thing for any male mammal to understand and put up with is the rhythmicity of the female. The hurt look on the face of any pooch when he finds that his ladylove has turned overnight from the gentle receptive "bitch of his dreams," to an irritable, snarling bundle of teeth and claws reflects his master's dismay at the ever-changing personality facets of his womenfolk. He can readily understand a straightforward, honest creature like himself, whose moods respond to the ups-and-downs of his social and business affairs. But a Jekyll-and-Hyde creature, whose disposition varies from gay to morose and from tender to savage for no apparent reason, has him stymied.

The menstrual cycle in women is controlled by the interplay of several hormones. If it stopped there, it would be all right; but it doesn't. The day-to-day concentration of each of these hormones in her blood profoundly affects not only such fundamental functions as body temperature, pulse rate, digestion, and amount of physical energy, but even her mental and emotional reactions. The Jane Smith of February 5th may be quite a different girl on February 20th. But give her time—she'll be back to Jane Smith again by March 5th.

Failure to understand the biology of females has created the aura of mystery always surrounding women. Menstruation, childbirth, and lactation inspire something of the same awe, if not fear, in the hearts of present-day males that they did to the cavemen thousands of years ago.

Remnants of this gullible attitude still linger in the male psyche. Of nine men given careful psychiatric study because they had murdered women, the underlying motive in each instance was women-fear! Most men's firm conviction that women possess "feminine intuition" is a deep-grained hang-over from the past. Even now no ship can safely sail the seas until it has been protected by the female charm of a woman trying to hit it with a bottle of champagne. Few knights dare go forth to combat, whether in armor or in a B-29, without a magic talisman from some wench.

Look at the words which men use to describe women—"bewitching," "enchanting," "charming," "stunning," and "fascinating." And what does a woman do to you? "She haunts you with her magic"; "She holds you in her spell" or "attracts you with her witchery," "hypnotizes you," "binds you with her sorcery." In contrast, what do you do to her? You "make" her, and that's that.

So closely are mystery, sex and romance linked in the minds of the innocent that when he discovers, after about ten years of close association, his wife is made of pretty ordinary clay after all, he feels cheated and often paddles off in a new direction after a more "bewitching" charmer.

A woman's constant griping about her delicate health is enough to drive a man to drink—if he needs to be driven. His ire reaches the flash point when he notices that these frequent indispositions do not interfere in any way with her pleasurable activities. That a woman can be too ill to beat a meal out of a cookstove, but quite well enough to go out to a restaurant is incomprehensible to a man; but it presents no problem in logic to another woman.

Most doctors agree that women have tougher, more resistant bodies, far better equipped to withstand the stresses and strains of modern living than men. Of the seventeen diseases which kill most Americans, year after year the toll among men is greater in all but four. Despite the hazards of childbirth, the death rate for females is lower than for males in every age group. And they outlive men by nearly five years. Yet women claim they're sick much of the time. They not only claim it—they are!

They suffer from minor physical disturbances nearly twice as often as men. Even when you eliminate "female complaints" they are still sick twenty per cent oftener. A few years ago doctors coined a fine new word with which to scare people—"psychosomatic"—which simply means "pertaining to the mind-body relationship." That's where women shine! Since they are more emotional than men, what goes on in their heads is far more likely to kick up a rumpus in their bodies. Junior's drinking the freezing compound out of the refrigerator may cause his mother incapacitating abdominal cramps. Best treatment: a box of candy or a dozen roses. But don't smirk; she wasn't faking. They were real cramps. The female mechanism has an extraordinary penchant for breaking down in nonessential departments for flimsy reasons. It is ungallant—but useful—to liken it to the old model T Ford. Things were always dropping off it or getting out of whack—but the contraption kept on going.

The allegation that women talk all the time is libel. It takes a pretty sturdy specimen to dish out more than eight hours of conversation a day. Why does she talk so much? Because she's naturally hairbrained and thinks everything she says is interesting? No. Women talk almost twice as much as men because they are, by nature, vocal animals and can't help it!

Females outgab males by a wide margin—for a reason. A young

lion isolated from other lions at birth will learn, by instinct, to roar when he grows up; but no baby can learn to make with the words without hearing his elders. If babies learned only from their fathers, it is unlikely that human speech would survive many generations.

Nature has guaranteed that babies shall learn to talk (or go nuts) at an early age by exposing them to a continuous barrage of female conversation from birth on. Women are impelled to talk more than men, *instinctively.* That this greater loquacity is not just a bad habit is shown by the fact that girl babies begin to pronounce words earlier than boys. At the age of two years, the average girl can use twice as many words as the average boy; but soon thereafter she draws ahead of the Geiger counter and only rough estimates of total wordage per square second are available. Nobody will ever know how many happy homes are gassed out by the incessant rattling of a woman's high-pitched voice, but one of the commonest complaints heard in divorce courts is, "She talks too much."

Mysterious as are the ways (and means) of a woman's body, you really need your bifocals when you try to glimpse her mind.

Why a woman will spend days pawing through teeming department stores searching for a blouse of exactly the right shade, or draperies that shall be green, "definitely green, but not too green, and of course not that horrid, sickening green," surpasseth the understanding of any man.

Her eternal preoccupation with color and color shades puts a heavy cross on the shoulders of any man who tries to live with her. He is not only called upon to eat combinations of food chosen for appearance rather than taste; but even when he dines out, he must patronize a restaurant whose interior décor is charming, without regard for the food.

Basically, woman's passion for color is not due to vanity nor to any desire to annoy, but to the intensity of her color perception. It means more to a woman and gives her greater pleasure because she actually *sees* more color.

With their diapers on, it is almost impossible to tell male and female infants apart. But try waving Christmas tree lights over the crib. It will be the girl who breaks into a smile, her eyes eagerly following the bright colors. From earliest infancy, the female human has far better prismatic sense than the male. And color blindness is one of the commonest eye defects of men, but it is rare in women.

Not long ago a young New Yorker, bursting with pride, took his out-of-town sweetheart to the top of the RCA Building to show her his home town. Her chance remark that his magnificent city was "real cute" prompted him to stalk off in bitter indignation. Neither he nor any of those who justified his desertion had ever noticed the innumerable toy towns in department-store windows at Christmastime, with their miniature houses, tiny churches, and flea-sized pedestrians dodging doodlebug automobiles. Women are much less impressed by size or quantity than men; and they don't think quantitatively. New York did not look like a mighty city to this girl; it was nothing more than a whole lot of toy buildings.

Men have been shocked at female "ignorance" and "stupidity" from the beginning of time—for few women are interested enough in the external world of big, important things to know how it's made or to care what makes it tick. Theirs is the inner world of people and personalities. That there is nothing wrong with the female brain is shown by the fact that girls do better than boys in school from kindergarten to the end of high school. But then something happens and the boys pass them up. Never again do women, as a class, become serious contenders as far as intellectual pursuits are concerned. Their keen eyes are fixed on the shimmering rainbow of personal relationship.

Their future roles can even be predicted by the way male and female infants play in a sand pile. Psychologists have observed that boys usually scatter all the sand near them to the four points of the compass; and then, in a spirit of high adventure, they crawl off to a new place and again throw sand *away* from them. But a girl baby is more likely to scoop sand *toward* her with wide circular motions until she has it all piled around her. Then she sits cooing at her elders in quiet enjoyment of her "home."

But does all this biologic thinking apply to the "modern" woman? The advocate of sex equality answers with an emphatic "No"; the psychologist a tentative "Maybe"; but the biologist, before crawling under the table, says, "It applies to women, period." For, basically, they haven't changed in the last few thousand years; they only look different on the outside. The same psychic impulse that once made her fuss with her fig leaf impels her to straighten her seams today. "Modern woman" is a contradiction in terms . . . there ain't no such animal. She'll change only as fast as she can repeal the present laws of biology. Until then, it's smart to know your women!

GEORGE ANTHEIL

Glandbook for the Questing Male

IF UPON one fine spring morning I have just arrived in New York City and am sitting at my favorite New York *Café du Dome* (which happens to be in the St. Moritz), and feeling somewhat slightly my oats I choose to look long and lingeringly upon the passing femininity of this choice part of the city I hope that no one will misunderstand me. I am simply in full pursuit of my hobby . . . glands. By this I mean, endocrinologically speaking, that I am merely attempting at first glance to determine the "articulation" of the various ladies passing by.

As I sit here upon the sidewalk, calmly imbibing my sickly green Pernod, I will, sooner or later glance up. Far away a piece of gaily printed silk will be gradually taking the form of a girl. I will try to catch sight of her at a distance, for this will give me more time to make up my mind about other and more subtle points when she comes near enough for me to look swiftly at her eyes, teeth, and skin. Later in this article I will attempt to outline briefly the most salient points to be determined from some distance, and the follow-up and recheck at the distance of a few feet. The reader, however, will at first have to be patient and see how old Massa himself works; later comes the solution and you can have your try. You may have to plow through a small mess of preliminary scientific data in order to understand somewhat of the fundamental principles, but it will be worth it.

The piece of printed silk is now somewhat nearer. Gathering an eyeful I speculate "Ah, blonde and short. Rather full-chested. She's a very well sexually articulated female and probably will make a most excellent mother in the unknown future. Her eyes are wide-spaced, too. She looks as if she blushes easily . . . all, all postpituitary qualities. She's very womanly and fights with a woman's weapons, nevertheless she's very sentimentally suggestive, as Louis Berman would say. She'll have to fall in love with you first, or you'll have to tell her you'll marry her. Perhaps you'll just say that you love her and let it go at that. She has it coming to her—she's the prototype of *The Little Heroine,* that steel-fingered little miss who hangs on, fighting through thick and thin for 'her man' and she usually gets him.

"Here comes Number 2. She's really very handsome. Heavy bushy hair. Sporty mannish dress. Aggressive walk. Will probably grow up to run her father's business. Too much adrenal cortex for yours truly. Sign off.

"Here comes Number 3. What a figure! Balanced, sleek, and beautiful. Eyes brilliant; she's devastating. She's wide-eyed too, a sign of the thyroid as well as the pituitary. A beautiful intelligent girl and one difficult to know. But one oh so well articulated.

"Here is another, Number 4, almost like Number 3. Marvelous figure, sleek, balanced body. She will be less difficult to know. Remark her eyes which are just a little too brilliant and her bosom which is just a little too small. Each one alone might mean nothing; together they spell 'Dementia Americana' especially in connection with the hyperthyroid woman. This one hasn't enought pituitary to balance her excessive thyroid. Here lurks a background of excitability, sleeplessness, night-clubs, social engagements, and post-war madness. She would probably kill you through sheer exhaustion in a month. Men will run away from her after a time.

"Here comes Number 5, tall, goodlooking, good figure, slightly longish limbs—the ideal of dressmakers of several years ago. Her bony but prettily intellectual forehead, her arresting but pensive eyes proclaim, for those attuned, the pre-pituitary. If I but knew her I could discuss Jean Cocteau, Louis Aragon, and Stravinsky with her, and she will be perfectly *au courant*: nevertheless she will be womanly and sentimental enough; she too is well articulated."

Lost as I am in the roseate haze, sooner or later a chill will pass over me and my sixth sense will become screamingly alert. Every nerve tense, I shall rudely awake to gaze fearfully at Number 6, beautiful Miss Baby Face. If she is rich she will probably be dressed in very striking fashion; from a distance I shall immediately and certainly know that I am looking at someone extraordinary. If she is very poor she will nevertheless be strangely dressed even though it is in inverse Greenwich Village or even Communist fashion. Of one thing I am certain . . . her dress will be bizarre for this part of the world and for this part of New York. Especially she will have very finely chiseled features, almost as if cut out of soap, and she will walk very very gracefully. Her hair will be silken, her waist narrow, and her bosom smallish. Her hair will be silken in all cases, and her features finely chiseled; but if her bosom is even regulation size it may simply mean that she has a pituitary compensation and therefore has a more intelligent brain resting within this childish exterior. But most certainly of all, if she has beauty (and she probably will), it will be of a far-off kind. If I take a fancy to her, follow her home, somehow or another make her acquaintance, and if she comes to know me well, Heaven help me! She will run off with other men and look at me innocently and tell me that she did not know that it was wrong. She will repeatedly break my heart. Otherwise and in other important matters she will be unsatisfactory; she will be flighty, talk, and not pay attention at such moments when attention should most be paid. She is pure Miss Thymo-centric and when she comes along I shall hastily try to look the other way. If luck is with me I shall not be shot down in my tracks and my pocket will not be picked.

So much for the preliminaries—now to get back to the gutter, as it were. For the purposes of sidewalk study I shall attempt the most drastic simplification of the essentials of gland-centrics ever undertaken. In other words, we now attempt to extract from the bewildering complexities of a science the bare rudiments of a sport. And let serious students of endocrinology as a science lie wherever, in their shocked surprise, they may fall.

When Girl Number 1 walked towards me I saw at once that she belonged to the postpituitary type of female. Even from a distance I saw that this was so as she was *short*. When women are short, oval faced, pretty, and fairly full-breasted they are postpituitaries.

Likewise, even from a distance I could see from her mannish walk that Girl Number 2 was masculoid. The masculoid girl is inevitably adrenal, although she can be feminine enough if her adrenals are otherwise balanced. Nevertheless she always remains boyish and mannish at least in her psychic outlook . . . she is the huntswoman, the aviatrix, the up-and-doer, the future lady senator and business woman of affairs. For the gentleman sitting at the café table and interested in an acquaintanceship or two, the adrenal woman is problematic and upon the whole not as good a bet as her less dynamic but more delectable sisters, the pituitary and the thyroid.

Of course, women being Woman, both of these latter girls will pose as sportswomen if that be the prevailing mode.

Girl Number 3 interested me considerably . . . a shapely girl with that surplus of spiritual, intellectual, and imaginative beauty supplied by a good pituitary balance added to her obvious thyroid dominance. She was, if anything, a little too perfect, matchless, unattainable.

But as far as attainability was concerned Girl Number 4 electrified me, and she was, in her way, quite as beautiful and somewhat similar to Number 3. Here was the classical hyperthyroid—one of those types among which are often found the most sexually vicious and dangerously interesting of the female sex. She and the postpituitary, whose excessive excitement-chasing has caused an overflow of her pituitary balance, are the two principal feminine types of today who live life at its fastest tempo; they have that explosive emotional urge exhibited by the young ladies of the "Cradle Mob" who wanted the "thrill" of shooting down harmless people in cold blood. Here are "classical" hyperthyroids and postpituitaries. Nothing will ever tame or satiate these women; they are, literally, "wild women."

Inasmuch as our sidewalk analyst would hardly be likely to look twice at unattractive femininity it so happens that our present article will be devoted only to beautiful women. It was by no accident that Providence sent one fine postpituitary and two superb thyroids so neatly my way. So far we have passed by the ugly subthyroid, the adrenal masculoid, and the gawky feminine prepituitary.

Girl Number 5 (the good looking model out of *Vogue*) is symptomatic of the times; she is the woman intellectual, the feminine thinker, the writer, the woman composer, the guiding flame leading into new spiritual worlds.

Insofar as beautiful women are concerned there appeared only one who really frightened me—Number 6. The badly compensated thymo-centric woman is a fooler; she is in actuality a kind ot feminine "castrate;" still she can be, as has been stated before, very beautiful. She is not very sexual however and uses sex rather than let sex use her. A great many "ladies of the pavement" belong to this glandular type; sex means so little to them that they see no human reason why such a trivial thing should not be made to produce an easy income. On the other hand the "womanly woman" the fine postpituitary is horror stricken by the prostitute's trade; to market sex promiscuously terrifies her. *Sex means too much to her*. She may well become a devoted mistress or even achieve a certain degree of promiscuity herself, but she will never enter

"This is Mr. Phelps—he's buying a piece of the show."

the ranks of Polly Adler's Finishing School, that is, with any real success, for she has not that cool detachment, natural to the thymo, which goes to make for real advancement in this profession. The thymo-centric is born to it as a pussycat is born to back alleys. Miss Uncompensated Thymo here finds herself comfortably at home.

There are as many combinations of type as there are women. But the "classical" and fundamental dominants regularly come to the fore, the beautiful highstrung thyroid, the sexy pituitary, the masculine adrenal, and the fluffy thymus. These four types often have variations so distantly removed from the original dominants that they may be at first hard to determine. Remember that none of us are simple human beings, made up of one cloth. But for purposes of a sidewalk glandbook, it is safe to assume that each will be definitely inclined toward one recognizable type.

Things are, of course, not always what they seem. There is, for instance, the matter of her walk. Through corsetage, brassieres and what not, a lady might quite often conceal (and probably does) a number of things. But she cannot refrain forever from walking as nature intended. Then too she cannot very well change her height. Diet, exercise, corsetage, and good dressmaking may conceal the width of her hips and shoulders, and she may even so wear her hair and hats as to hide her true forehead, but she cannot completely conceal unusual length or shortness of her legs nor an unusual brightness of her lovely eyes. Woman's delight in unconsciously simulating many of her sisters' endocrine types will cause her to comb down her hair over that bumpy forehead, or to drop belladonna into her eyes (if she be pituitary), thereby imitating almost exactly the hyperthyroid. Another day she may elect to become babyish and capricious, pluck her eyebrows, and accent cosmetically whatever delicate sculpturesqueness her face possesses. She need only complete the job by washing her hair with a good shampoo and so attain that natural silky fineness which characterizes the thymo-centric.

Forewarned, forearmed. You will no longer so easily be taken in; you will remember that the very last and all-comprehensive decision can come only from the medical laboratory, but that temporarily there are quite a number of salient and important features easily discoverable and for which we hardly need blood-tests or X-rays. If, for instance, she walks very gracefully, the chances are that she is a thymo-centric or a thyroid; if she walks boyishly or angularly she is probably an adrenal or a prepituitary; if she walks gracefully but nervously (and has the other signs in the bargain) she will be hyperthyroid. A postpituitary, especially one who is a little too sufficient, will walk with that well-known delicious amble known as "sexy."

Therefore for our sidewalk professor who is, we assume, unable to induce *each* lady to sit down, permit him to examine exhaustively her fingernails, peer through a magnifying glass at her skin texture, or to guess too accurately as to the extent of her corsetage, we should assemble the following little INDEX arranged specially for those who would glance slyly and decide quickly. Furthermore, as we are not considering freak, ugly, or circus types, it is perhaps not improper or insulting to beautiful women to arrange them in the order of their obvious accessibility, or "sexual articulation." For some kind of order we must have.

TYPE A

DOMINANT GLAND: postpituitary (excessive).

ACCESSIBILITY: extremely high. Strong tendency toward nymphomania.

OUTSTANDING CHARACTERISTICS AT TWENTY FEET:

Walk: sexy, rolling.

Build: slight, delicate.

Height: short, very definitely below average.

Bust: ample, usually tightly brassiered.

OUTSTANDING CHARACTERISTICS AT FIVE FEET:

Eyes: large and far apart, but not extremely brilliant.

Face: oval, often very strikingly beautiful but always chiseled rather than moulded.

Skin: fine, soft, moist, hairless.

Hair: inclined toward ash-blonde or one of the sandy indistinct tints, if not true blonde. (This is a tendency, not a rule).

Teeth: crowded closely together, and long.

PERSONALITY: thrill-chasing, roving, inconstant; very strongly sexed.

TYPE A-1

DOMINANT GLANDE: pre-pituitary.

ACCESSIBILITY: high, imaginative and very open to suggestion.

OUTSTANDING CHARACTERISTICS AT TWENTY FEET:

Walk: rangy, loping.

Build: lean, somewhat gangling.

Height: tall, very definitely above average.

Bust: large for this slender build.

OUTSTANDING CHARACTERISTICS AT FIVE FEET:

Eyes: large, and far apart, but not extremely brilliant.

Face: bony, especially as to forehead, and high cheekbones.

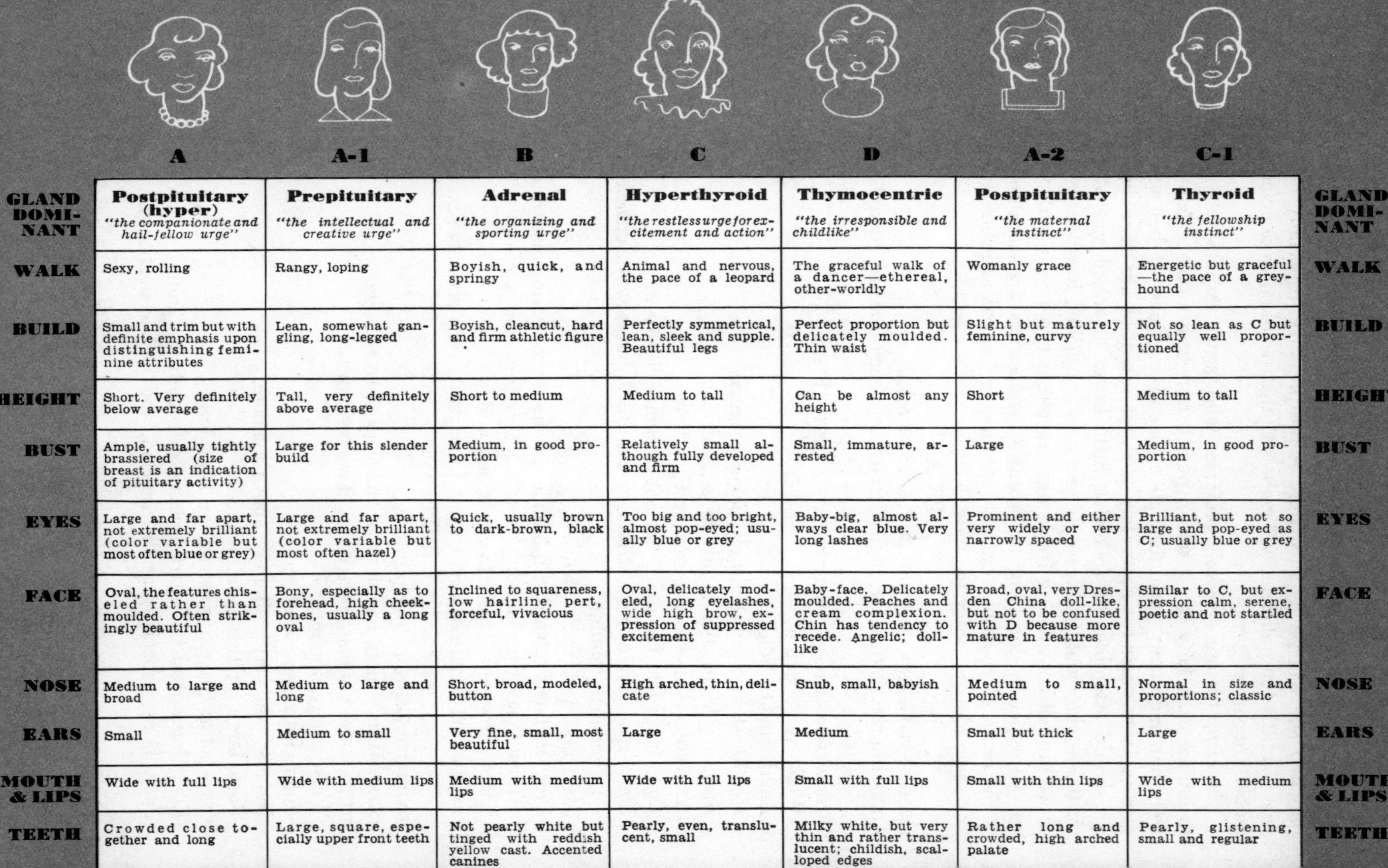

	A	A-1	B	C	D	A-2	C-1	
GLAND DOMINANT	**Postpituitary (hyper)** *"the companionate and hail-fellow urge"*	**Prepituitary** *"the intellectual and creative urge"*	**Adrenal** *"the organizing and sporting urge"*	**Hyperthyroid** *"the restless urge for excitement and action"*	**Thymocentric** *"the irresponsible and childlike"*	**Postpituitary** *"the maternal instinct"*	**Thyroid** *"the fellowship instinct"*	GLAND DOMINANT
WALK	Sexy, rolling	Rangy, loping	Boyish, quick, and springy	Animal and nervous, the pace of a leopard	The graceful walk of a dancer—ethereal, other-worldly	Womanly grace	Energetic but graceful—the pace of a greyhound	WALK
BUILD	Small and trim but with definite emphasis upon distinguishing feminine attributes	Lean, somewhat gangling, long-legged	Boyish, cleancut, hard and firm athletic figure	Perfectly symmetrical, lean, sleek and supple. Beautiful legs	Perfect proportion but delicately moulded. Thin waist	Slight but maturely feminine, curvy	Not so lean as C but equally well proportioned	BUILD
HEIGHT	Short. Very definitely below average	Tall, very definitely above average	Short to medium	Medium to tall	Can be almost any height	Short	Medium to tall	HEIGHT
BUST	Ample, usually tightly brassiered (size of breast is an indication of pituitary activity)	Large for this slender build	Medium, in good proportion	Relatively small although fully developed and firm	Small, immature, arrested	Large	Medium, in good proportion	BUST
EYES	Large and far apart, not extremely brilliant (color variable but most often blue or grey)	Large and far apart, not extremely brilliant (color variable but most often hazel)	Quick, usually brown to dark-brown, black	Too big and too bright, almost pop-eyed; usually blue or grey	Baby-big, almost always clear blue. Very long lashes	Prominent and either very widely or very narrowly spaced	Brilliant, but not so large and pop-eyed as C; usually blue or grey	EYES
FACE	Oval, the features chiseled rather than moulded. Often strikingly beautiful	Bony, especially as to forehead, high cheekbones, usually a long oval	Inclined to squareness, low hairline, pert, forceful, vivacious	Oval, delicately modeled, long eyelashes, wide high brow, expression of suppressed excitement	Baby-face. Delicately moulded. Peaches and cream complexion. Chin has tendency to recede. Angelic; dolllike	Broad, oval, very Dresden China doll-like, but not to be confused with D because more mature in features	Similar to C, but expression calm, serene, poetic and not startled	FACE
NOSE	Medium to large and broad	Medium to large and long	Short, broad, modeled, button	High arched, thin, delicate	Snub, small, babyish	Medium to small, pointed	Normal in size and proportions; classic	NOSE
EARS	Small	Medium to small	Very fine, small, most beautiful	Large	Medium	Small but thick	Large	EARS
MOUTH & LIPS	Wide with full lips	Wide with medium lips	Medium with medium lips	Wide with full lips	Small with full lips	Small with thin lips	Wide with medium lips	MOUTH & LIPS
TEETH	Crowded close together and long	Large, square, especially upper front teeth	Not pearly white but tinged with reddish yellow cast. Accented canines	Pearly, even, translucent, small	Milky white, but very thin and rather translucent; childish, scalloped edges	Rather long and crowded, high arched palate	Pearly, glistening, small and regular	TEETH

SKIN	less	have hair on arms and legs	ways somewhat pigmented; bothered by body hair	neath it. High warm color, perspires readily	thin-skinned to translucent degree	moist, flushes easily	Same as C	SKIN
HAIR	Inclined toward ash-blonde or one of the sandy indistinct tints	Blonde to ash-blonde	Curly to almost kinky. Usually thick, coarse and too dry. Most often brunette, but all real redheads belong to this type	Luxurious, inclination towards brunette or deep reds; tendency to be too rich in oils	Exceptionally silky, tendency to be too dry. Fine texture better guide than color which is always mixed, e.g. dirtyish blonde, blackish brown	Thick, with tendency toward golden blonde or any shades on the blonde side	Same as C	**HAIR**
VOICE	Variable in pitch, but always somewhat husky	Variable	Altoish to low	Variable, usually rich full mezzo	Thin, piping	High, clear	Variable	**VOICE**
HANDS	Small	Large	Squarish, short-fingered	Long tapering fingers, graceful, beautiful	Childish, pudgy	Small, very feminine	Long	**HANDS**
FINGER-NAILS	Medium, small moon	Heavy and ridged, very little moon	Thick, brittle	Medium, very translucent, large moon	Very thin, break off easily	Medium	Medium, beautifully arched, classic, big moon	**FINGER-NAILS**
ANKLES & LEGS	Womanly, well turned ankle, good calf, not over or underly muscular, full thighs, rounded, chubby knees	Long, usually thick ankles, small thighs	Muscular, very sculpturesque ankle; small hard thighs, solid	Sleek, beautifully moulded, not muscular, good unmoulded ankles	Can be well shaped though not much calf, thin ankle	Graceful, womanly, well-turned	Same as C	**ANKLES & LEGS**
FEET	Small	Large	Long and narrow	High arched, fine	Often flat-footed, never large	Small	High arched, medium	**FEET**
PERSON-ALITY	"The Eternal Feminine with a supercharger." Thrill-chasing, roving, inconstant very strongly sexed	"The Soul of an Artist." Pensive, thoughtful, masculoid, but also daring and imaginative. High in curiosity and intellectual acquisitiveness	"The Emancipated Woman." Masculoid, intelligent, good business-sense, has inclination towards manly interests. Can be very explosive, vicious, "neurasthenic." Courageous, sporty, aggressive	"The Beautiful and Damned." Restless, sleepless, never tires, subject to palpitation of the heart. Can eat like a horse and stay thin, drink like a fish and stay sober. Emotionally and intellectually quick-triggered	"The Beautiful and Dumb." The soul of a child, quixotic, flighty, cruel, but often trusting as well. Dangerous; always gets acquitted by juries because "everything went black"	"The little heroine herself"—with a will of iron. Strongest of all in the maternal instinct—a natural mother. Sentimental, emotional; all the traditional feminine psychic traits — the womanly woman	"The girl scout." Pleasant, frank, open, poetic, vivacious; the pal, the comrade	**PERSON-ALITY**
ACCESSI-BILITY	Will come much more than halfway; highest in accessibility; highest (with Type C) in susceptibility	Very high. May be reasoned with, especially by sophistry on advanced intellectual-moral grounds	High rating because of innate potentialities, but never a sure-thing gamble as this type varies between extremes of enthusiasm and reserve	Very susceptible to quick impulsive persuasion; (given C rating on accessibility chiefly because frequency of nymphomania among pituitary and adrenal types raises their already high average) very high	Low; variable; apt to look more interested and interesting than they are	Coyness is a postpituitary quality; never actuated by desire apart from sentiment; low	Low; sisterly	**ACCESSI-BILITY**
	A	**A-1**	**B**	**C**	**D**	**A-2**	**C-1**	

Skin: fine, soft, moist.

Hair: blonde to ash-blonde.

Teeth: large, square; especially upper front teeth.

PERSONALITY: pensive, thoughtful, masculoid, but also daring and imaginative.

TYPE B

DOMINANT GLAND: adrenal.

ACCESSIBILITY: high, usually masculoid; this type often develops a kind of psychic and physical nymphomania: it would seem that even as a woman the adrenal remains essentially masculine in psyche. She wishes, if married, to be the Don Juan of the family, and to have more affairs than her husband. Being of the quick-trigger type she probably will also have many divorces.

OUTSTANDING CHARACTERISTICS AT TWENTY FEET:

Walk: boyish, quick and springy.

Build: boyish; tendency towards muscularity or clean-cut hard and firm athletic figure; the ideal of the modern college magazine illustration.

Height: short to medium.

Bust: medium; fairly good proportions.

OUTSTANDING CHARACTERISTICS AT FIVE FEET:

Eyes: quick, usually brown.

Face: rather forceful, pert, inclination towards squareness and low hair line. Vivacious.

Skin: usually freckled.

Hair: curly to almost kinky. Usually coarse. Color often most unexpected, as black among Scandinavians and yellow for Italians. All real red heads belong to this glandular type.

Teeth: accented canines; teeth slightly inclined toward red-brown coloring; not real white.

PERSONALITY: masculoid, intelligent, good business women, has an inclination towards the world of affairs, politics, manly interests. Can be very explosive, vicious, "neurasthenic," capable of strange and incomprehensible acts that harm herself more than others.

TYPE C

DOMINANT GLAND: thyroid (excessive, or hyperthyroid.)

ACCESSIBILITY: high.

OUTSTANDING CHARACTERISTICS AT TWENTY FEET:

Walk: animal, and nervous.

Build: very remarkable. Perfectly symmetrical. Limbs just the right proportion in relation to rest of body. Head neither too large nor too small. Tendency towards leanness. No tremendously developed muscles. Sleek and supple. Very beautiful legs.

Height: medium to tall.

Bust: somewhat smaller and more firm than pre-pituitary (A2)

OUTSTANDING CHARACTERISTICS AT FIVE FEET:

Eyes: too brilliant and big: "pop-eyed."

Face: oval, delicate modeling of all the features, *wide high brow*, long eyelashes, general expression one of suppressed excitement.

Skin: soft, moist, no fat beneath it.

Hair: luxurious, inclination towards brunette, or deep reds.

Teeth: pearly, even, translucent.

PERSONALITY: restless, sleepless, never tires, subject to palpitation of the heart, too gay one moment and too depressed in the next; explosive crises are too often a form of this type's psychic expression.

TYPE D

DOMINANT GLAND: thymus.

ACCESSIBILITY: variable, but apt to look both more interested and more interesting than she is. Thus given fourth ranking in place of the first ranking that you might expect.

OUTSTANDING CHARACTERISTICS AT TWENTY FEET:

Walk: the graceful walk of a dancer.

Build: in perfect proportion, but delicately moulded. Thin waist.

Height: can be almost any height.

Bust: apt to be immature, arrested.

OUTSTANDING CHARACTERISTICS AT FIVE FEET:

Eyes: baby-big; almost always blue. Very long eyelashes.

Face: delicately moulded, almost as if cut in soap. "Peaches and cream" complexion. Chin has a faint tendency to recede, or become weak and babyish. Angelic; doll-like.

Skin: unusually delicate, reminiscent of roseate translucent marble.

Hair: exceptionally silky, the fine texture a better guide than the color, which is almost always mixed, as for example dirtyish blonde, blackish brown.

Teeth: milky white, but very thin and rather translucent.

PERSONALITY: the soul of a child, intelligent, quixotic, flighty, cruel, but often trusting as well. But not the personality of other "normal" human beings. Dangerous: the kind that always gets acquitted by juries because "everything went black."

This, then, in the order of their accessibility, completes the listing of the four basic types of glandular dominants. And for the sidewalk analyst, it is about here that the alphabet stops. There's no point in going on to X or Z, for though those women may well have hearts of gold, they are so unappealing to the eye of the nympholept that he seldom wastes a second glance on them.

But there are two variants of Type A and Type C that must be listed next, and it is most important to list them because they are, on the score of accessibility, exceptions that prove the rule. Although they belong to those two glorious categories, the post-pituitary, and the thyroid, in which the excessives (Types A and C listed above) both look interesting and are as interested as they look, these are not the excessives but merely the dominants, and the sad fact that they are twice as hard to interest as the excessives, while almost as interesting to look at, must be accepted philosophically as one of the hazards of the course of the questing male.

TYPE A2

Dominant Gland: post-pituitary.

Accessibility: in contrast to the excessive (Type A), the post-pituitary dominant will probably want to see the engagement ring first. In any event, it will at least be necessary to tell her that you will love her dearly, and positively forever.

Outstanding Characteristics at Twenty Feet:

Walk: womanly.

Build: slight, rather delicate, but not as sharply moulded as the thymo-centric (Type D). Earthy, sexy, but not heavy.

Height: short.

Bust: large.

Outstanding Characteristics at Five Feet:

Eyes: prominent and either very widely or very narrowly spaced.

Face: broad oval, and very Dresden China doll-like, but not to be confused with the true baby-face of the thymo-centric (Type D).

Skin: roseate, creamy, warm, moist, flushes readily.

Hair: thick, with tendency toward golden blonde or any of the shades on the blonde side.

Teeth: rather long and crowded.

Personality: "The little heroine herself"—with steely little fingers and a will of iron.

TYPE C1

Dominant Gland: thyroid.

Accessibility: low.

Outstanding Characteristics at Twenty Feet: (these are exactly the same as C above, but not quite so lean.)

Outstanding Characteristics at Five Feet: (these too are exactly similar to C, with the exception of the eyes, which are brilliant but not so "pop-eyed" as C; likewise expression is calm, serene, and poetic, instead of startled and bursting with pent-up excitement.

Personality: pleasant, frank, open, poetic, vivacious; the pal, the comrade.

The above four central types will complete our index of pretty and beautiful women. They are the four primary colors of the palette, and practically every other feminine color, or type-personality, can be mixed from them. As I have noted before, in endocrinology there are no "pure" types; there are merely dominants around which the body chemistry swings. It will be your pleasure to single out by yourself which is which and in exactly what ratio she is this and in exactly what ratio she is that; these are merely the prime colors, the fundamentals. Oftentimes it may be necessary to refer back to the various original glandular processes themselves to finish your decoding in such style as becomes an amateur endocrine hobbyist. In this way, gradually, lovely ladies will take themselves apart before your very eyes and become a fine tenebrous network . . . the history of their lives written upon one tooth alone. Fascinating prospect, isn't it?

She's No Longer Faithful If–

You are reading the evening paper and call her attention to the headlines MAN SHOOTS HIS MISTRESS AND HER LOVER. She turns pale and changes the conversation.

You suspect a certain shady and talkative gentleman of being her lover. The three of you are together. During the conversation she slightly underlines the word "gentleman," does it several times. "You are a gentleman, aren't you?" She is afraid of him. He talks too much.

She does not return home with the bracelet she wore when she left the apartment this morning. You call her attention to the fact. "I have left it at the jeweler's to be repaired," says she. In several days it returns. The jeweler has repaired nothing. She forgot it, but went back to fetch it . . . from the apartment in which she forgot that she owned it.

He is a "friend of the family," the next most familiar face of your household, and it is perhaps only natural that she should know more about his romantic affairs than you. One day, however, this mysterious knowledge of hers is no longer up to date. She pumps you lightly but tenaciously about the latest affair of your friend. Curiously, and for the first time in years, he has told you all about it, "it" being the little actress of a current play. Your mistress turns a little white. He has left her, and he wants her to know it: she had better stop ringing him up, too, otherwise he will hint even more broadly, that for some time, she too has been his mistress. Before she married you or came to take her abode with you in sin, her only friends were men, and she was notorious for her dislike of women. Now, however, she meets a woman whom you never see but whom she sees day in and month out. The woman friend has problems which often need to be discussed and the brow of your pretty little mistress is often wrinkled with care.

Life has taken on a more serious aspect. She spends a great deal of time with "her."

She has been unpunctual all of her life, but she suddenly starts to develop an unheard-of punctuality. She says that she will be home at six, and she is home at six.

She had been indifferent for months or even years, but she suddenly develops an unheard-of tenderness for you and the worries of your special world. Last week, however, your best masculine friend has ceased to come to your house, for no good reason whatsoever. Formerly he came to see you every day.

A certain friend of yours has always been a very nice chap, very well behaved, courteous to your opinions and your foibles, and a perfect gentleman in your house, in which he appears often. He is married, and in a distant and perfectly proper way your mistress admires and respects him. His wife is ill and undergoes a serious operation, and he is worried and lonely, and your mistress is worried too, and often indeed during these months of illness does she go to see the sick woman. One day his wife is well, and your friend no longer calls, as is no more than to be expected. However, weeks later, you call attention to the fact that he has not appeared at all, and you are somewhat surprised by your mistress's faint but unmistakable irritation with this fact. "Oh him! He is tied to the apron strings of his wife."

She has never wept. But now she cries easily, at the cinema, or while she is in bed with a novel of frustrated and secret love, such as *Wuthering Heights.*

She has always been naturally secretive, but she now leaves all of her correspondence around openly for you to read. But once upon a time you inadvertently open one of her letters, and doesn't she make a terrific scene about it. "You do not trust me . . . well, then, you can read everything!" She throws heaps of letters before you. Her life is ultra open and above board. Still, she meets the mail man first.

She has never taken any interest in bridge, motoring, polo, or golf, but suddenly she takes a terrifying interest in one or another of these, or in something equally thrilling that keeps her away from home for long and protracted periods. Whatever it is, it is very evidently doing her a great deal of good: she is, in fact, a new woman, with a new flash in her eye, and a new bounce in her step.

She has always loved Mozart, Bach, and Stravinsky. Last night, however, you heard her playing Ravel, Schumann, *and* Chopin.

For a number of years she has not been interested in her appearance, but she suddenly has the hairdresser and the beauty salon completely change her over into another and different woman, decidedly much much gayer: she also becomes a furious participant of weight-reducing sports. In some elusive way, however, all this does not seem to be meant for you.

You are dumbfounded when out of Christmas or birthday season she makes you (upon your own money) an elaborate present. She has eased her conscience.

She has always been as healthy as a young horse, but she suddenly, in the early twenties, develops "heart attacks." Accordingly you must be very careful with her, catering to her every whim; you must be especially cautious not to bring on another "attack" by an undue and unjust fit of jealousy. Your doctor is mystified, and advises X-ray, which, mysteriously, is never quite taken. She suddenly sickens, really loses weight, and becomes nervous and irritable. Your business is pressing, and you cannot possibly go to Bermuda, but she does, and alone. Later your detective agency with branches all over the world will tell you that "he" went to Bermuda two weeks earlier, but with that girl from the now defunct *Scandals.* Your mistress was really ill, but her illness was the illness of desperation. There is no case; you take her back; she becomes well; and you both live happily ever after.

She hardly ever puts on a bold make-up, but today she came home with flaming over-emphasis upon her lips and cheeks, and with a breezier, bravado manner, as well. If you look at her when you know that she does not think you are looking (mirror) you will see that she looks at you anxiously.

She has never been apparently jealous. She has been jealous at various times in the history of your family life, but she would rather have bitten out her tongue than admit it. Lately she has promoted situations which have automatically developed into jealous scenes of such hair-raising histrionics that Sarah Bernhardt herself could hardly have done them as much justice. Curiously you were innocent. She is losing her lover and her faith, and you are the unwelcome recipient of this transference.

She is an incurable smoker and has tried several times lately to give up this habit. During the first several weeks hell has always broken out in the household. At last she says "Darling, I must give up smoking; I don't want to make you miserable meanwhile, so I think I shall go away to some nice little quiet place for several months and have my tantrums there." You are only too glad to say "yes." Three months later she comes home completely cured; nevertheless you still find mysterious lip-sticked ends of her favorite brands in the fireplace, or in the flowerbed just outside of her bedroom window. She really had intended to give up smoking during these past three months, but how was she to know that Ralph would leave her for someone else. Her jangled nerves just had to have the smoothness of nicotine to come back and face you. In three days from now you will say some slight thing or another that will set her into a whirling fuzzy tantrum of grief; she will cry and moan and lock herself up in her room and when you come up to apologize for something you have not done, she will graciously forgive you. At that moment she will light a cigarette. "I just must have one . . . just one." As you are in the wrong, you will not then have the heart or the courage to stop her. From thenceforth she will again come out openly with her smoking. Next year she will go through "the cure" again, but the locale will be changed. Different men go to different places.

She leaves the house upon summer mornings in well-pressed and laundered linens, but she returns in the evening with these selfsame linens (such suits wrinkle easily) immaculate. She says that she has been shopping and to the cinema. If that is true, she did not wear her dress at all during her shopping tour, nor did she drive about from store to store sitting tightly in her little Alfa-Romeo. Moreover, the movie theater is apparently equipped with such electric irons as are peculiar to gentlemen's apartments, as alack, you one day discover when she throws away a linen suit slightly branded with an iron not belonging to your household.

You are a painter, writer, composer, or sculptor. You have worked hard and regularly last year, but during the past three months you have worked most irregularly. Your mistress is plainly worried: she does not know when to leave the house, or when to return to it; your irregular habits could prove very embarrassing, should you take it into your head to go about visiting some of your very best friends during this period of stagnation. Accordingly she urges you to work; she lectures and scolds; she purchases a new typewriter, a new Steinway, music paper, clay, or even discovers for you a most presentable and new feminine model of exacting spiritual curves. You do start working again, but she herself again absents herself the whole livelong day.

She says that she has stayed overnight with a girl friend, and has returned at eleven o'clock this morning. She eats a *very* hearty meal at lunchtime but after tea her eyelids will become heavy and show an inclination to droop. Thereupon you serve her with a heavy supper and take her to a six-act and very important play. During the play she will fall asleep.

She does not make women friends easily, but she does make friends with the wife of your best friend, who is, to say the least, a rather unattractive and unfriendly sort of female. You are astonished to hear your mistress (she who legally or not shares your fireside and roof) laughingly address your friend's wife as follows:—"Darling, I have just observed your husband's car in front of Ciro's, and, unless I need glasses, he was stepping into it with that dangerously attractive Finnish girl we all met at the party last Saturday . . . now darling . . . you *really* must watch him." After this peals of tinkling laughter, which, to you, sound a little grim. She is not going to let your friend cheat *on her*.

She is reading a scientific note in the newspaper—"although the light of a great number of stars in the heavens still reach us . . . the stars themselves are no longer there." She looks at you sadly and sideways, and there is a suspicion of a tear in her eye. She is having a rare attack of conscience; years ago you called her "my guiding star."

You are absent from home a great deal. Your maid has always been deathly afraid of her. Without any reason whatsoever, the maid overnight becomes unbearably arrogant. You expect your mistress to discharge her upon the spot, but she does not. Two weeks later you see the maid on her night off, wearing one of your mistress's most expensive dresses. You are astonished later, to find that it was a gift.

In this day of uncanny dial telephones and right numbers immediately reached by mechanical means it will set one to thinking when suddenly, since last month, every time *you* answer the phone (and *not* your mistress) a masculine voice says, "Sorry, wrong number." The situation is pressing and he must take the chance of bumping into you in trying to telephone to her. He talks to her but he hangs up on you.

If she spends all of her time in the department stores of your city, and still comes home day after day with nary a purchase, it may be that she is frightened that you might follow her. A big department store is an A-1 Alibi; in the first place every woman spends hours in them, and, in the second place, try to find anybody in one.

This afternoon your friend has had a terrible business calamity, and this 4 a.m. *your mistress* has received a telegram from him

"Roger and I quarreled and he thinks I've gone home to Mother."

threatening suicide at 5 a.m. sharp. Your little Mother Confessor's respect for human life prompts her to go; he is actually saved, but several months later unaccountably disappears from the vicinity.

A telegram has arrived at home from Leopold Stokowski who wants to engage you for his orchestra, but he must see you tomorrow and no other day. You have disappeared out of town and your mistress does not know where you are, nor what to do. She telephones your friend, who under this particular press of circumstances so dear and so important to you, tells her that you may be reached at the apartment of a certain little actress. Your mistress telephones you. The telegram was a hoax—you sent it yourself. Your mistress's telephone call under these circumstances discloses the relationship between her and your best male friend to be of a special nature.

She is an excellent cook and in the roseate past has gladly cooked excellent meals for the male friends you occasionally brought home to dinner. One male friend persists, and every time she now cooks dinner for you both, the soup is full of salt and the roast is burnt. (However poised a woman may be otherwise, she needs perfect equanimity to cook for her lover, and that balance is deeply disturbed by the possibly alert eye of her husband.)

Recently you both have met a married couple and all four of you have become close friends. Since then your mistress's drinking has undergone a subtle and gradual change, and she now invariably becomes intoxicated whenever you meet this married couple *ensemble* although she refrains if the gentleman is alone. (She does not mind living with you, but she can no longer bear the thought of the other couple living together.)

She has a healthy respect for the town scandal monger.

She has always worn clothes of pure white or somber gray; her new evening dress is of flaming scarlet and cut down to HERE.

She has always loved dancing and there is no just cause for suspicion in spite of the fact that within the last several weeks her ballroom dancing has improved almost to professional standards. However when she says of her sleek-haired dancing partner . . . "I am so concerned about Tony . . . he has a really fine mind, and is terribly depressed about his present life; he comes of gentle birth . . . could we not do something about him, Henry?" . . . then you have cause for alarm. Tony is a gigolo and has no other fine feelings except those in his feet. If you look at him at this moment, you will find his eyes glittering at your Hispano-Suiza moored across the street.

Formerly when you were both children and in love, distance and separation was a terrible and agonizing thing, and reunions after an absence of three months were the tearful and throbbing ones of two bleeding hearts. But now, just as she descended from the train which brought her from far away, she seemed more womanly, more capable, and more definitely "sex appeal." As you fall into one another's arms, you have that inexplicable and fascinating feeling that you are embracing a strange woman.

She has gone to Monte Carlo especially to play baccarat. After three months she has returned with her Bugatti, jewels, furs, and bank balance in exactly the same condition as the day you put her, her car, and her luggage upon the Midi-Express.

She is away upon a summer vacation and writes:—"*I have just met the most ridiculous little man*—." Her next letter is poetic, the sea is very beautiful, the landscape is marvelous, and the world is a strange, mysterious and thoroughly ecstatic place. She refers to that funny little man in a postscript—"The young scrapegrace I wrote you about—he is still idiotically following me around; as a matter of fact he seems to be madly in love with me—*really* my darling it is too *too* funny—if you *could only see* him!"

The next letter is in a more serious vein; she is plainly enjoying her vacation, but a little apprehensive that people might misunderstand. Her letter begins thoughtfully, "Arthur dearest, the only thing that worries me about Jean . . . his name is Jean . . . is that he makes such an *ass* of himself! It would be dreadful if some garbled word concerning his antics found its way back to you, poor darling, working away there at your hot city office; you certainly have enough business trouble to worry about. You will know by this token that your little dove is in summer flight, and merely stretching her wings a little bit to see how attractive they look. Besides you need *only to see* Jean to know that *I* could *never* take such a fellow seriously, not even for one moment."

A fourth letter arrives:—"I am now definitely worried. Perhaps I had better cut short my vacation and come back home. Jean has besieged me with his attentions, and I *feel* that people may commence to talk. For instance I met that flirtatious Miss "Q" yesterday and she *did* look at me in the *queerest* way. Perhaps that is because I saw both of them together all day the day before . . . do you know that I found they had taken a long walk down the beach together, and disappeared, Heaven knows where, until late evening!"

Months later, after her return, you find a hidden snapshot, dedicated simply "To Joan, from Jean" and a little heart. Jean is tall, blond, and very very handsome.

Your mistress, a dancer, has become stranded in South America. She has sent you a cable to this effect, and you somewhat bewildered, have sent her the money. (Brazilian and Argentine laws stipulate that no dancer may enter the country without a return ticket because of the age-old wicked "Road to Buenos Aires" which still traps the girls of five continents.) She does not return, but after another month, sends you another cable for an additional sum—as "irregular ship-sailings" have prevented her return.

You do not answer this second cable. In two months' time she will return of her own accord for in the last analysis no South American will marry any other than one of his own countrywomen . . . he would be disinherited if he did. Therefore you will have your mistress back in a very reconciliatory and contrite mood, ready to accept and believe your story that you did not receive her second cable.

She has recently bought a box of very expensive monogrammed writing paper. Day after day it disappears, although she never writes a letter.